10 probs   closed book
3 probs   law of Sins, Cos,
              Logs

1 prob   Trig Identity

Wasy

Plane

Trigonometry

NATHAN O. NILES

Associate Professor
Department of Mathematics
U. S. Naval Academy
Annapolis, Maryland

Lecturer in Mathematics
McCoy College
The Johns Hopkins University
Baltimore, Maryland

NEW YORK · JOHN WILEY & SONS, INC.

London · Chapman & Hall, Limited

PLANE

TRIGONOMETRY

Preface

This book was written to give a modern flavor to trigonometry. The present trend is away from the computational part and toward the analytical aspects of the subject. By introducing the concept of a function in terms of domain and range, it is brought to the student's attention that trigonometric functions are evaluated at an angle or at a real number. This definition of a function permits the transition from the concept of the trigonometric functions of angles to the concept of the trigonometric functions of real numbers to be eased by noting that the main difference between these concepts is the terminology used for the argument of the functions. The analytical aspects of trigonometry are then discussed with respect to real numbers as well as angles.

For pedagogical reasons the concept of trigonometric functions of angles is first introduced and followed by a chapter on applications of the right triangle. Then in Chapter 4 the trigonometric functions of real numbers are introduced. After this chapter the student has a clear understanding of an equation such as $x = \cos 8t$, where the argument $8t$ is a real number. This will help the student in his future scientific courses.

To save time in the numerical computations, the slide rule solution of triangles has been introduced. The discussion on slide rule solutions of triangles is based on slide rules in which the S- and T-scales are on the slide and which are based on the D-scale on the body of the rule.

(A deci-trig slide rule was used for the illustrative examples.) However, for those who might still desire the usual method of logarithmic solutions the use of the slide rule has been made optional without any loss of continuity. To further shorten the time spent on numerical calculations, the oblique triangles are solved by using the Law of Sines and the Law of Cosines. For those who still desire to solve triangles by the Law of Tangents and the half-angle formulas these methods are given in the Appendix.

There are several novel features included. The radian measure of an angle is introduced early and is used interchangeably with the degree measure of an angle. The student is always curious as to how the values of the trigonometric functions are calculated. One advantage of using the radian measure of an angle is that it offers a splendid opportunity to evaluate the trigonometric functions by means of using infinite series. An example is given in the text. The last article in the chapter on identities treats the trigonometric elimination of parameters. Some of the problems in the chapter on identities include types employing trigonometric substitutions such as are encountered in integration. The addition formulas for the trigonometric functions are based on the distance between two points and on the unit circle. The last chapter includes a discussion of scalar and alternating products of plane vectors.

The definitions used throughout the book conform with the definitions found in standard texts of more advanced courses. There are numerous problems which afford the student an opportunity for drill work. The proofs are rigorously given, but are explained in a language the student can understand.

This book is arranged to supply the needs of trigonometric courses of varying length. A brief course might include Chapters 1, 2, 4, 5, and first part of 6, 7, 8, and 9.

As there are numerous books on plane trigonometry, it is an almost impossible task to check them all for repetition of proofs and problems. I am deeply indebted to all of the authors whose books I have used in class and whose books I have read over the past years. A book that was extremely helpful in the trigonometric functions of real numbers was *Principles of Mathematics* by Allendorfer and Oakley published by McGraw-Hill Book Company, in 1955. If I have used any material which an author feels is exclusively his, my apologies, and full credit is due him.

I wish to thank Professor S. S. Saslaw, co-author of *Plane and Spherical Trigonometry*, published by The United States Naval Institute in 1948, for his critical and helpful reading of the manuscript in its rough form, and to thank Professors J. P. Hoyt and T. M. Moore for their criticisms and suggestions, and J. R. Gorman and A. K. Karwath for their splendid help in reading proof. To all my colleagues, who in their many discussions and arguments gave me several ideas for problems and methods of presentation, my heartiest thanks.

NATHAN O. NILES
U. S. NAVAL ACADEMY
ANNAPOLIS, MD.

February, 1959

Preface to the Student

Trigonometry is not a difficult subject. It is logical and its study requires that you do a conscientious job. When studying mathematics, read carefully the discussion and the illustrative examples before attempting to do the problems. In reading mathematics, read the equations and symbols as though they were written out in words. After all, they are only symbols used to denote certain ideas. Thus to read $c = \sqrt{a^2 + b^2}$, we would read "c is equal to the square root of a squared plus b squared." Work out the illustrative examples on a separate piece of paper until you understand each step. Look them over carefully. They are included for your benefit. Be careful and do not use the $=$ sign as a punctuation mark. Mathematics is a game played according to certain rules. Play by the rules and you win. Violate the rules and you are penalized!

A question that some student always asks is, "Where is this used?" Trigonometry is used in many subjects. Some of these are surveying, astronomy, navigation, harmonic analysis, electronics, and many branches of engineering. As your mathematical maturity develops you will be able to see other places where it can be used.

Good luck to you in your study of trigonometry.

NATHAN O. NILES

Contents

Fundamental Concepts

1-1. INTRODUCTION

Trigonometry was originally used to solve problems in astronomy and land measurement. The word is derived from two Greek words meaning the measurement of triangles. As modern mathematics and science developed, the scope of trigonometry broadened until it became an indispensable tool in mathematical analysis, the physical sciences, and many branches of engineering.

Many of you have already worked with or seen the definitions of the trigonometric functions in terms of an angle. These may have been considered in books on plane geometry or algebra where the sine and cosine functions of an angle were discussed. They are very common and useful in the computational work of solving triangles and similar problems. However, in more advanced mathematics courses and allied subjects the concept of the trigonometric functions

1

of real numbers* is vitally important. We will first discuss the trigonometric functions of angles and work with them in solving right triangles. Then in Chapter 4 we shall study the trigonometric functions of real numbers.

Whenever a subject is studied for the first time, there are new definitions to learn. Once the basic definitions are formulated, we can then proceed to find out how to work with them.

We shall see how the values of the trigonometric functions may be obtained, how they might be used, and how the trigonometric functions behave algebraically. To this end, we need to know something about directed lines, the rectangular coordinate system, and angles.

1-2. DIRECTED LINES

A directed line is a line to which a positive and a negative direction has been assigned. In Fig. 1-2-1, let the direction of line l to the right

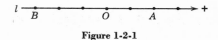

Figure 1-2-1

of point O be assigned positive (indicated by the arrow on the line) and the direction to the left of O be assigned negative. The distance, or length of the line segment, between any two points A and B on a line is the measure of the separation between the two points. The **directed distance** *from* point A *to* point B is the length of the line segment as well as the direction *from A to B*. The symbol used to denote the *directed distance* **from** A **to** B is AB.

Theorem: For any two points A and B on a directed line

(1-2-1) $$AB = -BA.$$

Thus, in Fig. 1-2-1, if $AB = -5$, then $BA = 5$.

The *absolute value* of a number, N, is indicated by the symbol $|N|$. For N positive, $|N| = N$. For N negative, $|N| = -N$. Thus $|3| = 3$ and $|-3| = -(-3) = 3$.

---

* In this book we will consider "real" numbers to be the ordinary numbers with which we usually work. The word "real" distinguishes them from another collection of quantities called "complex numbers." When we speak of numbers we will mean real numbers unless otherwise specified.

The distance *between* any two points A and B on a directed line is $|AB|$.

The position of any point P on a line, l, is given by a number which represents the directed distance, measured in terms of some suitable unit, from a point O called the origin. This number is called the *coordinate of the point P on line l*. If the distance between each mark on line l, of Fig. 1-2-1, is one unit, the coordinate of point A is 2, and the coordinate of point B is -3. Every real number can be considered as the coordinate of one and only one point on a directed line. There is a one-to-one correspondence between the real numbers and the coordinates of points on a directed line. This means that for any real number there is only one point on the line, and for any point on the line there is only one real number associated with it.

Theorem: *If A, B, and C are any three points on a directed line, then*

(1-2-2) $$\boldsymbol{AC = AB + BC.}$$

(a)

A B C +

(b)

B A C +

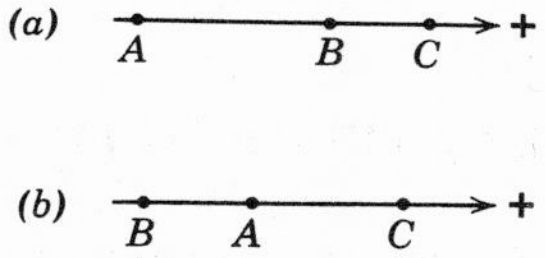

Figure 1-2-2

Proof: For the arrangement of the points shown in Fig. 1-2-2(a) the theorem is evident. For the arrangement shown in Fig. 1-2-2(b) we have

$$BA + AC = BC.$$

Hence $$AC = -BA + BC.$$

Since $$-BA = AB,$$

we have $$AC = AB + BC.$$

The proof for other possible arrangements is left as an exercise for the student.

▶ **EXERCISES**

In problems 1 through 4 show that $AC = AB + BC$, where A, B, and C are any three points on a directed line.

In problems 5 through 7 show that the directed distance from point P_1 to point P_2 is given by $NP_2 - NP_1$.

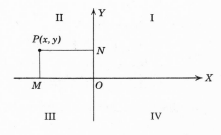

8. Consider the three points A, B, and C to be on a directed straight line. Find the required part.

(a) $AB = 2$, $BC = 3$, find AC.   (b) $AB = -2$, $BC = 3$, find AC.
(c) $AC = 7$, $AB = 2$, find BC.   (d) $CA = -2$, $BC = 3$, find AB.

9. The coordinates of points P_1 and P_2 on a straight line are given. Find the distance from P_1 to P_2 and the distance between P_1 and P_2.

(a) $P_1 = 4$, $P_2 = -2$.   (b) $P_1 = 2$, $P_2 = 5$.
(c) $P_1 = -3$, $P_2 = -7$.   (d) $P_1 = -2$, $P_2 = 2$.

1-3. THE RECTANGULAR COORDINATE SYSTEM

In the preceding article we saw that real numbers could be used to locate a point on a line. We then set up a coordinate system on a line. In a similar manner we shall now set up a coordinate system to locate a point in a plane.

Figure 1-3-1

Let two directed perpendicular lines in the plane intersect at point O (Fig. 1-3-1). Call one of these lines the X-axis, and the other line the Y-axis. The X-axis is usually drawn horizontal with the *positive* direction to the *right*. The Y-axis is usually drawn vertical with the *positive* direction *up*. These axes divide the plane into four regions called quadrants, numbered I, II, III, and IV. We denote quadrant I as QI and so forth for the other quadrants. We now set up a coordinate system on each of these axes with the origin at O.

Let P be any point in the plane. Through P draw a line perpendicular to the Y-axis intersecting it at N. Also draw a line through P perpendicular to the X-axis intersecting it at M.

Definition: *The directed distance* **OM** *is the* **x-coordinate** *or* **abscissa** *of point* P, *and is denoted by* **x**. *The directed distance* **ON** *is the* **y-coordinate** *or* **ordinate** *of point* P, *and is denoted by* **y**.

An ordered pair of numbers is a pair in which the order matters. Thus, the ordered pair $(-3, 7)$ is not the same as the ordered pair $(7, -3)$; x and y are called the rectangular coordinates of point P and are written as the ordered pair (x, y). We are thus able to assign to each point in the plane an ordered pair of real numbers. To each ordered pair of real numbers there corresponds only one point in the plane. We thus have a one-to-one correspondence between a point and its rectangular coordinates. The symbol used to denote that *any* point P has coordinates x and y is $P(x, y)$.

The coordinates of a point may be negative since directed distances were used in the definition of rectangular coordinates.

Example 1. Plot (locate) the points $A(3, 4)$, $B(-2, 5)$, $C(-1, -3)$, and $D(4, -2)$.

Solution: Draw two directed perpendicular lines and mark on them units of a suitable size. See Fig. 1-3-2.

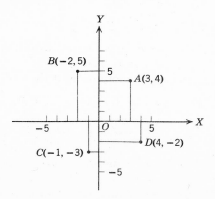

Figure 1-3-2

For point A, the abscissa equals 3 units and the ordinate equals 4 units. Mark them off and thus locate A. For point B, the abscissa equals -2 units and the ordinate equals 5 units.

The distance between any two points $P_1(x_1, y_1)$ and $P_2(x_2, y_2)$ in the rectangular coordinate system is given by the formula

(1-3-1) $$P_1P_2 = \sqrt{(x_2 - x_1)^2 + (y_2 - y_1)^2}.^*$$

The proof follows. Construct the right triangle P_1CP_2 with the line segment P_1P_2 as hypotenuse. (See Fig. 1-3-3.) The side parallel to

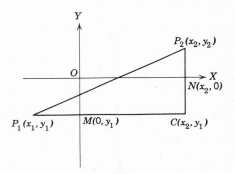

Figure 1-3-3

the X-axis is the line segment P_1C, and the side parallel to the Y-axis is the line segment CP_2. From the Pythagorean Theorem, we have

$$(P_1P_2)^2 = (P_1C)^2 + (CP_2)^2.$$

Using equation 1-2-2, we have

$$P_1C = P_1M + MC.$$

The definition of the abscissa gives us $MC = x_2$ and $MP_1 = x_1$. Hence, $P_1M = -x_1$. We thus have $P_1C = -x_1 + x_2$, or $P_1C = x_2 - x_1$. Similarly using the definition of the ordinate, we find

$$CP_2 = CN + NP_2 = -y_1 + y_2, \text{ or } CP_2 = y_2 - y_1.$$

Thus,

$$P_1P_2 = \sqrt{(x_2 - x_1)^2 + (y_2 - y_1)^2}.$$

Since $(x_2 - x_1)^2 = (x_1 - x_2)^2$ and $(y_2 - y_1)^2 = (y_1 - y_2)^2$, it makes

---

* The symbol $\sqrt{\ }$ denotes the *nonnegative* square root. Hence, P_1P_2 is considered to be positive.

no difference which point is taken as P_1 and which as P_2. The above proof depends upon equation 1-2-2, which is true for any arrangement of three points on a straight line; hence, the formula is true regardless of the location of the two points.

Example 2. Find the distance between $A(-3, 7)$ and $B(2, -1)$.

Solution: Use equation 1-3-1 to obtain

$$P_A P_B = \sqrt{[2 - (-3)]^2 + (-1 -7)^2} = \sqrt{(5)^2 + (-8)^2},$$
$$P_A P_B = \sqrt{89}.$$

The distance **from** the origin **to** the point $P(x, y)$ is called the *radius vector of P*. The radius vector, denoted by $\boldsymbol{r}$, is always positive and is given by the formula

(1-3-2) $$r = \sqrt{x^2 + y^2}.$$

The proof is left as an exercise for the student.

▶ **EXERCISES**

1. State the algebraic signs of the coordinates of a point in
   (a) QI.   (b) QII.   (c) QIII.   (d) QIV.

2. Prove formula 1-3-2, $r = \sqrt{x^2 + y^2}$.

3. Plot the following points. Beside each point write its coordinates. State the value of the abscissa, ordinate, and radius vector. State the quadrant in which each point lies.
   (a) (4, 3).   (b) (5, -12).   (c) (-6, 8).   (d) (-8, -15).
   (e) (4, -3).   (f) (-4, 1).   (g) (-1, -2).   (h) (8, 15).

4. Find the unknown coordinate or radius vector for the point P.
   (a) (7, 24).   (b) (3, -4).   (c) (, 5), $r = \sqrt{29}$, P in QII.
   (d) (-6,), $r = 10$, P in QIII.
   (e) (3,), $r = \sqrt{63}$.   (f) (-24,), $r = 25$.

5. Find the distance between the given points.
   (a) (2, 3), (7, 7).   (b) (2, 3), (-4, 6).
   (c) (-2, 2), (-4, -3).   (d) (-5, -1), (-3, -5).
   (e) (6, -7), (6, 3).   (f) (-3, 1), (-1, 10).

6. Prove that the distance, d_h, between any two points on a horizontal line is given by the absolute value of the difference of their abscissas.

7. Prove that the distance, d_v, between any two points on a vertical line is given by the absolute value of the difference of their ordinates.

8. Prove the distance formula 1-3-1, when (*a*) P_1 is in the second quadrant and P_2 is in the first quadrant; (*b*) P_1 is in the fourth quadrant and P_2 is in the second quadrant.

9. Show that the triangle with vertices at (6, 3), (4, −3), and (2, 1) is a right triangle.

10. Find the perimeter of the triangle with vertices at (−2, 1), (1, −3), and (4, 3).

1-4. THE GENERATION OF POSITIVE AND NEGATIVE ANGLES

In trigonometry we like to consider an angle as being generated by a half-line rotating about its end point. A half-line, or ray, is that part of a line which lies to one side of a fixed point on the line. The fixed point is the end point of the half-line.

Definition: An angle is generated by rotating a half-line about its end point from some initial position to some terminal position. The measure of an angle is the amount of the rotation.

The initial position is called the **initial side**; the terminal position is called the **terminal side** and the end point is called the **vertex** of the

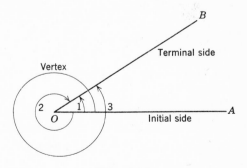

Figure 1-4-1

angle. When we talk about an angle, we will mean the measure of the angle.

In Fig. 1-4-1, angles 1, 2, and 3 represent a few of the many angles associated with this position of the initial and terminal sides of angle

AOB. If the rotation of the terminal side is in a *counterclockwise sense*, the angle is considered to be *positive*. If the rotation of the terminal side is in a *clockwise sense*, the angle is considered to be *negative*. The sense of rotation is indicated by an arrow on a curved line. A *directed angle* is one which has been assigned a sense.

The unit of measurement for angles may be degrees, radians, or mils.* *One* degree *is the measure of an angle whose vertex is at the center of a circle and which intercepts an arc equal in length to $\frac{1}{360}$th of the circumference*. An angle of one degree may be further divided into 60 equal parts each of which is called a *minute*. Each minute may be further subdivided into 60 equal parts each of which is called a *second*. The familiar symbols °, ′, ″, stand for *degrees, minutes,* and *seconds*, respectively. The radian is defined in Art. 1-5.

No limit is placed on the magnitude of an angle. If a half-line makes one complete revolution in a counterclockwise sense, it will generate *one angle* of 360°. Two complete revolutions in a counterclockwise sense is *one angle* of 720°. Thus half-lines *OA* and *OB* may serve as the initial and terminal sides of many angles.

Definition: *Angles having the same initial sides and the same terminal sides are called* **coterminal** *angles.*

Angles are frequently designated by Greek letters such as α (alpha), β (beta), γ (gamma), θ (theta), φ (phi).

Example. Draw angles θ of measure 30°, −45°, 390°. Indicate by φ an angle coterminal with angle θ.

Solution: See Fig. 1-4-2.

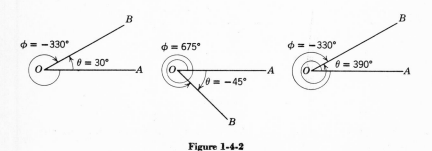

Figure 1-4-2

* The mil is discussed in the appendix.

▶ **EXERCISES**

Draw the following angles. Indicate by arrows the direction and extent of the rotation. Name the initial and terminal sides. Also, for each angle indicate two coterminal angles, one positive and one negative.

1. 60°.   **2.** 135°.   **3.** 240°.   **4.** 300°.

5. −30°.   **6.** −150°.   **7.** −225°.   **8.** −330°.

9. 420°.   **10.** 540°.   **11.** −390°.   **12.** −540°.

13. 150°.   **14.** 270°.   **15.** 315°.   **16.** −270°.

17. 30°.   **18.** 45°.   **19.** 120°.   **20.** 180°.

1-5. RADIAN MEASURE

Definition: A radian is the measure of an angle whose vertex is at the center of a circle and which intercepts an arc on the circle equal in length to the radius of the circle.

We shall now obtain a relation between degrees and radians. From geometry we know that central angles are proportional to the arcs they intercept. For Fig. 1-5-1, we have

$$\frac{\angle AOC}{\angle AOB} = \frac{\overset{\frown}{ABC}}{\overset{\frown}{AB}}.$$

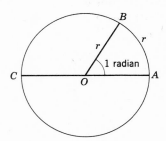

Figure 1-5-1

$\angle AOC = 180°$, $\angle AOB = 1$ radian, and $\overset{\frown}{ABC}$ is one half of the circumference of a circle or πr. Thus, we have

$$\frac{180°}{1 \text{ radian}} = \frac{\pi r}{r}.$$

On cross multiplying we obtain,

(1-5-1)   **π radians = 180°.**

For arithmetical computation in this book we will use the number 3.14 as an approximation to the value of π.*

Using the value of $\pi = 3.14$, we have

(1-5-2)   **1 radian** $= \dfrac{180°}{\pi} =$ **57.3°**, approximately,† and

(1-5-3)   **1°** $= \dfrac{\pi}{180°} =$ **0.0175** radian, approximately.

The ability to quickly convert degrees to radians or radians to degrees should be mastered. This conversion may be performed by making use of formulas 1-5-1, 1-5-2, and 1-5-3. Frequently, an angle in radians is expressed as a fraction of π. For example, $60° = \pi/3$ radians.

When no unit of measurement of an angle is stated, the radian is always understood to be the unit. Thus, an angle of 30 is an angle of 30 radians, whereas an angle of 30° is an angle of 30 degrees.

Example 1. Express the given angle measure in radian measure.

(*a*) 30°.   (*b*) 25°.

Solution: (*a*) Since $30° = \frac{1}{6}(180°)$ we have from formula 1-5-1

$$30° = \frac{\pi}{6} \textbf{ radians.}$$

(*b*) Since 1° = 0.0175 radian, 25° = 25(0.0175) = **0.4375 radian.**

Example 2. Express the given angle measure in degrees.

(*a*) $\frac{2}{3}\pi$.   (*b*) 1.3.

Solution: (*a*) Since formula 1-5-1 tells us

$$\pi \text{ radians } = 180° \text{ we have}$$
$$\tfrac{2}{3}\pi = \tfrac{2}{3}(180°) = \textbf{120°}.$$

(*b*) From formula 1-5-2 we have 1 radian = 57.3°,

hence   1.3 radians = (1.3)(57.3°) = **74.5°.**

---

* The value of π has been computed to many decimal places. To 10 decimal places $\pi = 3.1415926536$. The more accurate values of π are used when more accuracy in a problem is desired.

† The equality symbol is used for approximations for convenience.

The conversion of degrees to radians or of radians to degrees is readily done on the slide rule by using proportions.

Example 3. Use the slide rule to convert 4.6 radians to degrees.

Solution: Use the proportion $\dfrac{\pi}{180°} = \dfrac{4.6}{x}$, and make the slide rule setting as shown in Fig. 1-5-2.

Thus, **4.6 radians = 264°**.

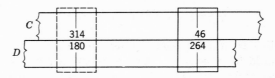

Figure 1-5-2

One of the many uses of radian measure is to find the length of an arc of a circle. In Fig. 1-5-3, let *S* be the length of arc on the circumference of a circle of radius *r* intercepted by a central angle, **θ**,

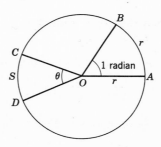

Figure 1-5-3

measured in radians. From plane geometry we know that in a circle, arcs are proportional to their central angles. Let angle *AOB* be of magnitude one radian; then arc *AB* is of length *r*. Form the proportion

$$\frac{S}{r} = \frac{\theta \text{ radians}}{1 \text{ radian}}.$$

Thus (1-5-4) $S = r\theta$ (θ measured in radians).

Example 4. Find the length of arc of a circle of radius 8 in. which subtends a central angle of 67°.

Solution: To use formula 1-5-4, the angle must first be expressed in radians. Hence $67° = 67(0.0175) = 1.17$ radians (approximately), and we have

$$S = (8)(1.17) = \textbf{9.36 in.}$$

▶ **EXERCISES**

1. Convert the angle measure from degrees to radians.

(a) $45°$.   (b) $270°$.   (c) $60°$.   (d) $210°$.

(e) $\pi°$.   (f) $2\pi°$.   (g) $\dfrac{3\pi}{2}°$.   (h) $\dfrac{\pi}{4}°$.

(i) $121.5°$.   (j) $207° \, 12'$.   (k) $341° \, 26'$.   (l) $415.3°$.

2. Convert the angle measure from radians to degrees.

(a) 2π.   (b) $\dfrac{3\pi}{4}$.   (c) $\dfrac{17\pi}{90}$.   (d) $\dfrac{5\pi}{3}$.

(e) 0.056.   (f) 1.2.   (g) 3.   (h) 5.16.

(i) $\dfrac{2}{\pi}$.   (j) $\dfrac{3}{2\pi}$.   (k) $\dfrac{4}{\pi}$.   (l) 1.6π.

Use formula 1-5-4, $S = r\theta$, for problems 3 through 7.

3. Find S if $r = 10$ ft, $\theta = 0.5$.

4. Find S if $r = 8$ in., $\theta = 67°$.

5. A ship sailed a circular course about an anchored buoy. If the angle between the lines of sight from the ship to the buoy was $105°$ while the ship traveled a distance of 1 mile, how far was the ship from the buoy?

6. A pendulum of length 9.6 ft swings through an arc of $17° \, 25'$. How long was the arc described by its mid-point?

7. The length of a pulley belt is 35 ft. If the pulley is 10 in. in diameter, how many revolutions does it make as the belt makes one complete revolution?

8. Show that the area of a sector of a circle of radius, **r**, and of central angle, **θ**, in radians, is $A = \frac{1}{2}r^2\theta$. (Hint: Use Fig. 1-5-4 and the fact that in a given circle the areas of two sectors are proportional to their central angles. Sector $ABCOA$ is intercepted by a central angle of π radians. Find area of AOB.)

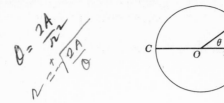

Figure 1-5-4

Use the formula of problem 8, $A = \frac{1}{2}r^2\theta$, for problems 9 through 14.

9. Find A, if $r = 6.3$ in., $\theta = 3.6$.

10. Find r, if $A = 14.7$ ft², $\theta = 0.5$.

11. Find θ, if $r = 135$ yds, $A = 575$ ft².

12. Find the area of a sector of a circle of radius 5 ft and central angle 51°.

13. A searchlight with a range of 1250 ft can turn through an angle of 135°. Find the area over which it can be played.

14. A circular sector has a perimeter of 235 ft and a central angle of 130°. Find its area.

1-6. THE STANDARD POSITION OF AN ANGLE

An angle is in **standard position** if the vertex is at the origin and the *initial side* is placed on the *positive X-axis*. The angle is called a second quadrant angle if the terminal side is in the second quadrant

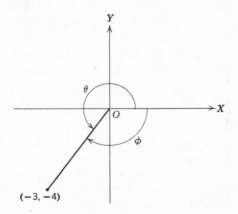

Figure 1-6-1

and likewise for the other quadrants. If the terminal side coincides with an axis, the angle is called a quadrantal angle.

Example. Draw an angle in standard position whose terminal side passes through the point $(-3, -4)$.

Solution: See Fig. 1-6-1. θ is a positive angle and ϕ is a negative angle.

▶ **EXERCISES**

Draw an angle in standard position whose terminal side passes through the given point. Indicate by θ one of the positive angles and by ϕ one of the negative angles thus formed. Name the quadrant of the angle.

1. $(10, 12)$.	**2.** $(-7, 2)$.	**3.** $(0, 3)$.
4. $(12, -5)$.	**5.** $(-3, -10)$.	**6.** $(2, 0)$.
7. $(1, -5)$.	**8.** $(-1, 0)$.	**9.** $(-4, -7)$.
10. $(0, -4)$.	**11.** $(-5, -5)$.	**12.** $(-9, -6)$.

1-7. FUNCTIONS

Whenever there is a relationship between two collections (or sets) of numbers, it defines a function. There are many ways of expressing the relationship, such as tables, charts, and formulas.

The cost of sending a package by parcel post is determined by its weight. The postman can find the correct cost by using a table giving the costs for certain weights.

Charts may be used to convey information such as the number of students taking a course in trigonometry in certain years.

The formula $A = \pi r^2$ enables us to find the area of a circle if we know the radius.

Each of the above methods sets up a correspondence between two collections of numbers.

Definition: One of the collections is called the **domain** *of the function. The other collection is called the* **range** *of the function. An element of the range of the function is called an* **image**.

We now give the definition of a function.

Definition: *A function is a rule which assigns to each element of the domain of the function one and only one element of the range of the function.*

Whenever a symbol is used to denote an arbitrary element of a set, containing more than one element, it is called a *variable*. If the set contains only one element, then the symbol is called a *constant*. It is customary to let letters in the last part of the alphabet such as u, v, x, y, z, etc., denote variables and letters in the first part of the alphabet denote constants.

Special notations are used for functions. The rule part of the function is usually designated by f, g, T, *sin*, and other symbols. Usually x represents an arbitrary element of the domain of the function and is called the *independent variable of the function*. The letter y may be used to represent an arbitrary image and is called the *dependent variable* of the function. The symbol $f(x)$ denotes the image assigned to x by the function f. There are two ways of reading the symbol $f(x)$, "f **at** x" and "f **of** x". The former is more elegant as it denotes the value of the function f at the number x. However, the common usage in reading $f(x)$ is "f **of** x". In conformance with this usage, we shall speak of f **of** x for general values of x and for a specific value of x, say $x = a$, we shall read $f(a)$ as "f **at** a". The expression $y = f(x)$ also represents the value of the function at x. The independent variable of the function is sometimes called the *argument* of the function. Other symbols such as $T(\theta)$, $g(z)$ and so forth would be used to represent other functions.

The symbol $f(x)$ plays a dual role in mathematics. It stands for the function f itself and it also stands for the value of the function **at** a particular value of x. This ambiguity, however, will not usually cause confusion. Suppose $f(x) = x^2$, then $f(-2)$ stands for the value of the function at $x = -2$, or $f(-2) = (-2)^2 = 4$.

In specifying a particular function it is necessary to specify all parts of the function either directly or indirectly. Usually in elementary mathematics no mention is made of either the domain or range of the function, it being assumed that they are obvious or easily determined. In this book the rule will be specified by equations or formulas. Thus, for $f(x) = x^2$ it is obvious that the domain consists of the set of all real numbers, while the range consists of the set of all nonnegative numbers. The rule states that an image is obtained by squaring an element of the domain. For $f(x) = \sqrt{x}$, it is evident that the domain and range consist of all $x \geq 0$. (Read: x is greater than or equal to zero.) If we wish to restrict the domain to certain values, then we must specifically state the domain. Suppose we wished to restrict the domain to only those numbers between and including 1 and 2 for the function $f(x) = x^2$. We would then write $f(x) = x^2$, $1 \leq x \leq 2$. (Read: x is greater than or equal to one and less than or equal to two.)

Trigonometry is the study of the properties of certain quantities whose values are determined by the values of a variable angle or real number. Hence, they are functions of the angle measure or real number from which their values are determined.

▶ **EXERCISES**

1. If $f(x) = 2x - 3$, find $f(1), f(0), f(-3)$.

2. If $f(u) = \dfrac{u^2 - 3}{u + 1}$, find $f(2), f(-2), f(a + h)$.

3. If $f(x) = \dfrac{1 - x^2}{1 + x^2}$, find $f(3), f(-3)$. Show that $f(-x) = f(x)$.

4. Name the argument of the functions: (a) $f(x)$. (b) $f(y)$. (c) $F(z)$. (d) $T(\phi)$. (e) $\sin (\theta)$. (f) $gd(u)$. (g) $\sinh (t)$.

5. Express the radius of a circle as a function of its area.

6. State the domain and range of the function. Write out in words the rule of the function.

(a) $f(x) = 3x$. (b) $f(x) = \dfrac{3}{x - 2}$. (Hint: division by zero is not an allowable algebraic process.)

(c) $f(x) = \dfrac{x + 1}{x - 1}$. (d) $f(x) = \sqrt{25 - x^2}$. (e) $f(x) = \sqrt{x^2 - 25}$.

(f) $f(x) = |x|$. (g) $f(x) = 2x + 1$, $-1 \leq x \leq 3$.
(h) $f(x) = x^2 - x + 1$, $-3 \leq x \leq 0$.

7. Express the abscissa of a point as a function of its ordinate and radius vector.

8. Express the ordinate of a point as a function of its abscissa and radius vector.

Trigonometric Functions (Angles)

2-1. DEFINITION OF THE TRIGONOMETRIC FUNCTIONS OF ANY ANGLE

In the last article, we saw that a function is a rule and that a common symbol used to denote the function is f. We also saw that the symbol $f(x)$ stands for the function itself and for the value of the function at x. We shall here define a class of functions called the *trigonometric functions*. There are six such functions: the **sine** function, the **cosine** function, the **tangent** function, the **cotangent** function, the **secant** function, and the **cosecant** function. Instead of using a single letter to represent each trigonometric function, we shall use three letters for each function (their abbreviations); thus, **sin** for the *sine function*, **cos** for the *cosine function*, **tan** for the *tangent function*, **cot** for the *cotangent function*, **sec** for the *secant function*, and **csc** for the *cosecant function*. Hence, the symbol $sin\ (\theta)$ represents the sine function evaluated at θ. (The symbol $sin\ \theta$ is commonly read

18

"sine of θ.") It is customary when using the abbreviations of the trigonometric functions to omit the ( ) signs surrounding the argument. When we wish to speak of all of the trigonometric functions without specifying a particular one, we will use the symbol $T(\theta)$.

A peculiarity of functional notation should now be pointed out. The symbol f may be used to represent many different rules. That is, if we set $f(x) = (something)$ the quantity to the right of the equals sign will give the rule. For example, if $f(x) = x^3$, the rule is to cube the elements of the domain. If $f(x) = \sqrt{x}$, the rule is to take the square root of the elements of the domain. However, for the trigonometric functions, the rule is implied by the function symbol. That is, *sin* **always** implies the rule for the sine function. Similar statements are true for the symbols of the other trigonometric functions.

In the definitions that follow we will state the domain and range of the trigonometric functions even though they should be evident with a little thought.

Let P be any point *different from* 0 on the terminal side of θ in standard position (Fig. 2-1-1 on page 20), that is, $r \neq 0$. (Read: r not equal to zero.)

Then the trigonometric functions of θ are defined as in Table 2-1:

TABLE 2-1

Function	Domain	Range
$\sin \theta = \dfrac{\text{ordinate of } P}{\text{radius vector of } P} = \dfrac{y}{r}.$	All angles.	$-1 \leqq \dfrac{\text{All real}}{\text{numbers}} \leqq 1.$
$\cos \theta = \dfrac{\text{abscissa of } P}{\text{radius vector of } P} = \dfrac{x}{r}.$	All angles.	$-1 \leqq \dfrac{\text{All real}}{\text{numbers}} \leqq 1.$
$\tan \theta = \dfrac{\text{ordinate of } P}{\text{abscissa of } P} = \dfrac{y}{x}.$	All angles for which $x \neq 0.$	All real numbers.
$\cot \theta = \dfrac{\text{abscissa of } P}{\text{ordinate of } P} = \dfrac{x}{y}.$	All angles for which $y \neq 0.$	All real numbers.
$\sec \theta = \dfrac{\text{radius vector of } P}{\text{abscissa of } P} = \dfrac{r}{x}.$	All angles for which $x \neq 0.$	All real numbers $\leqq -1$ and $\geqq 1.$
$\csc \theta = \dfrac{\text{radius vector of } P}{\text{ordinate of } P} = \dfrac{r}{y}.$	All angles for which $y \neq 0.$	All real numbers $\leqq -1$ and $\geqq 1.$

These ratios, although defined in terms of the coordinates of the point $P(x, y)$, depend only on the fact that P is *any* point on the terminal side of θ, different from the origin, for if we choose any other

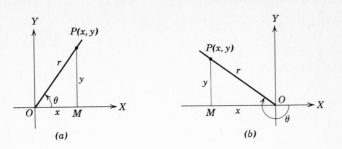

Figure 2-1-1

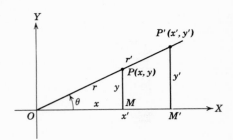

Figure 2-1-2

point $P'(x', y')$ on OP, with radius vector r', where $r' \neq 0$ (see Fig. 2-1-2), we obtain from the definition of the trigonometric functions $\sin \theta = \dfrac{y'}{r'}$, $\cos \theta = \dfrac{x'}{r'}$, $\tan \theta = \dfrac{y'}{x'}$, etc., but from the similar triangles OMP and $OM'P'$ we see that $\dfrac{y}{r} = \dfrac{y'}{r'}$, $\dfrac{x}{r} = \dfrac{x'}{r'}$, $\dfrac{y}{x} = \dfrac{y'}{x'}$, etc. Hence the value of $\sin \theta$, or of any other trigonometric function, *depends* only on the *measure* of angle θ and *not* on the position of point P on the terminal side of θ.

Since coterminal angles have the same initial and terminal sides and the trigonometric functions depend only on the position of the terminal side, we state the

Theorem: *A trigonometric function of an angle is equal to the same trigonometric function of its coterminal angles.*

Notes on the definitions:

1. Recall that θ represents the *measure* of angle θ. Since no units of measurement have been specified in the above definitions, θ may be measured in degrees or radians. In Chapter 4 we will show that every real number may be included in the domain of the trigonometric functions.

2. The restriction in the domain of tan θ, cot θ, sec θ, and csc θ is due to the algebraic rule that does not allow division by zero.*

3. The abbreviations for the names of the trigonometric functions are written without a period.

4. In this book the use of the abbreviations without a symbol for the argument is avoided.

5. The trigonometric functions may be grouped into pairs called cofunctions; that is *sine* and *cosine, tangent* and *cotangent, secant* and *cosecant.* In each of these pairs *each function* is the *cofunction of the other.*

Example. Write out in words the rule implied by the symbol *sin θ*.

Solution: For any point (other than the origin) on the terminal side of an angle, θ, in standard position form the ratio of the ordinate to the radius vector.

▶ **EXERCISES**

Write out in words the rule implied by the symbols: (*a*) cos θ. (*b*) tan θ. (*c*) cot θ. (*d*) sec θ. (*e*) csc θ.

2-2. SIGNS OF THE TRIGONOMETRIC FUNCTIONS

The algebraic signs of the trigonometric functions of any angle depend on the signs of the ordinate, the abscissa, and the radius vector of any point on its terminal side. As the terminal side passes from one quadrant to another, the radius vector always remains

---

* The fraction $a/b = c$ implies that $a = b \cdot c$. If $a = 0$ and $b \neq 0$, then $0 = b \cdot c$, which is true for $b \neq 0$ only if $c = 0$. Hence, $0/b = 0$, for $b \neq 0$. If $a \neq 0$ and $b = 0$, the fraction $a/0$ has *no meaning*. For $a = 0 \cdot c$ implies that $a = 0$ which is contrary to the hypothesis that $a \neq 0$. If $a = 0$ and $b = 0$, the fraction is *indeterminate*. For this implies $0 = 0 \cdot c$ which is true for all values of c.

positive, while there is always a change in the sign of the abscissa or the ordinate. In the first quadrant both coordinates are positive; in the second quadrant the abscissa, x, is negative and the ordinate, y, is positive; in the third quadrant both x and y are negative; and in the fourth quadrant x is positive and y is negative. Table 2-2 summarizes the signs of the trigonometric functions.

TABLE 2-2

Quadrant of the angle θ	Positive functions	Negative functions
I	All.	None.
II	$\sin \theta$, $\csc \theta$.	$\cos \theta$, $\sec \theta$, $\tan \theta$, $\cot \theta$.
III	$\tan \theta$, $\cot \theta$.	$\sin \theta$, $\csc \theta$, $\cos \theta$, $\sec \theta$.
IV	$\cos \theta$, $\sec \theta$.	$\sin \theta$, $\csc \theta$, $\tan \theta$, $\cot \theta$.

The value of trigonometric functions at an angle may be approximated by using Fig. 2-2-1. The abscissa, ordinate, and radius vector of any point within or on the circle may be determined from the graph; then by use of the definitions the value of the trigonometric functions may be computed. The circle of radius 10 was chosen for convenience.

Example 1. Use Fig. 2-2-1 to find approximately the values of the trigonometric functions at 130°.

Solution: Draw the angle 130° in standard position. For convenience read the coordinates of the point P where the terminal side intersects the circle.

Thus $\qquad x = -6.4$, $y = 7.7$, and $r = 10$.

From the definitions we have approximately

$$\sin 130° = \frac{7.7}{10} = 0.77. \qquad \csc 130° = \frac{10}{7.7} = 1.3.$$

$$\cos 130° = \frac{-6.4}{10} = -0.64. \qquad \sec 130° = \frac{10}{-6.4} = -1.6.$$

$$\tan 130° = \frac{7.7}{-6.4} = -1.2. \qquad \cot 130° = \frac{-6.4}{7.7} = -0.83.$$

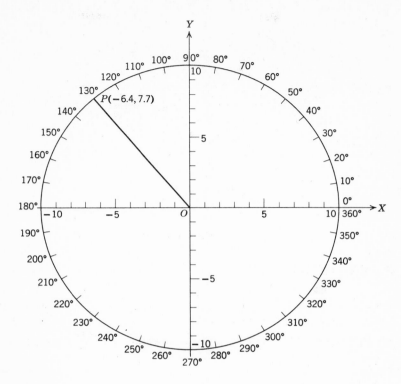

Figure 2-2-1

Example 2. Find the trigonometric functions at an angle in standard position whose terminal side passes through $(-1, -\sqrt{3})$.

Solution: Let θ be the angle and sketch θ in standard position as shown. (Fig. 2-2-2.) Since $x = -1$ and $y = -\sqrt{3}$, we have $r = 2$. Then from the definitions we obtain

$$\sin\theta = \frac{y}{r} = -\frac{\sqrt{3}}{2}. \qquad \csc\theta = \frac{r}{y} = \frac{2}{-\sqrt{3}} = \frac{-2\sqrt{3}}{3}.$$

$$\cos\theta = \frac{x}{r} = \frac{-1}{2}. \qquad \sec\theta = \frac{r}{x} = \frac{2}{-1} = -2.$$

$$\tan\theta = \frac{y}{x} = \frac{-\sqrt{3}}{-1} = \sqrt{3}. \qquad \cot\theta = \frac{x}{y} = \frac{-1}{-\sqrt{3}} = \frac{\sqrt{3}}{3}.$$

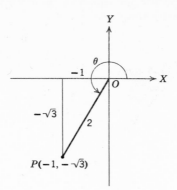

Figure 2-2-2

▶ **EXERCISES**

1. Use Fig. 2-2-1 to find approximately the trigonometric functions at the angle whose measure is: (*a*) 50°. (*b*) 60°. (*c*) 125°. (*d*) 260°. (*e*) 340°. (*f*) $\dfrac{\pi}{5}$· (*g*) $\dfrac{7\pi}{5}$· (*h*) $\dfrac{5\pi}{7}$· (*i*) $\dfrac{11\pi}{9}$· (*j*) 5.76. (*k*) 2.36. (*l*) 0.366.

2. Use a suitable coterminal angle to find the approximate trigonometric functions at the angle whose measure is: (*a*) − 40°. (*b*) − 150°. (*c*) $\dfrac{-7\pi}{6}$· (*d*) $\dfrac{-5\pi}{4}$· (*e*) 430°. (*f*) 640°. (*g*) − 560°. (*h*) − 850°.

3. State the quadrants in which: (*a*) sin θ is positive, (*b*) cos θ is positive, (*c*) tan θ is positive, (*d*) sin θ is negative, (*e*) cos θ is negative, (*f*) tan θ is negative.

4. In the definitions of the trigonometric functions of an angle in standard position let $r = 1$, and write the definitions of tan θ, cot θ, sec θ, and csc θ in terms of sin θ and cos θ.

5. Find the trigonometric functions at an angle in standard position whose terminal side passes through the given point.

(*a*) (3, 7). (*b*) (− 5, 4). (*c*) (− 12, − 13). (*d*) (16, − 9).
(*e*) (− 4, − 3). (*f*) (4, 7). (*g*) (1, − 1). (*h*) ($\sqrt{3}$, − 1). (*i*) (− 2, 5).
(*j*) ($3\sqrt{2}$, $4\sqrt{2}$).

6. In the following table, two of the functions of an angle have the signs as indicated. State the quadrant of the angle and the signs of the other trigonometric functions.

	(a)	(b)	(c)	(d)	(e)	(f)	(g)	(h)	(i)	(j)	(k)	(l)
Quadrant												
$\sin \theta$	−	+					+					
$\cos \theta$		−	+			+				−	−	
$\tan \theta$	+		+	−	−					+	−	
$\cot \theta$						+		−				−
$\sec \theta$				+			+		−			
$\csc \theta$				−				+	−			−

2-3. GIVEN ONE TRIGONOMETRIC FUNCTION, TO DETERMINE THE OTHERS

If we know the value of one of the trigonometric functions of an angle and the quadrant in which it lies, we can find the values of the other trigonometric functions. The method, in general, consists of drawing the angle in standard position, finding from the given conditions a point on the terminal side of the angle and using the co-ordinates and radius vector of this point in the definitions of the trigonometric functions to obtain their values.

Example 1. Given that $\tan \theta = -\frac{3}{4}$ and that θ is an angle in the second quadrant, find the other trigonometric functions at θ.

Solution: From the definition $\tan \theta = y/x$, we have

$$\frac{y}{x} = -\frac{3}{4}.$$

Any point in the second quadrant whose coordinates are in the ratio $-\frac{3}{4}$ lies on the terminal side of θ. A few points of this kind are: $(-4, 3)$, $(-8, 6)$, and $(-1, \frac{3}{4})$. Let us choose the point $P(-4, 3)$, for convenience.

Draw the angle in standard position as shown in Fig. 2-3-1. From the relation

$$r = \sqrt{x^2 + y^2},$$

we have $$r = \sqrt{16 + 9} = 5.$$

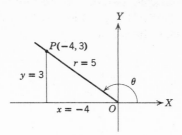

Figure 2-3-1

Hence,

$$\sin \theta = \frac{y}{r} = \frac{3}{5}. \qquad \cos \theta = \frac{x}{r} = -\frac{4}{5}. \qquad \tan \theta = \frac{y}{x} = -\frac{3}{4}.$$

$$\csc \theta = \frac{r}{y} = \frac{5}{3}. \qquad \sec \theta = \frac{r}{x} = -\frac{5}{4}. \qquad \cot \theta = \frac{x}{y} = -\frac{4}{3}.$$

If the quadrant in which the angle lies is not specified, then there are generally **two** nonnegative angles less than 360° which have the same value for a specific trigonometric function.

Example 2. Given that $\sin \theta = -\frac{5}{13}$, find the other trigonometric functions at θ.

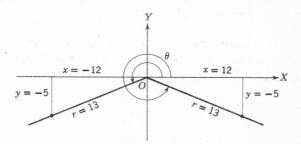

Figure 2-3-2

Solution: Since the quadrant of θ is not specified, two angles less than 360° will satisfy the given condition. One is a third quadrant angle and the other is in the fourth quadrant. (Fig. 2-3-2.) From the definition

$$\sin \theta = \frac{y}{r},$$

we have
$$\frac{y}{r} = -\frac{5}{13}.$$

Since r is always positive, we choose $y = -5$ and $r = 13$. From the relation $x^2 + y^2 = r^2$,

we find
$$x = \pm\sqrt{r^2 - y^2},$$

and thus
$$x = \pm\ 12.$$

Hence,

$\sin\theta = -\frac{5}{13}.$	$\cos\theta = \mp\frac{12}{13}.$	$\tan\theta = \pm\frac{5}{12}.$
$\csc\theta = -\frac{13}{5}.$	$\sec\theta = \mp\frac{13}{12}.$	$\cot\theta = \pm\frac{12}{5}.$

▶ **EXERCISES**

Find the trigonometric functions at an angle that satisfies the given conditions.

1. $\tan\theta = \frac{4}{3}$, θ in QI. **2.** $\sin\theta = \frac{3}{5}$, θ in QII.

3. $\cos\theta = \frac{4}{5}$, θ in QIV. **4.** $\sec\theta = -\frac{13}{5}$, θ in QIII.

5. $\cot\theta = -\frac{8}{15}$, θ in QII. **6.** $\sin\theta = \frac{12}{13}$, θ in QII.

7. $\sin\theta = -\frac{1}{10}$, θ in QIV. **8.** $\cos\theta = -\frac{1}{17}$, θ in QIII.

9. $\cos\theta = \frac{2}{29}$, θ in QIV. **10.** $\tan\theta = \frac{5}{3}$, θ in QIII.

11. $\sin\theta = -\frac{9}{41}$, θ in QIV. **12.** $\sec\theta = -\frac{41}{40}$, θ in QII.

13. $\tan\theta = -\frac{5}{12}$. **14.** $\sin\theta = \frac{3}{4}$.

15. $\cos\theta = -\frac{5}{12}$. **16.** $\cot\theta = -\frac{7}{24}$.

17. $\sec\theta = \frac{5}{3}$. **18.** $\csc\theta = -\frac{13}{12}$.

19. $\tan\theta = 1$. **20.** $\sin\theta = -\frac{3}{7}$.

21. $\cos\theta = \frac{2}{5}$. **22.** $\cot\theta = 3$.

23. $\tan\theta = \frac{9}{40}$. **24.** $\cos\theta = -\frac{40}{41}$.

25. $\sin\theta = 0.62$, θ in QI. **26.** $\cos\theta = -0.28$, θ in QII.

27. $\tan\theta = -2.6$, θ in QIV. **28.** $\cot\theta = 10$, θ in QIII.

29. $\sec\theta = 7.6$, θ in QI. **30.** $\csc\theta = -4.5$, θ in QIII.

31. State the nonnegative angles less than $360°$ which are not included in the sentence immediately preceding Example 2 on page 26.

2-4. EXACT VALUES OF THE TRIGONOMETRIC FUNCTIONS AT 30°, 45°, AND 60°

In the next two articles we shall see how the exact values of the trigonometric functions at a few special angles may be found. The student should bear in mind that to find these values we only need to find the coordinates (x, y) and the radius vector r of any point on the terminal side of the angle when placed in standard position. . We use the word *exact* to mean precise. Thus, the exact value of the square root of three may be expressed as $\sqrt{3}$, while to three decimal places the approximate value of the square root of three is 1.732. Similarly, the symbol π represents an exact number and its approximate value to three decimal places is 3.142.

From plane geometry the student should recall that in a 30°-60°-90° triangle the sides opposite these angles are proportional to the numbers 1, $\sqrt{3}$, and 2, respectively. See Fig. 2-4-1.

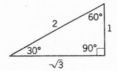

Figure 2-4-1

Trigonometric Functions at 30°

Draw angle 30° in standard position (Fig. 2-4-2). Since any point

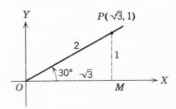

Figure 2-4-2

may be chosen on the terminal side, choose $OP = 2$. Then P has coordinates $(\sqrt{3}, 1)$. From the definitions of the trigonometric functions, we have

$$\sin 30° = \frac{y}{r} = \frac{1}{2}. \qquad\qquad \csc 30° = \frac{r}{y} = \frac{2}{1} = 2.$$

$$\cos 30° = \frac{x}{r} = \frac{\sqrt{3}}{2}. \qquad\qquad \sec 30° = \frac{r}{x} = \frac{2}{\sqrt{3}} = \frac{2\sqrt{3}}{3}.$$

$$\tan 30° = \frac{y}{x} = \frac{1}{\sqrt{3}} = \frac{\sqrt{3}}{3}. \qquad \cot 30° = \frac{x}{y} = \frac{\sqrt{3}}{1} = \sqrt{3}.$$

Trigonometric Functions at 60°

Draw angle 60° in standard position (Fig. 2-4-3). Choose $OP = 2$.

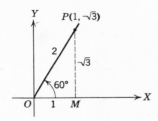

Figure 2-4-3

Then the coordinates of point P are $(1, \sqrt{3})$. From the definitions of the trigonometric functions, we have

$$\sin 60° = \frac{y}{r} = \frac{\sqrt{3}}{2}. \qquad\qquad \csc 60° = \frac{r}{y} = \frac{2}{\sqrt{3}} = \frac{2\sqrt{3}}{3}.$$

$$\cos 60° = \frac{x}{r} = \frac{1}{2}. \qquad\qquad \sec 60° = \frac{r}{x} = \frac{2}{1} = 2.$$

$$\tan 60° = \frac{y}{x} = \frac{\sqrt{3}}{1} = \sqrt{3}. \qquad \cot 60° = \frac{x}{y} = \frac{1}{\sqrt{3}} = \frac{\sqrt{3}}{3}.$$

Trigonometric Functions at 45°

In plane geometry it is shown that an isosceles right triangle has its sides proportional to the numbers 1, 1, and $\sqrt{2}$. See Fig. 2-4-4.

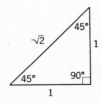

Figure 2-4-4

Draw angle 45° in standard position (Fig. 2-4-5). Choose $OP = \sqrt{2}$. Then the coordinates of point P are (1, 1). From the

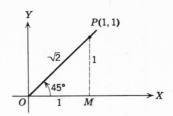

Figure 2-4-5

definitions of the trigonometric functions, we have

$$\sin 45° = \frac{y}{r} = \frac{1}{\sqrt{2}} = \frac{\sqrt{2}}{2}. \qquad \csc 45° = \frac{r}{y} = \frac{\sqrt{2}}{1} = \sqrt{2}.$$

$$\cos 45° = \frac{x}{r} = \frac{1}{\sqrt{2}} = \frac{\sqrt{2}}{2}. \qquad \sec 45° = \frac{r}{x} = \frac{\sqrt{2}}{1} = \sqrt{2}.$$

$$\tan 45° = \frac{y}{x} = \frac{1}{1} = 1. \qquad \cot 45° = \frac{x}{y} = \frac{1}{1} = 1.$$

The trigonometric functions at an integral multiple of 30° or 45° whose terminal side does not coincide with one of the coordinate axes is readily found by placing the 30°-60°-90° or 45°-45°-90° triangle in such a way that the appropriate angle occurs in standard position.

Example. Find the exact values of the trigonometric functions at 120°.

Solution: Place the 30°-60°-90° triangle in the position as shown in Fig. 2-4-6. Then point $P(-1, \sqrt{3})$ has a radius vector $r = 2$, and

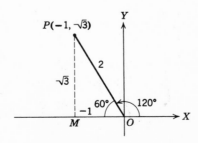

Figure 2-4-6

from the definitions we have

$$\sin 120° = \frac{\sqrt{3}}{2}.$$

$$\csc 120° = \frac{2}{\sqrt{3}} = \frac{2\sqrt{3}}{3}.$$

$$\cos 120° = \frac{-1}{2}.$$

$$\sec 120° = \frac{2}{-1} = -2.$$

$$\tan 120° = \frac{-\sqrt{3}}{1} = -\sqrt{3}.$$

$$\cot 120° = \frac{-1}{\sqrt{3}} = \frac{-\sqrt{3}}{3}.$$

2-5. TRIGONOMETRIC FUNCTIONS AT QUADRANTAL ANGLES

A quadrantal angle is an angle in standard position whose terminal side coincides with one of the coordinate axes. For these angles one of the coordinates of a point on the terminal side must be zero. Since division by zero is not an admissible algebraic operation, two of the trigonometric functions for each quadrantal angle will not exist.

Example. Find the trigonometric functions at 180°.

Solution : Draw the angle in standard position as in Fig. 2-5-1. For

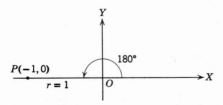

Figure 2-5-1

convenience choose point $P(-1, 0)$ as a point on the terminal side. Then $x = -1$, $y = 0$, and $r = 1$. Using the definitions we have

$$\sin 180° = \frac{y}{r} = \frac{0}{1} = 0.$$

$$\csc 180° = \frac{r}{y} = \frac{1}{0} \text{ (does not exist)}.$$

$$\cos 180° = \frac{x}{r} = \frac{-1}{1} = -1.$$

$$\sec 180° = \frac{r}{x} = \frac{1}{-1} = -1.$$

$$\tan 180° = \frac{y}{x} = \frac{0}{-1} = 0.$$

$$\cot 180° = \frac{x}{y} = \frac{-1}{0} \text{ (does not exist)}.$$

▶ **EXERCISES**

1. Draw the angles in standard position and calculate the exact values of their trigonometric functions.

(a) 150°. (b) 210°. (c) 240°. (d) 300°. (e) 0°. (f) 90°. (g) 270°.

(h) $\dfrac{3\pi}{4}$. (i) $\dfrac{7\pi}{4}$. (j) $\dfrac{13\pi}{6}$. (k) $\dfrac{13\pi}{3}$. (l) $-30°$. (m) $-210°$. (n) $\dfrac{-4\pi}{3}$.

2. (a) Complete the table with the exact value of the functions.

θ	0°	30°	45°	60°	90°	180°	270°
$\sin \theta$							
$\cos \theta$							
$\tan \theta$							

(b) Make a table similar to the table in part a for θ in radians.

3. Show that the following statements are true. The notation $\sin^2 \theta$ means $(\sin \theta)^2$.

(a) $\sin^2 30° + \cos^2 30° = 1$.

(b) $1 + \tan^2 \dfrac{\pi}{4} = \sec^2 \dfrac{\pi}{4}$.

(c) $1 + \cot^2 \dfrac{\pi}{6} = \csc^2 \dfrac{\pi}{6}$.

(d) $2 \sin 30° \cos 30° = \sin 60°$.

(e) $\cos^2 30° - \sin^2 30° = \cos 60°$.

(f) $\cos 30° = \sqrt{\dfrac{1 + \cos 60°}{2}}$.

(g) $\sin \dfrac{\pi}{6} = \sqrt{\dfrac{1 - \cos \pi/3}{2}}$.

(h) $\cos^2 \dfrac{\pi}{6} \left(1 + \tan^2 \dfrac{\pi}{6}\right) = 1$.

4. Find the exact values of the following expressions.

(a) $\tan^2 30° \sec 60° \sin 45°$.

(b) $\sin^2 90° \cos^2 60° \sec 60°$.

(c) $\cos^2 \pi \tan \dfrac{\pi}{4} \sec \dfrac{\pi}{3}$.

(d) $\csc \dfrac{\pi}{2} \sin^2 \dfrac{\pi}{3} - \cos^2 \dfrac{\pi}{6}$.

(e) $\cot 30° - \sin \dfrac{\pi}{3} \sec \dfrac{\pi}{6}$.

(f) $\sec^2 45° \sin 60° - 3 \tan \dfrac{\pi}{6}$.

(g) $\sin \pi \cos 2\pi + \tan \dfrac{\pi}{3} \cot \dfrac{\pi}{3}$.

(h) $\sin 45° \cos 45° (\tan 45° + \cot 45°)$.

2-6. TRIGONOMETRIC FUNCTIONS OF POSITIVE ACUTE ANGLES

In the last two articles, the trigonometric functions of a few special angles were found by employing special techniques. The exact values of the trigonometric functions of other angles can also be found. However, the results are rather cumbersome. It is shown in higher mathematics that the values of the trigonometric functions of angles for which the trigonometric functions exist can be found by using infinite series which converge. (The words "infinite series" and "converge" are fully defined in standard texts on Calculus.) In Art. 2-7 we will show that the trigonometric functions of any angle can be expressed in terms of trigonometic functions of a positive acute angle.

An infinite series for $sin\ \theta$, where θ is the radian measure of the angle, is given by

$$\sin \theta = \theta - \frac{\theta^3}{3!} + \frac{\theta^5}{5!} - \frac{\theta^7}{7!} + \cdots.$$

(The three dots at the end mean that the rest of the terms follow the same pattern.) The product of the positive integers from 1 to n is called *factorial n* and is denoted by *n!* Thus $5! = 1 \cdot 2 \cdot 3 \cdot 4 \cdot 5 = 120$.

If θ is small, $sin\ \theta$ is easily computed from this series. For a large θ, suitable reductions can be made.

Example 1. Compute the value of *sin 0.2* correct to four decimal places.

Solution: Substitute $\theta = 0.2$ in the infinite series for $sin\ \theta$.

Thus $\qquad \sin 0.2 = 0.2 - \dfrac{(0.2)^3}{3!} + \dfrac{(0.2)^5}{5!} - \dfrac{(0.2)^7}{7!} + \cdots.$

$$\sin 0.2 = 0.20000 - \frac{0.00800}{6} + \frac{0.00032}{120} - \frac{0.0000128}{5040} + \cdots.$$

$$\sin 0.2 = 0.20000 - 0.00133 + 0.000003 - 0.000000002 + \cdots.$$

As the fourth and following terms will not here affect the fourth decimal place, we need only to add the first three terms to obtain

$$\sin 0.2 = 0.1987.$$

If a greater number of decimal places in the answer is required, it is only necessary to use more terms of the infinite series. The method of using infinite series to find the values of trigonometric functions is used by the electronic computing machines.

The trigonometric functions of many positive acute angles have been computed and placed in tables for easy reference. Table I in the back of this book gives the values of the trigonometric functions for an angle θ measured in degrees and radians. The angles are listed at intervals of 10' and the values of their trigonometric functions are accurate to four decimal places.

In using Table I we note that angles from 0° to 45° are listed in the left-hand column, and those from 45° to 90° are listed in the right-hand column. The validity of this arrangement will be shown in Chapter 3 when we show that cofunctions of acute complementary angles are equal. The value of the trigonometric function of an angle is found on the same line as the angle. If the angle is listed at the *left* of the page, the column heading is at the *top* of the page. If the angle is listed at the *right* of the page, the column heading is at the *bottom* of the page. A few examples of the use of Table I follow.

To find *sin 27°40'*, we note that the angle is listed at the *left*. Hence, we use the column name at the *top* and find **sin 27°40' = 0.4643**.

To find *tan 1.0879*, we note that the angle (in radians) is listed at the *right*. Hence, we use the column name at the *bottom* and find **tan 1.0879 = 1.907**.

To find the angle whose trigonometric function is known, we reverse the process. Thus, to find θ, given that *cot θ = 0.5169* and θ a positive acute angle, we look in the *cot θ* columns until the number 0.5169 is found. Noting that *cot θ* is at the *bottom* of the column, we read the angle at the *right*. Hence, for *cot θ = 0.5169*, we have θ = **62°40'** or **1.0937 radians**.

If the angle, or the trigonometric function of the angle for which we are looking, is not listed in the table we find it by a process called *linear interpolation*. This process assumes that if an angle lies between two entries in the table, then its trigonometric functions lie a proportional distance between the trigonometric functions listed. The method will be illustrated in the following examples. Interpolation will not give more accuracy than the listed values in the table.

Example 2. Find sin 27°37'.

Solution: Clearly, 27°37' lies between 27°30' and 27°40' and sin 27°37' lies between sin 27°30' and sin 27°40'. To find out where it lies make the following schematic diagram.

$$10\left[7\left[\begin{matrix}\theta \\ 27°30' \\ 27°37' \\ 27°40'\end{matrix}\right.\right.\qquad\left.\left.\begin{matrix}\sin\theta \\ 0.4617 \\ ]x \\ 0.4643\end{matrix}\right]26.\right.$$

Clearly, $27°37'$ lies $\frac{7}{10}$ of the way from $27°30'$ to $27°40'$, and $\sin 27°37'$ should lie a proportional way from 0.4617 to 0.4643.

The difference between the two entries 0.4617 and 0.4643, namely, 0.0026, is called the *tabular difference*. For convenience, the tabular difference usually omits the decimal point and the zeros immediately following the decimal point and is written as an integer.

Form the proportion $\frac{7}{10} = \frac{x}{26}$ and obtain

$$x = 18.2.$$

Since we cannot gain greater accuracy by interpolation, this value of x is rounded off to the nearest integer. Thus $x = 18$.

The value of $x = 18$ is in this case added to 0.4617 to obtain **$\sin 27°37' = 0.4635$**.

Note: The value of x is either added to or subtracted from the number from which x is measured in order to make the final result lie between the tabular entries.

Example 3. Find $\cot 62°14'$.

Solution: Since $62°14'$ lies between $62°10'$ and $62°20'$, form the schematic diagram

$$10\left[4\left[\begin{matrix}\theta \\ 62°10' \\ 62°14' \\ 62°20'\end{matrix}\right.\right.\qquad\left.\left.\begin{matrix}\cot\theta \\ 0.5280 \\ ]x \\ 0.5243\end{matrix}\right]37.\right.$$

Form the proportion $\qquad\dfrac{4}{10} = \dfrac{x}{37};$

hence $\qquad\qquad\qquad x = 14.8.$

Rounded off to the nearest integer we have $x = 15$.

Here $x = 15$ must be subtracted from 0.5280 to make the result lie between the tabular entries. Thus we find

$$\cot 62°14' = 0.5265.$$

Example 4. Find θ in degrees where θ is a positive acute angle, given that $\csc \theta = 2.716$.

Solution: Form the schematic diagram

$$10\begin{bmatrix}x\begin{bmatrix}21°30' & & 2.729 \\ & & 2.716 \end{bmatrix}13 \\ 21°40' & & 2.709\end{bmatrix}20.$$

Hence
$$\frac{x}{10} = \frac{13}{20}$$

and
$$x = 6.5.$$

When the number to be rounded off ends in **5**, it is customary to round the number off to the nearest *even* integer. Thus, we have here $x = 6$.

Adding 6 to 21°30' we have

$$\theta = 21°36'.$$

Example 5. Find cos 0.4761.

Solution: Form the schematic diagram

$$30\begin{bmatrix}20\begin{bmatrix}0.4741 & & 0.8897 \\ 0.4761 & & \end{bmatrix}x \\ 0.4771 & & 0.8884\end{bmatrix}13.$$

Hence
$$\frac{20}{30} = \frac{x}{13}$$

and
$$x = 8.7,$$

or
$$x = 9 \text{ to the nearest integer.}$$

Thus **cos 0.4761 = 0.8888.**

When more accuracy in a problem is desired, tables with more places must be used. The procedure of interpolation and obtaining values from such tables is the same as for the four-place tables just discussed.

▶ **EXERCISES**

1. Use the infinite series $\sin \theta = \theta - \dfrac{\theta^3}{3!} + \dfrac{\theta^5}{5!} - \dfrac{\theta^7}{7!} + \cdots$, to compute *sin θ* accurate to four decimal places. (*a*) 0.1. (*b*) 0.5. (*c*) 1.0. (*d*) 1.2. (*e*) 30°. (*f*) 10°. (*g*) 3°.

2. Use the infinite series $\cos \theta = 1 - \dfrac{\theta^2}{2!} + \dfrac{\theta^4}{4!} - \dfrac{\theta^6}{6!} + \dfrac{\theta^8}{8!} + \cdots$, to compute *cos θ* accurate to four decimal places for the values of θ in problem 1.

Use Table I to find the value of the trigonometric functions in problems 3 through 14.

3. sin 8°20′. **4.** sin 0.7709. **5.** cos 52°20′.

6. cos 0.7883. **7.** tan 30°10′. **8.** tan 1.0007.

9. cot 28°40′. **10.** cot 1.3352. **11.** sec 45°20′.

12. sec 0.0349. **13.** csc 36°50′, **14.** csc 1.2683.

In problems 15 through 20 find the value of θ in degrees, where θ is a positive acute angle.

15. sin θ = 0.1248. **16.** cos θ = 0.9996. **17.** tan θ = 1.530.

18. cot θ = 0.5969. **19.** sec θ = 1.074. **20.** csc θ = 1.275.

In problems 21 through 26 find the value of θ in radians where θ is a positive acute angle.

21. sin θ = 0.9492. **22.** cos θ = 0.5050. **23.** tan θ = 0.4487.

24. cot θ = 1.530. **25.** sec θ = 1.318. **26.** csc θ = 2.381.

In problems 27 through 42 find by interpolation the value of the trigonometric functions.

27. sin 37°37′. **28.** sin 47°42′. **29.** cos 36°38′.

30. cos 61°29′. **31.** tan 23°54′. **32.** tan 73°06′.

33. cot 62°11′. **34.** cot 3°44′. **35.** sec 71°46′.

36. csc 31°59′. **37.** sin 0.8752. **38.** cos 1.3071.

39. tan 0.1273. **40.** cot 0.8368. **41.** sec 1.0000.

42. csc 0.2143.

In problems 43 through 54 find the value of θ in degrees to the nearest minute where θ is a positive acute angle.

43. sin θ = 0.0766. **44.** sin θ = 0.7324. **45.** cos θ = 0.7482.

46. cos θ = 0.2715. **47.** tan θ = 0.3300. **48.** tan θ = 1.301.

49. cot θ = 4.349. **50.** cot θ = 0.8932. **51.** sec θ = 1.183.

52. sec θ = 1.472. **53.** csc θ = 2.181. **54.** csc θ = 1.393.

In problems 55 through 66 find the value of θ in radians, where θ is a positive acute angle. (Use Table I.)

55. $\sin \theta = 0.1316$.   **56.** $\sin \theta = 0.9107$.   **57.** $\cos \theta = 0.2456$.
58. $\cos \theta = 0.9813$.   **59.** $\tan \theta = 0.4054$.   **60.** $\tan \theta = 1.573$.
61. $\cot \theta = 5.602$.   **62.** $\cot \theta = 0.8126$.   **63.** $\sec \theta = 1.067$.
64. $\sec \theta = 1.748$.   **65.** $\csc \theta = 1.313$.   **66.** $\csc \theta = 2.188$.

67. What conclusion can you obtain when you compare the values of $\sin \theta$ and θ if θ is measured in radians and approaches zero?

2-7. VALUES OF THE TRIGONOMETRIC FUNCTIONS OF ANY ANGLE

An angle in standard position greater than 360° is coterminal with a *nonnegative* angle less than 360°. A negative angle in standard position is coterminal with a *nonnegative* angle less than 360°. For

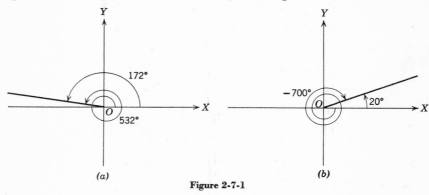

(a)   (b)

Figure 2-7-1

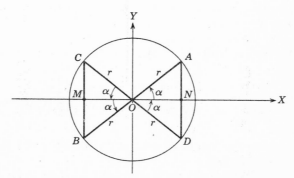

Figure 2-7-2

example, 532° is coterminal with 172°, and $-700°$ is coterminal with 20°. See Fig. 2-7-1.

Since coterminal angles have the same values for their trigonometric functions, we need only consider the problem of finding values of trigonometric functions of nonnegative angles less than 360°.

Draw a circle of radius r with its center at the origin. See Fig. 2-7-2.

Draw two diameters making equal angles, α, with the X-axis, where α is a *positive acute angle*. Let the diameters intersect the circle at A, B, C, and D. Draw lines AD and BC, thus forming the two isosceles triangles AOD and BOC. We know from geometry that AD and BC are both perpendicular to the X-axis, as the X-axis bisects the vertex angle of the isosceles triangles. We thus have four congruent right triangles. The *ordinates* of the points A, B, C, and D are *numerically equal* as are their *abscissas*. The *radius vector* of each point is r. Recalling the definitions of the trigonometric functions of an angle in standard position, we see that the trigonometric functions of angles **XOC** or **$(180° - \alpha)$**, **XOB** or **$(180° + \alpha)$**, and **XOD** or **$(360° - \alpha)$** are *numerically* equal to the *same* trigonometric functions of the angle **XOA** or **(α)**. For example, $|\sin (180° - \alpha)| = \sin \alpha$, $|\tan (360° - \alpha)| = \tan \alpha$, $|\cos (180° + \alpha)| = \cos \alpha$, and so forth.

Using functional notation we have $|T(\theta)| = T(\alpha)$, where θ is any angle in standard position and α is the related angle to θ.

Definition: *The related angle is the **positive acute angle** between the terminal side of the given angle and the X-axis. For quadrantal angles the related angle is 0° if the terminal side lies on the X-axis, and is 90° if it lies on the Y-axis.*

The algebraic sign to be used in evaluating the trigonometric functions of an angle is determined by the quadrant in which the terminal side of the given angle lies.

To find the value of the trigonometric function of an angle we follow the

Reduction Rule.

1. Sketch the given angle in standard position and determine the related angle.

2. Determine the algebraic sign from the required trigonometric function and the quadrant of the angle.

3. Find the value of the *same* trigonometric function of the related angle.

Example. Find the value of the following functions:

(*a*) sin 150°.   (*b*) cos 150°.   (*c*) tan 200°.

(*d*) cot 475°.   (*e*) sin (− 220°).

Solution: Draw each angle in standard position and find the related angle.

(*a*) Since 150° is a second quadrant angle (Fig. 2-7-3), sin 150° is positive. Its related angle is 30°. Hence, **sin 150° = sin 30° = $\frac{1}{2}$**.

(*b*) Since 150° is a second quadrant angle, cos 150° is negative.

Hence,   **cos 150° = − cos 30° = − $\frac{\sqrt{3}}{2}$.**

(*c*) The related angle is 20° (Fig. 2-7-4). The tangent of a third quadrant angle is positive. Hence,

$$\textbf{tan 200}° = \textbf{tan 20}° = \textbf{0.3640.}$$

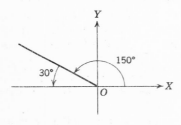

Figure 2-7-3

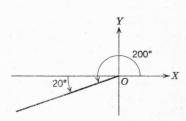

Figure 2-7-4

(*d*) The related angle is 65° (Fig. 2-7-5). The cotangent of a second quadrant angle is negative.

Hence,   **cot 475° = cot 115° = − cot 65° = − 0.4663.**

(*e*) The related angle is 40° (Fig. 2-7-6). The quadrant is the second.

Hence,   **sin (− 220°) = sin 40° = 0.6428.**

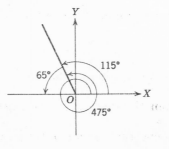

Figure 2-7-5

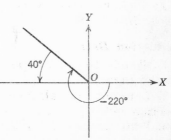

Figure 2-7-6

▶ **EXERCISES**

1. Express the given trigonometric function in terms of the same function of a positive acute angle:

(a) sin 125°.   (b) cos 225°.   (c) tan 352°28′.
(d) cot 94°.   (e) sec 262°58′.   (f) csc 341°.
(g) sin 425°.   (h) cot 1243°.

2. Use Table I to evaluate the trigonometric function:

(a) sin 123°.   (b) cos 223°10′.   (c) tan 175°20′.
(d) cot 307°30′.   (e) sec 145°10′.   (f) csc 207°.
(g) sin (−324°10′).   (h) cos (−28°).   (i) tan 198°.
(j) sin 301°07′.   (k) cos 100°11′.   (l) csc (−117°20′).

3. Find θ where $0° \leqq \theta < 360°$:

(a) sin θ = −0.3420, cos θ > 0.
(b) cos θ = −0.8450, tan θ > 0.
(c) tan θ = 1.339, sin θ < 0.
(d) cot θ = −0.5509, sec θ < 0.
(e) sec θ = 1.139, tan θ > 0.
(f) csc θ = 1.620, sec θ < 0.
(g) sin θ = 0.6078.   (h) cos θ = −0.6264.
(i) tan θ = −0.7500.   (j) cot θ = 0.5509.
(k) sec θ = −1.307.   (l) csc θ = −1.025.

4. Complete the table with the exact value of the trigonometric function.

θ	120°	135°	150°	180°	210°	225°	240°	270°	300°	315°	330°	360°
sin θ												
cos θ												
tan θ												
cot θ												
sec θ												
csc θ												

5. Make a table similar to the one in problem 4. Use radian measure for the angle θ.

2-8. TRIGONOMETRIC FUNCTIONS OF $(-\theta)$

The trigonometric functions of a negative angle may be found by using the reduction rule of Art. 2-7. It is convenient, however, to have a special relationship at our disposal.

Draw any angles θ and $-\theta$ in standard position. In Fig. 2-8-1, θ was drawn as a second quadrant angle for convenience. Choose points $P(x, y)$ and $P'(x', y')$ on the terminal sides at a distance $r = r'$ from the origin as shown in Fig. 2-8-1. From the congruent

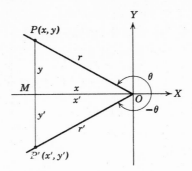

Figure 2-8-1

triangles (Why?) OMP and OMP', we can see that $x = x'$, $y = -y'$, and $r = r'$.

From the fundamental definitions we obtain

$$\sin (-\theta) = \frac{y'}{r'} = \frac{-y}{r} = -\sin \theta,$$

$$\cos (-\theta) = \frac{x'}{r'} = \frac{x}{r} = \cos \theta,$$

$$\tan (-\theta) = \frac{y'}{x'} = \frac{-y}{x} = -\tan \theta,$$

(2-8-1)

$$\cot (-\theta) = \frac{x'}{y'} = \frac{x}{-y} = -\cot \theta,$$

$$\sec (-\theta) = \frac{r'}{x'} = \frac{r}{x} = \sec \theta,$$

$$\csc (-\theta) = \frac{r'}{y'} = \frac{r}{y} = -\csc \theta.$$

Example. $\sin (-50°) = -\sin 50°.$

$\tan (-160°) = -\tan 160° = -(-\tan 20°) = \tan 20°.$

▶ **EXERCISES**

1. Evaluate the following trigonometric functions:
(a) sin $(-42°)$.   (b) cos $(-57°30')$.   (c) tan $(-126°)$.
(d) sin $(-205°)$.   (e) cos $(-131°17')$.   (f) tan $(-350°)$.
(g) sec $(-252°)$.   (h) csc $(-303°)$.

2. Prove the relations of (2-8-1) for:
(a) θ in QI.   (b) θ in QIII.   (c) θ in QIV.

The Right Triangle

3-1. INTRODUCTION

In this chapter we will show a few of the uses of trigonometry which involve solving a right triangle. From geometry we know that a triangle has three sides and three angles. The solution of a triangle is the determination of the three unknown parts when three parts, one of which must be a side, are known.

The angles of a right triangle will be denoted by **A, B,** and **C,** with **C** being the right angle unless otherwise indicated. The sides opposite the angles will be denoted by **a, b,** and **c,** respectively. The angles other than the right angle have a sum of 90°. Each of the acute angles is called the *complement* of the other.

In Fig. 3-1-1 is shown a right triangle *ACB*. Side *c* is called the *hypotenuse*, side *a* is the *opposite* side to angle *A*, and side *b* is the *adjacent* side to angle *A*.

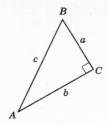

Figure 3-1-1

3-2. TRIGONOMETRIC FUNCTIONS OF AN ACUTE ANGLE OF A RIGHT TRIANGLE

When we place the acute angle, **A**, of the right triangle ACB, in

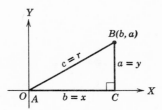

Figure 3-2-1

standard position (see Fig. 3-2-1), we have from the fundamental definitions of the trigonometric functions:

$$\sin A = \frac{y}{r} = \frac{a}{c} \text{ or } \textbf{sin (acute angle)} = \frac{\textbf{opposite side}}{\textbf{hypotenuse}}.$$

$$\cos A = \frac{x}{r} = \frac{b}{c} \text{ or } \textbf{cos (acute angle)} = \frac{\textbf{adjacent side}}{\textbf{hypotenuse}}.$$

$$\tan A = \frac{y}{x} = \frac{a}{b} \text{ or } \textbf{tan (acute angle)} = \frac{\textbf{opposite side}}{\textbf{adjacent side}}.$$

$$\cot A = \frac{x}{y} = \frac{b}{a} \text{ or } \textbf{cot (acute angle)} = \frac{\textbf{adjacent side}}{\textbf{opposite side}}.$$

$$\sec A = \frac{r}{x} = \frac{c}{b} \text{ or } \textbf{sec (acute angle)} = \frac{\textbf{hypotenuse}}{\textbf{adjacent side}}.$$

$$\csc A = \frac{r}{y} = \frac{c}{a} \text{ or } \textbf{csc (acute angle)} = \frac{\textbf{hypotenuse}}{\textbf{opposite side}}.$$

The above relations are known as the definitions of the trigono-metric functions of an *acute angle of a right triangle.*

If we now place angle B, of the same right triangle ACB, in standard position (Fig. 3-2-2), we obtain:

$$\sin B = \frac{b}{c}. \qquad \cos B = \frac{a}{c}. \qquad \tan B = \frac{b}{a}.$$

$$\csc B = \frac{c}{b}. \qquad \sec B = \frac{c}{a}. \qquad \cot B = \frac{a}{b}.$$

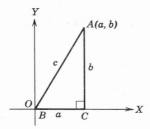

Figure 3-2-2

Comparing the trigonometric functions of angle A to those of angle B, we find that

$$\sin B = \frac{b}{c} = \cos A. \qquad\qquad \csc B = \frac{c}{b} = \sec A.$$

$$\cos B = \frac{a}{c} = \sin A. \qquad\qquad \sec B = \frac{c}{a} = \csc A.$$

$$\tan B = \frac{b}{a} = \cot A. \qquad\qquad \cot B = \frac{a}{b} = \tan A.$$

Since A and B are acute complementary angles,* we may say that *cofunctions of acute complementary angles are equal.* Two angles whose sum is 90° are said to be *complementary angles.* Thus, angles of 200° and −110° are complementary angles. In Chapter 7 we can use suitable formulas to show that the cofunctions of any two com-plementary angles are equal. This fact explains why the tables of trigonometric functions of angles need be compiled only for angles from 0° to 45°.

————————————

* Since B is the angle *complementary* to A, $\sin B = \sin$ [angle complementary to A] which is written as *cos A.* Thus the abbreviation cos A may be called the complementary sine of A.

The student should become so familiar with the definitions of the trigonometric functions of an acute angle of a right triangle that he can quickly write down the functions that relate any three parts of a right triangle.

Example. For the given right triangle ACB (Fig. 3-2-3) find **a** in terms of **B** and **c**.

Solution:

$$\cos B = \frac{a}{c}.$$

Hence, $\qquad\qquad\qquad a = c \cos B.$

The student should strive to be able to write the answer without writing down the first step.

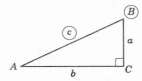

Figure 3-2-3

▶ **EXERCISES**

Using the trigonometric functions of an acute angle of a right triangle, write a formula for the unknown parts of the right triangle in terms of the given parts. The given parts, other than the right angle, are circled.

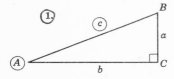 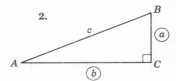

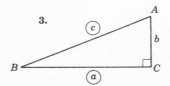 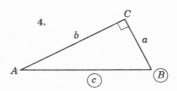

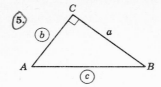

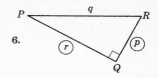

6.

7.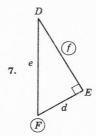

Use Fig. 3-2-4 for problems 8 through 11.

8. (a) Find x in terms of y and θ.
   (b) Find x in terms of z and θ.

9. (a) Find y in terms of z and θ.
   (b) Find y in terms of x and θ.

10. (a) Find z in terms of x and θ.
    (b) Find z in terms of y and θ.

11. (a) Find θ in terms of x and y.
    (b) Find θ in terms of x and z.
    (c) Find θ in terms of y and z.

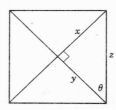

Figure 3-2-4

12. Given the right triangle PQR in Fig. 3-2-5:

(a) Express RQ as a function of θ.

(b) Express PQ as a function of θ.

(c) Show that $\sin^2 \theta + \cos^2 \theta = 1$.

(d) Show that $\tan \theta = \dfrac{\sin \theta}{\cos \theta}$.

(e) Show that $\sec \theta = \dfrac{1}{\cos \theta}$.

(f) Show that $\csc \theta = \dfrac{1}{\sin \theta}$.

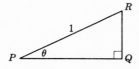

Figure 3-2-5

13. Given the right triangle ACB in Fig. 3-2-6:

(a) Express AC as a function of α.

(b) Express AB as a function of α.

(c) Show that $1 + \cot^2 \alpha = \csc^2 \alpha$.

(d) Show that $\sin \alpha = \dfrac{1}{\csc \alpha}$.

(e) Show that $\cot \alpha = \dfrac{1}{\tan \alpha}$.

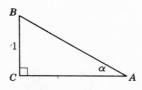

Figure 3-2-6

14. Given the right triangle DEF in Fig. 3-2-7:

(a) Express ED as a function of x.

(b) Express FD as a function of x.

(c) Show that $1 + \tan^2 x = \sec^2 x$.

(d) Show that $\sin x = \dfrac{\tan x}{\sec x}$.

(e) Show that $\cot x = \dfrac{1}{\tan x}$.

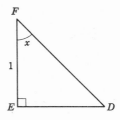

Figure 3-2-7

3-3. SIGNIFICANT FIGURES

When data are obtained by use of a measuring instrument, its accuracy is dependent upon the characteristics of the instrument. It is customary to let the number of digits in a number indicate the degree of accuracy. These digits are called **significant figures**. The digits 1, 2, 3, $\cdots$ 9 are always considered significant. The digit zero is not considered significant if its only purpose is to locate the decimal point; otherwise, it is significant. For example, the numbers 2.03, 567, 0.00962, and 302,000 are numbers with three significant figures.

Many times the zero at the right end of a number may or may not be significant. To know for sure some inside information is needed, such as how the measurements were made. If we say that a distance d is 30 ft, then the zero is significant if $29.5 < d < 30.5$. The use of the "scientific" or "standard" notation of numbers indicates the significance of the final zero. In this notation the number is written as a product of the form $n \times 10^k$, where $1 \leqq n < 10$ (read: n is equal to or greater than 1 but less than 10) and k is an **integer**. For example, the numbers 302,000 and 0.00962 would be written as 3.02×10^5 and 9.62×10^{-3} to indicate three significant figures; whereas for five significant figures they would be written as

3.0200×10^5 and 9.6200×10^{-3}. In this book we shall consider the final zero or zeros to be significant for a number not in "standard" notation.

The "10-inch" slide rule may be used for computations involving numbers of not more than three significant figures. When more accuracy is required, logarithms should be used. In general, the answer to a computation is no more accurate than the least accurate number in the data. For example, consider the product of the approximate numbers 4.12 and 2.3. The next figure in each number is unknown. Let us denote it by u. The product of an unknown number and another number is also unknown. Hence, we get

$$
\begin{array}{r}
4.1\,2u \\
2.3u \\
\hline
u\ u\ uu \\
1\ 23\ 6\ u \\
8\ 24\ u \\
\hline
9.4u\ u\ uu
\end{array}
$$

Thus, the answer contains only two significant figures, namely, 9.4.

When solving triangles we may consider that *one- or two-place accuracy* in the sides corresponds to the *nearest degree* in the angles; *three-place accuracy* in the sides corresponds to *the nearest multiple of 10 minutes*, or *tenth of a degree* in the angles when using a deci-trig slide rule; *four-place* accuracy in the sides corresponds to the *nearest minute* in the angles; *five-place* accuracy in the sides corresponds to the *nearest tenth of a minute* in the angles.

As an exercise the student should write the following numbers using "standard" notation: (*a*) 125, (*b*) 0.176, (*c*) 0.0003070, (*d*) 7060.23.

3-4-A. SOLUTION OF RIGHT TRIANGLES—ARITHMETIC

The arithmetic solution of a right triangle employs the definitions of the trigonometric functions of an acute angle of a right triangle and the values of the trigonometric functions as found in Table I. The procedure to follow in solving a right triangle is to sketch the triangle approximately to scale, drawing a circle around the *given* parts. Write the trigonometric expression that involves *two* of the *known* parts and *one* of the *unknown* parts. Solve for the unknown part. The method is illustrated in the following examples.

Since the values of the trigonometric functions of angles given in Table I are accurate to four places, we shall use four places in the intermediate steps of problems and then round the answer off to the proper number of significant figures as discussed in Art. 3-3. That is, for three or less significant figures use Table I without interpolation. With four significant figures use Table I with interpolation to the nearest minute. For greater accuracy other tables and logarithms may be used.

Example 1. Solve the right triangle ACB in which $c = 7.25$, $A = 35°00'$.

Solution: Sketch the triangle (Fig. 3-4-1) and circle the given parts. Since $A + B = 90°$, we find $\boldsymbol{B = 55°}$.

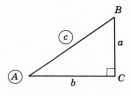

Figure 3-4-1

A trigonometric function that involves the two known parts A and c and the unknown part a is

$$\sin A = \frac{a}{c}.$$

Hence we have $\qquad\qquad \boldsymbol{a = c \sin A}.$

A formula to use for b which involves the two known parts is

$$\boldsymbol{b = c \cos A.}$$

Replacing c and A by their given values, we have

$$a = 7.25 \sin 35°00', \text{ and } b = 7.25 \cos 35°00'.$$

From Table I we find $\sin 35°00' = 0.5736$, and $\cos 35°00' = 0.8192$. Thus $a = 7.25\ (0.5736)$, and $b = 7.25\ (0.8192)$, or $\quad \boldsymbol{a = 4.16}$, and $\boldsymbol{b = 5.94}$ rounded off to three significant figures.

Example 2. Solve the right triangle ACB in which $a = 62.5$ and $b = 36.4$.

Solution: Sketch the triangle (Fig. 3-4-2). Circle the given parts. Either one of the acute angles may be found first.

Thus $$\tan B = \frac{b}{a},$$

$$\tan B = \frac{36.4}{62.5} = 0.5824.$$

From Table I we find

$B = 30°10'$ (to the nearest multiple of 10 minutes).

Then $A = 90° - B = 59°50'$.

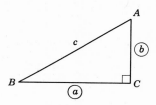

Figure 3-4-2

There are several ways to find c. The use of a trigonometric function is usually easier than the Pythagórean Theorem. Hence,

$$\csc B = \frac{c}{b},$$

and

$$c = b \csc B.$$

Thus, $c = (36.4) \csc 30°10'$.

$c = (36.4)(1.990),$

and $c = 72.4$ (to three significant figures).

3-4-B. SLIDE RULE SOLUTION OF THE RIGHT TRIANGLE

To solve any right triangle on a slide rule we need to know only two proportions. One is the proportion involving sines and the other is the proportion involving tangents.

The Sine Proportion

Consider the right triangle ACB of Fig. 3-4-3. From the definitions of Art. 3-2, we have

$$(3\text{-}4\text{-}1) \qquad \sin A = \frac{a}{c}.$$

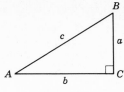

Figure 3-4-3

Dividing both sides of 3-4-1 by a we obtain

(3-4-2)
$$\frac{\sin A}{a} = \frac{1}{c}.$$

Recalling that $\sin 90° = 1$, we may write **formula 3-4-2** as

(3-4-3)
$$\frac{\sin A}{a} = \frac{\sin 90°}{c}.$$

In a similar manner we may obtain

(3-4-4)
$$\frac{\sin B}{b} = \frac{\sin 90°}{c}.$$

Combining formulas 3-4-3 and 3-4-4 we have

(3-4-5)
$$\frac{\sin A}{a} = \frac{\sin B}{b} = \frac{\sin 90°}{c}.$$

The ratios of formula 3-4-5, which we will call the *sine proportion* for right triangles, may be used to solve all right triangles except the one case where the two legs are given. Sides a, b, and c are read on the D-scale of the slide rule and angles A and B are read on the S-scale.

Example 1. Solve the right triangle ACB in which $c = 7.25$, $A = 35°$.

Solution: Sketch the triangle (Fig. 3-4-4) and circle the given parts. From $B = 90° - A$ we have $B = 55°$.

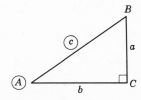

Figure 3-4-4

Using the sine proportion for right triangles we have

$$\frac{\sin 35°}{a} = \frac{\sin 55°}{b} = \frac{\sin 90°}{7.25}.$$

On the slide rule set 90° on the S-scale opposite 7.25 on the D-scale; opposite 35° on the S-scale read $\boldsymbol{a} = \boldsymbol{4.16}$ on the D-scale; opposite 55° on the S-scale read $\boldsymbol{b} = \boldsymbol{5.94}$ on the D-scale.

The Tangent Proportion

In any right triangle ACB (Fig. 3-4-3) where the two legs are known we may write,

(3-4-6) $$\tan A = \frac{a}{b}.$$

This may be rewritten as

(3-4-7) $$\frac{\tan A}{a} = \frac{1}{b}.$$

From Art. 2-4 we recall that $\tan 45° = 1$; hence formula 3-4-7 may be written as

(3-4-8) $$\frac{\boldsymbol{\tan A}}{\boldsymbol{a}} = \frac{\boldsymbol{\tan 45°}}{\boldsymbol{b}}.$$

The ratios of formula 3-4-8, which we shall call the *tangent proportion*, may be used to find angle A. Sides a and b are read on the D-scale and angle A is read on the T-scale. After angle A is found, the sine proportion may be used to complete the solution of the triangle.

Note: If side b is always taken as the *larger* leg, then angle A will always be *less* than 45°.

A convenient rule is stated below for solving a right triangle on the slide rule when two legs are given.

(1) *Set an index of the slide opposite the larger leg on the D-scale.*

(2) *Opposite the shorter leg on the D-scale read the smaller angle on the T-scale. (Leave the hairline at this setting on the D-scale.)*

(3) *Move the S-scale to the right until the smaller angle appears on the S-scale under the hairline.*

(4) *Opposite an index of the slide read the hypotenuse on the D-scale.*

(5) *Obtain the larger angle by subtracting the smaller angle from 90°.*

Example 2. Solve the right triangle ACB in which $a = 62.5$ and $b = 36.4$.

Solution: Sketch the triangle (Fig. 3-4-5). Circle the given parts. Use the above rule.

Thus we obtain $B = 30.2°$, $c = 72.4$, $A = 59.8°$.

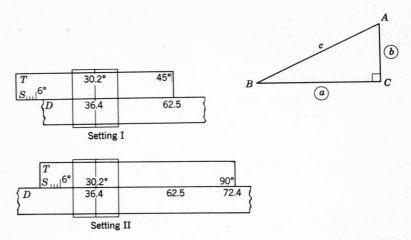

Figure 3-4-5

▶ **EXERCISES**

1. Solve the right triangle ACB. If a slide rule is used, round off the data to three significant figures.

(a) $a = 4$, $A = 35°$.

(b) $b = 5$, $A = 27°$.

(c) $a = 6$, $b = 8$.

(d) $a = 13$, $b = 9$.

(e) $a = 12.5$, $b = 8.7$.

(f) $a = 26.3$, $B = 41°30'$.

(g) $b = 0.46$, $A = 52°40'$.

(h) $b = 729$, $B = 28°10'$.

(i) $c = 6.29$, $A = 13°20'$.

(j) $c = 9.18$, $B = 30°10'$.

(k) $a = 147$, $c = 184$.

(l) $A = 34°15'$, $a = 843.2$.

(m) $B = 47°26'$, $c = 4.617$.

(n) $A = 23°30'$, $c = 627$.

(o) $B = 6°12'$, $c = 3720$.

(p) $a = 101$, $b = 116$.

(q) $a = 24.72$, $b = 33.14$.

(r) $b = 0.0253$, $c = 0.0489$.

(s) $b = 1.441$, $c = 3.465$.

(t) $A = 21°36'$, $b = 0.8214$.

2. An oblique triangle may be solved by means of two right triangles. Two right triangles are formed by drawing a perpendicular from one vertex to the opposite side or the opposite side produced. If an angle is known, draw the perpendicular so that one of the resulting right triangles contains two of the given parts.

Solve the following oblique triangles by the above method.

(a) $A = 30°$, $B = 50°$, $b = 10$.   (b) $A = 25°$, $C = 75°$, $a = 15$.
(c) $A = 42°$, $b = 10$, $c = 20$.   (d) $C = 70°$, $a = 12$, $b = 16$.
(e) $A = 20°$, $b = 5$, $a = 8$.   (f) $C = 55°$, $c = 27$, $a = 20$.
(g) $c = 26.3$, $C = 47°20'$, $A = 32°30'$.
(h) $a = 13.2$, $b = 24.7$, $C = 10°10'$.

3. In the oblique triangle given three sides a, b, c (Fig. 3-4-6), show that

$$x = \frac{b^2 + c^2 - a^2}{2c}.$$

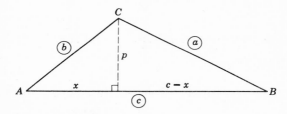

Figure 3-4-6

[Hint: Equate the expression for p in each triangle.]

4. Make use of problem 3 to solve the triangles.

(a) $a = 3$, $b = 4$, $c = 5$.   (b) $c = 10$, $b = 5$, $a = 9$.

3-5. ELEMENTARY APPLICATIONS

Many types of practical problems may be solved by means of a right triangle. A few of them are shown in this article.

Angles of Elevation and Depression

The **line of sight** of an object is the line joining the eye of an observer and the object. If the object is *above* a horizontal plane through the eye of the observer, the angle between the line of sight and this horizontal plane is called the **angle of elevation**. If the object is *below* this horizontal plane, the angle is then called the **angle of depression**.

Example 1. From the top of a building 85.0 ft high, the angle of depression of an automobile is $29°10'$. How far is the automobile from the foot of the building measured horizontally?

Solution: Sketch a triangle which represents the given conditions (Fig. 3-5-1). Circle the given parts. From plane geometry we know

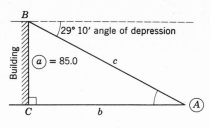

Figure 3-5-1

that $A = 29°10'$. Since we desire to find side b, we may write the formula $\cot A = \dfrac{b}{a}$, or

$$b = a \cot A. \text{ (The cot } A \text{ was chosen to avoid division.)}$$

Hence, we find

$$b = 85.0 \cot 29°10',$$

$$b = (85.0)(1.792),$$

and

$$\boldsymbol{b = \textbf{152 ft}} \text{ (rounded off to three significant figures).}$$

If the slide rule is used, the above triangle may be solved by finding $B = 90° - 29°10' = 60°50'$ and then using the sine proportion

$$\frac{\sin 29°10'}{85.0} = \frac{\sin 60°50'}{b}; \; \boldsymbol{b = \textbf{152 ft}}.$$

Course and Bearing

In navigation the north line is used as the reference line in measuring directions. It is usually represented by a vertical line.

The **course**, C_n, (Fig. 3-5-2) of a ship is the angle measured from the north *clockwise through the east* to the direction in which the ship is sailing. The bearing of **B from A** is the angle measured clockwise from the north to line AB, angle $\theta_{B/A}$ in Fig. 3-5-3. (The notation B/A means B relative to A.) Likewise, the bearing of A from B is the angle $\theta_{A/B}$.

In surveying, the direction or bearing of a line is given as the acute angle between the line and the north axis or the south axis. The north or south designation is given first, then the acute angle, and then the east or west designation. For example, in Fig. 3-5-4 the line OA has a bearing S 70° W.

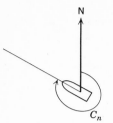

Figure 3-5-2   Figure 3-5-3

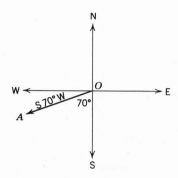

Figure 3-5-4

Example 2. A ship sails 15.5 miles on course 124.0°. It then sails 31.3 miles on course 214.0°. What course must it then sail to return to its starting point?

Solution: Make a sketch representing the given conditions (Fig. 3-5-5). We thus have a right triangle with two legs known. To find B use

$$\tan B = \frac{b}{a},$$

$$\tan B = \frac{15.5}{31.3},$$

$$\tan B = 0.4951,$$

$$B = 26°20'.$$

To find C_n, note that $\alpha = 56°$. (Why?)

Hence $\qquad\qquad \alpha + B = 56° + 26°20' = 82°20'$,

and $\qquad\qquad\qquad C_n = 90° - (\alpha + B)$,

or $\qquad\qquad\qquad \mathbf{C_n = 7°40'.}$

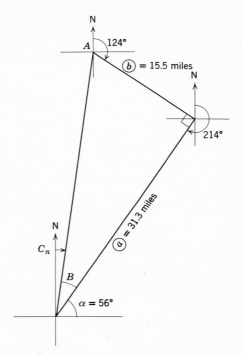

Figure 3-5-5

Vectors

Physical entities such as forces, velocities and accelerations, and any quantity that requires a direction as well as a magnitude to be completely described may be represented by a vector. A **vector** is defined as a line which has both *magnitude* and *direction*. When a vector is in a plane, its direction is relative to some fixed directed line. If the positive X-axis is the reference line, the direction of the vector is an angle in standard position. The direction of a vector is indicated graphically by a line segment with an arrow on one end, and its magnitude is indicated by the length of the line segment (Fig. 3-5-6).

Vectors are more fully discussed in Chapter 12.

The directed line segments OM and ON ($PN \perp OY$ and $PM \perp OX$), on the X-axis and Y-axis, respectively, are called the **X-component** and the **Y-component** of the vector. They are given as

$$v_x = v \cos \theta, \text{ and } v_y = v \sin \theta.$$

Clearly, $MP = ON$ and hence, if v_x and v_y are known, the magnitude v and direction θ of the vector can be determined by solving the right triangle OMP.

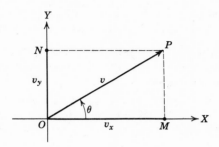

Figure 3-5-6

Example 3. If for a certain vector $v_x = 10$ and $v_y = 6$, find the magnitude and direction of the vector.

Solution: Sketch the right triangle (Fig. 3-5-7) and solve for v and θ.

$$\tan \theta = \frac{6}{10} = 0.6,$$

thus $\qquad \theta = \mathbf{31°}.$

$v = 10 \sec \theta = 10 \sec 31°,$

$v = (10)(1.167) = 11.67,$

and $\qquad v = \mathbf{12}$ (rounded off to be consistent with the given data).

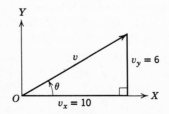

Figure 3-5-7

The slide rule solution would be the same as for solving a right triangle with two legs given. See page 55.

▶ **EXERCISES**

In the following problems, the height of an object means its height above the horizontal plane through the point of observation; distance means horizontal distance unless otherwise noted.

1. A rectangle is 26 in. by 14 in. What angle does the diagonal make with the longer side? How long is the diagonal?

2. The diagonal of a rectangle is 7.56 in. and the shorter side is 2.23 in. Find the angle the diagonal makes with the longer side and the length of the longer side.

3. A ladder 20 ft long is placed against a vertical wall such that its foot is 5 ft from the wall. What angle does the ladder make with the wall? How high does the ladder reach on the wall?

4. The angle of elevation of the top of a lighthouse from a point 225 ft from the base is 15°. Find the height of the lighthouse.

5. How long a shadow will be cast by a pole 100 ft high when the angle of elevation of the sun is 32.4°?

6. The lengths of the shadows of two vertical poles are 72.5 ft and 40.3 ft respectively. The first pole is 25 ft taller than the second. Find the angle of elevation of the sun and the length of each pole.

7. A tree 40 ft high stands beside a brook. From a point A, 600 ft away, the angle of elevation of the top of the tree is 3°20′. Find whether the brook is lower or higher than A and how much.

8. From a third story window the angle of depression of the foot of a building across the street is 37°. The angle of elevation of the top is 51°. If the street is 80 ft wide, find the height of the building.

9. A flagpole is on the top of a building 125 ft away. The angles of elevation of the top and of the foot of the flagpole are 70° and 67°, respectively. Find the length of the flagpole.

10. What is the height of a hill whose angle of elevation taken at the bottom is 46° and 100 yds further off, on a level with the bottom, the angle of elevation is 31°?

11. A lighthouse 25.00 ft high stands on the top of a cliff, and from a point on the seashore the angles of elevation of the highest and lowest points of the lighthouse are observed to be 47°12′ and 45°13′, respectively. Find the height of the cliff.

12. From the top of a building and from a window 30 ft below the top, the angles of depression of an object on the ground are 15°40′ and 10°00′, respectively. Find (*a*) the horizontal distance to the object and (*b*) the height of the building.

13. A patrol boat steamed 27 miles on course 31° and then steamed 18 miles on course 121°. Find the course to be set and the distance to be traversed in order to return to its starting point by the shortest route.

14. A ship is 14 miles due south of lighthouse *A*. Lighthouse *B* is 16 miles from *A* and bears 90° from *A*. What is the bearing of *B* from the ship?

15. A lighthouse bears 32.5° from a ship 5.5 miles away. The ship then sails in a northerly direction until the lighthouse bears 122.5° from the ship. How far did the ship sail and how far is it from the lighthouse?

16. A ship is sailing due south at a constant speed. At 6 A.M. a lighthouse is observed on a bearing of 270° at a distance of 14.5 nautical miles. At 6:30 A.M. its bearing is 285°. Find the rate at which the ship is sailing and the bearing of the lighthouse at 9 A.M.

17. Point *A* is 4.30 miles due north of point *C*. Point *B* is 2.20 miles due west of point *C*. Find the bearing of *A* from *B* and the distance *AB*.

18. A plot of land is in the shape of a right triangle *ACB*, where *C* is the right angle. *AC* = 355 ft and bears S 72°10′ W. *CB* = 253 ft and bears N 17°50′ W. Find the length and bearing of side *AB*. Also find the area of the plot.

19. A surveyor wishes to find the distance *AB* across a lake. From his position at *C* he finds *CA* = 357 yds and has a direction of N 25°20′ W. *CB* = 510 yds and has a direction of N 64°40′ E. Find the distance *AB*.

20. A surveyor walks 757 feet in the direction S 32°42′ E. He then walks 451 ft in the direction N 19°48′ E. If he then turns 90° and walks in a straight line to his starting point, find the total distance he walked.

21. Find v_x and v_y for the following vectors:

	(a)	(b)	(c)	(d)	(e)	(f)	(g)	(h)
v	12	15	6	20	25	32	57	128
θ	30°	135°	300°	180°	114°	182°	351°	−42°

22. Find v, the magnitude, and θ, the direction of the vector whose X- and Y-components are as indicated.

(a) $v_x = 12,\ v_y = 5.$ (b) $v_x = -135,\ v_y = 290.$
(c) $v_x = -24,\ v_y = -25.$ (d) $v_x = 348,\ v_y = -92.3.$

23. A force of 358.2 lbs acts in the direction N 58°13′ E. Find its north and east components.

24. A force has a west component of 567 lbs and a south component of 605 lbs. Find the magnitude and direction of the force.

25. Find the X- and Y-components of the 55 lb force acting in the direction shown (Fig. 3-5-8). (Note carefully the choice of axes.)

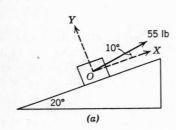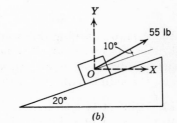

Figure 3-5-8

26. An airplane has a velocity of 350 mph on course 292°. How far north does it fly in one hour?

27. A particle has an acceleration of 6.25 ft/sec² in the direction making an angle of 22°30′ with the X-axis. Find the X- and Y-components of its acceleration.

Trigonometric Functions (Real Numbers)

4-1. INTRODUCTION

In the first three chapters we worked with the concept of the trigonometric functions of directed angles. There is another concept of trigonometric functions that is becoming increasingly important, the concept of the trigonometric functions of real numbers. The main difference between these two concepts is the terminology of the argument.

We will show that a real number can be represented by a length of arc of a unit circle in a manner similar to its representation by the coordinate of a point on a straight line. The coordinates of the end point of such an arc will serve as the basis of our definitions of the trigonometric functions of real numbers. We will then show the relation between real numbers and directed angles as well as between their trigonometric functions. The trigonometric functions of real numbers are not mysterious things. They are logical and play a tremendous role in engineering. We have tables listing the squares, cubes, square roots, cube roots, logarithms, and other properties of numbers. The student might then ask, "Why not trigonometric functions of numbers?" This chapter will show that the answer to this question is in the affirmative.

A course in trigonometry, based on the ideas of this chapter, can be developed without the concept of an angle. This point of view is taken in advanced courses in mathematics.

4-2. THE UNIT CIRCLE

A circle is defined in geometry as the locus of a point in a plane at a given distance from a fixed point in the plane. The fixed point is called the center of the circle and the distance from the center to the circle is called the radius. A **unit circle** is defined as a circle with the length of its radius one unit.

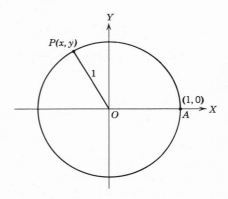

Figure 4-2-1

Let the center of the unit circle be placed at the origin of the rectangular coordinate axes. See Fig. 4-2-1. The distance from any point $P(x, y)$ on the unit circle to the origin is equal to one unit. Hence, we have $OP = 1$. Using the formula for the distance between two points,

$$P_1P_2 = \sqrt{(x_2 - x_1)^2 + (y_2 - y_1)^2},$$

we obtain

$$OP = \sqrt{(x - 0)^2 + (y - 0)^2} = 1, \text{ or}$$

(4-2-1) $$x^2 + y^2 = 1.$$

This equation is called the *equation of a unit circle whose center is at the origin.* Any point whose coordinates satisfy the equation $x^2 + y^2 = 1$ is on the unit circle, and conversely, the coordinates of any point on the unit circle satisfy the equation.

The length of the circumference of any circle of radius r is given by the formula $C = 2\pi r$. For a unit circle the circumference is equal in length to 2π units.

The length of arc along a curve is fully discussed in the calculus. To consider it fully would take more mathematical maturity than this book presupposes, for it is a profound concept. For our consideration we shall use the following intuitive idea of measuring the length of arc on a circle. Lay a piece of string along the arc and cut it off at the end points of the arc. Straighten the string out and measure its length. This length is said to be the *length of arc.* When we talk about an arc, we will mean the length of arc.

The arc on the unit circle which begins at the point $(1, 0)$ and is laid off in a *counterclockwise* sense is said to be a *positive arc.* If the arc is laid off in the *clockwise* sense, it is said to be a *negative arc.* A one-to-one correspondence may be set up between the real numbers and the arcs on a unit circle. This representation of real numbers is determined by the length of arc and its direction of measurement. The arc of the unit circle which starts at the point $(1, 0)$ and ends at point P, the terminal point, is called the representative arc of the real number with which it is associated. We shall frequently use the symbol u for the real number whose representative arc starts at the point $(1, 0)$. The arc is also denoted by u. A *positive* real number is denoted as $u > 0$ and a *negative* real number is denoted as $u < 0$. The number 0 is denoted by $u = 0$, an arc of zero length. For any real number u there is one and only one pair of coordinates (x, y) for the terminal point of the representative arc u.

If the terminal point $P(x, y)$ of the arc u is in the first quadrant, then u is said to be a *first quadrant arc.* If the terminal point of u is in the second quadrant, then u is said to be a second quadrant arc; similarly for third and fourth quadrant arcs.

In Fig. 4-2-2 representative arcs for several real numbers u are shown. For clarity in the sketches, arcs of more than one revolution are shown by multiple lines (parts b and d). These multiple lines should of course coincide with each other as they are on the unit circle. The terminal point $P(x, y)$ is considered to be at a distance of one unit from the center of the circle.

The use of π in expressing some real numbers is convenient as it equals one-half of the total circumference of the unit circle. Thus

$\pi/2$ is one-quarter of the circumference; $\pi/6$ is one-twelfth of the circumference and so forth.

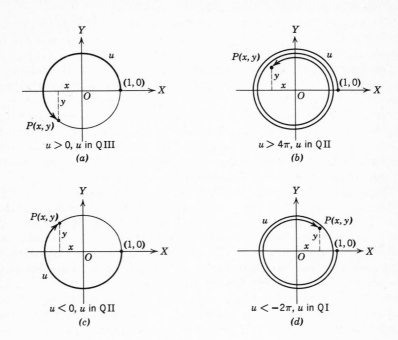

Figure 4-2-2

Example. Draw an arc on a unit circle representing the following real numbers: (a) π, (b) -2π, (c) 9.42.

Solution: See Fig. 4-2-3.

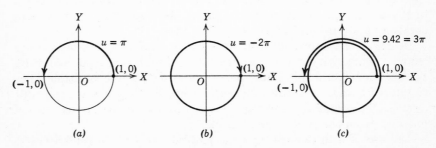

Figure 4-2-3

Coterminal arcs are defined as arcs on the unit circle with their initial point at $(1, 0)$ and having the *same point* $P(x, y)$ as their terminal point. Thus, the arcs representing the real numbers $\dfrac{\pi}{3}$ and $\dfrac{7\pi}{3} = \dfrac{\pi}{3} + 2\pi$ are coterminal arcs. In general representative arcs of the real numbers u and $u \pm 2n\pi$, $n = 0, 1, 2, \cdots$ are *coterminal arcs*. The number u may be either positive or negative. Figure 4-2-4 shows several numbers u and v whose representative arcs are coterminal.

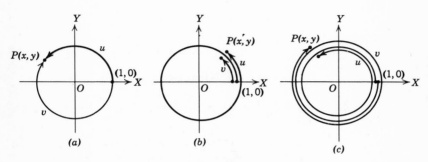

Figure 4-2-4

▶ EXERCISES

1. On a strip of paper reproduce Fig. 4-2-5 shown on page 70. Paste the tab under the other end of the strip, thus forming a circular ruler. The circular ruler (Fig. 4-2-6) so-formed has a radius of one inch. With a compass draw a unit circle of radius one inch, with its center at the origin of the rectangular coordinate axes. Place the edge of the circular ruler over the circle so that the mark 0 coincides with the point $(1, 0)$. Draw the representative arcs for the following real numbers:

(a) 1.   (b) 2.   (c) 3.   (d) 4.   (e) 5.   (f) 6.   (g) 1.3.   (h) 2.8.
(i) 3.4.   (j) 0.5.   (k) 4.7.   (l) 5.2.   (m) 7.   (n) 8.   (o) 9.   (p) 10.

2. Do the same as in problem 1 for the negatives of the above numbers.

3. Draw the representative arc u for the following real numbers. Indicate on your sketch an arc v coterminal with u.

Figure 4-2-5

$(a)\dfrac{\pi}{2}.$ $(b)\dfrac{3\pi}{2}.$ $(c)\dfrac{\pi}{4}.$ $(d)\dfrac{3\pi}{4}.$ $(e)\dfrac{7\pi}{4}.$ $(f)-\pi.$ $(g)-2\pi.$

$(h)-\dfrac{5\pi}{4}.$ $(i)-\dfrac{3\pi}{2}.$ $(j)-\dfrac{\pi}{2}.$ $(k)\,2\pi.$ $(l)\,3.14.$ $(m)\,6.28.$

$(n)-1.05.$ $(o)-0.78.$ $(p)-4.71.$

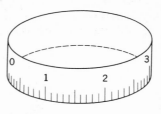

Figure 4-2-6

4. Define: (a) a third quadrant arc, (b) a fourth quadrant arc.

5. Is there more than one representative arc whose coordinates of its terminal point are (x, y)? How many?

6. Given one coordinate of the terminal point of a representative arc, find the other coordinate and draw two representative arcs $u < 2\pi$ having the given coordinate of the terminal point in the quadrant indicated.

$(a)\ x = -\frac{3}{5},\text{QII.}$ $(b)\ y = \frac{5}{13},\text{QI.}$ $(c)\ x = \frac{24}{25},\text{QIV.}$

$(d)\ y = -\frac{8}{17},\text{QIII.}$ $(e)\ x = \frac{9}{41},\text{QI.}$ $(f)\ y = -\frac{21}{29},\text{QIV.}$

$(g)\ x = -\frac{144}{145},\text{QII.}$

4-3. TRIGONOMETRIC FUNCTIONS OF REAL NUMBERS

For each real number, u, there is one and only one pair of coordinates (x, y) which are the coordinates of the terminal point of the representative arc u on the unit circle that starts at $(1, 0)$ (Fig. 4-3-1). Hence, the coordinates x and y are functions of the real number u.

The trigonometric functions of the real number u are defined in Table 4-3. The appropriate notes on the definitions of the trigonometric functions of angles on page 21 apply to these definitions.

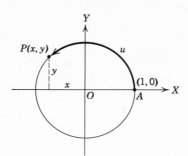

Figure 4-3-1

TABLE 4-3

Function	Domain	Range
$\sin u = y$.	All real numbers.	$-1 \leqq$ All real numbers $\leqq 1$.
$\cos u = x$.	All real numbers.	$-1 \leqq$ All real numbers $\leqq 1$.
$\tan u = \dfrac{y}{x}$.	All real numbers for which $x \neq 0$.	All real numbers.
$\cot u = \dfrac{x}{y}$.	All real numbers for which $y \neq 0$.	All real numbers.
$\sec u = \dfrac{1}{x}$.	All real numbers for which $x \neq 0$.	All real numbers $\leqq -1$ and $\geqq 1$.
$\csc u = \dfrac{1}{y}$.	All real numbers for which $y \neq 0$.	All real numbers $\leqq -1$ and $\geqq 1$.

When we wish to talk about the trigonometic functions in general and do not care about specifying a particular trigonometric function, we will use the functional notation $T(u)$ which will stand for the *trigonometric functions of the real number* u.

The algebraic signs of the trigonometric functions of real numbers depend on the signs of the abscissa and ordinate of the terminal point $P(x, y)$ of the representative arc on the unit circle.

▶ **EXERCISES**

1. Define $\tan u$, $\cot u$, $\sec u$, and $\csc u$ in terms of $\sin u$ and/or $\cos u$.

2. Complete the following table.

Quadrant of the real number, u	Positive functions	Negative functions
I	all	
II		
III	tan u. cot u.	
IV		

3. Find the values of the trigonometric functions at the real number u, given the indicated coordinate and the quadrant of the terminal point of the representative arc, u.

(a) $x = \frac{3}{5}$, QI.　　　(b) $y = \frac{5}{13}$, QII.　　(c) $x = -\frac{4}{5}$, QII.

(d) $y = \frac{8}{17}$, QI.　　(e) $y = -\frac{12}{13}$, QIII.　(f) $x = -\frac{24}{25}$, QIII.

(g) $y = -\frac{15}{17}$, QIV.　(h) $x = \frac{144}{145}$, QIV.

4. A *quadrantal number* is defined to be a number such that the terminal point of its representative arc is on one of the coordinate axes. Show that all quadrantal numbers may be written as

$$\pm n\frac{\pi}{2}, \; n = 0, 1, 2, \cdots.$$

5. Find the values of the trigonometric functions at the following real numbers. [Hint: Find the coordinates of the terminal point of the representative arc.]

(a) 0. (b) $\frac{\pi}{2}$. (c) π. (d) $\frac{3\pi}{2}$. (e) -2π. (f) $-\frac{\pi}{2}$. (g) $-\pi$. (h) $-\frac{3\pi}{2}$. (i) 1.57.

(j) 7.85. (k) -3.14. (l) -9.42.

6. Compare the values of parts a, b, c, and d of problem 5 with the values of the trigonometric functions at angles of 0, $\pi/2$, π, and $3\pi/2$ radians.

7. Show that for all u, $T(u + 2\pi) = T(u)$.

8. Find a value of u for which $\tan u = \cot u$.

9. Can $\cos u = 2$? Why?

10. Can $\csc u = \frac{1}{2}$? Why?

11. Can $\sec u = 0$? Why?

12. Write out in words the rule implied by the symbols: (a) $\sin u$, (b) $\cos u$, (c) $\tan u$, (d) $\cot u$, (e) $\sec u$, (f) $\csc u$.

4-4. REAL NUMBERS AND DIRECTED ANGLES

In Art. 1-4 the generation of an angle was described as the rotation of a line segment about a vertex. In Fig. 4-4-1, as point P traverses the representative arc u, the line segment OP generates the angle θ, which is in standard position. The *angle θ is said to be associated with the representative arc u.*

Using the formula for the length of arc on a circle, namely, $S = r\theta$ (θ measured in radians), we see that for a unit circle, with $r = 1$

$$S = \theta.$$

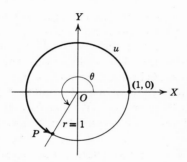

Figure 4-4-1

Denoting the arc length by u, we can say that the directed angle θ (measured in radians) associated with the representative arc u on the unit circle is equal to the length of u. That is,

(4-4-1) $$\theta = u \ (\theta \text{ in radians}).$$

If the real number u is positive, θ will be positive, and if the real number u is negative, θ will be negative. If $u = 0$, then $\theta = 0$.

In the definitions of the trigonometric functions of a directed angle θ in standard position, it was noted that any point $P(x, y)$, $r \neq 0$ could be chosen on the terminal side of the angle. Let us choose the point P, such that $r = 1$; then those definitions become

$$\sin \theta = \frac{y}{r} = y. \qquad \cos \theta = \frac{x}{r} = x. \qquad \tan \theta = \frac{y}{x}.$$

$$\csc \theta = \frac{r}{y} = \frac{1}{y}. \qquad \sec \theta = \frac{r}{x} = \frac{1}{x}. \qquad \cot \theta = \frac{x}{y}.$$

Comparing these to the definitions of the trigonometric functions of a real number we see that

(4-4-2) $$T(\theta) = T(u),$$

where u is a real number and θ is the directed angle, measured in radians, associated with the representative arc u. Hence, all of the formulas that have been and will be derived for the angle θ will be valid for the real number u.

From the formula $T(\theta) = T(u)$, we find

$$\sin 180° = \sin \pi \text{ (radians)} = \sin \pi,$$

$$\tan 3 = \tan 3(\text{radians}) = \tan \left[3\left(\frac{180°}{\pi}\right)\right] = \tan 171.9°.$$

The above relations point out the fact that we must be extremely careful in indicating the proper units of measurement of the argument of the trigonometric functions. If the argument is an angle measured in degrees, minutes, and seconds, the symbols °, ′, ″, must be used. Otherwise, when no symbol is used, the argument is an angle measured in radians or a real number. Thus, *sin* 30° is "the sine of an angle of 30 degrees." Whereas *sin* 30 is either "the sine of an angle of 30 radians" or its equivalent, "the sine of the real number 30."

The values of the trigonometric functions of real numbers may easily be found by considering the real number as an angle expressed in radians. Table II in the back of the book gives the values of the trigonometric functions of real numbers or of angles measured in radians accurate to four places.

Example 1. Find the value of the following trigonometric functions:

(a) sin 0.5, (b) sec 1.4, (c) cos 0.623.

Solution: Use Table II.

(a) **sin 0.5 = 0.4794.**

(b) **sec 1.4 = 5.883.**

(c) Since 0.623 is not found in the table, interpolation is required.

$$\begin{array}{ccc} u & & \sin u \\ 10\left[3\left[\begin{array}{c}0.620 \\ 0.623 \\ 0.630\end{array}\right.\right. & & \left.\left.\begin{array}{c}0.8139 \\ 0.8080\end{array}\right]x\right]59. \end{array}$$

$$\frac{3}{10} = \frac{x}{59} \text{ or } x = 17.7 \text{ (round off to } x = 18).$$

Hence,   **cos 0.623 = 0.8121.**

Example 2: Find the positive real number $u < 1.57$, for the following trigonometric functions:

(a) $\tan u = 1.369$, (b) $\sin u = 0.4908$.

Solution: Use Table II.

(a) For $\tan u = 1.369$, **$u = 0.94$.**

(b) Since 0.4908 is not listed in the body of the table under the sin u column, we must use interpolation. Thus,

$$
\begin{array}{cc}
u & \sin u \\
\end{array}
$$

$$
10\left[x\left[\begin{array}{cc} 0.510 & 0.4882 \\ & 0.4908 \end{array}\right]26\right]87.
$$

$$
\begin{array}{cc} 0.520 & 0.4969 \end{array}
$$

$$
\frac{x}{10} = \frac{26}{87},
$$

$$
x = 2.9 \text{ (round off to } x = 3\text{)}.
$$

Hence, for $\sin u = 0.4908$, **$u = 0.513$.**

▶ **EXERCISES**

1. Find the value of the trigonometric functions at the real number (use Table II):

(a) sin 0.06.   (b) cos 1.40.   (c) tan 1.00.
(d) cot 0.10.   (e) sec 0.48.   (f) csc 1.15.
(g) sin 1.471.   (h) cos 1.007.   (i) tan 0.125.
(j) cot 1.206.   (k) sec 1.307.   (l) csc 1.236.

2. Find the positive real number $u < 1.57$.

(a) sin u = 0.2474.   (b) cos u = 0.9759.   (c) tan u = 92.62.
(d) cot u = 0.5216.   (e) sec u = 1.133.   (f) csc u = 2.916.
(g) sin u = 0.6624.   (h) cos u = 0.7158.   (i) tan u = 2.259.
(j) cot u = 0.4344.   (k) sec u = 7.076.   (l) csc u = 5.161.

3. In calculus the ratio $\dfrac{\sin u}{u}$ is important. Find the value of this ratio for the following values of u:

(a) $u = 0.3$. (b) $u = 0.2$. (c) $u = 0.1$. (d) $u = 0.05$.
(e) $u = 0.01$.

What value does the ratio $\dfrac{\sin u}{u}$ approach as u approaches zero?

4. If $f(u) = \dfrac{1 - \cos u}{u^2}$, find (a) $f(0.2)$, (b) $f(0.1)$.

5. If $f(u) = \dfrac{\tan u - u}{u - \sin u}$, find (a) $f(0.2)$, (b) $f(0.1)$.

6. For a weight hanging on a vibrating spring the displacement, velocity, and acceleration of the weight at any time t sec are given by the respective expressions

$$S = \tfrac{1}{2}\cos 3t, \qquad v = -\tfrac{3}{2}\sin 3t, \qquad a = -\tfrac{9}{2}\cos 3t,$$

where S is measured in ft, v in ft/sec, and a in ft/sec².
Find S, v, and a at the following times:

(a) $t = 0.1$. (b) $t = 0.2$. (c) $t = 0.4$.

7. The displacement of a vibrating spring under certain conditions is given by $x = \tfrac{1}{10}\sin 10t - t\cos 10t$. Find the displacement x ft at the following times t sec.

(a) $t = 0.01$. (b) $t = 0.02$. (c) $t = 0.05$. (d) $t = 0.1$.
(e) $t = 0.15$.

8. The equation of a shaft with flexible bearings rotating at its critical speed is given by $y = y_0 \cos (\pi x/2L)$. If for a shaft of length $L = 120$ in., $y_0 = 1$ in., find y for x equal to

(a) 10 in. (b) 50 in. (c) 100 in.

9. The area of a segment of a circle of radius r, bounded by an arc of the circle and its chord is given by the formula $A = \tfrac{1}{2}r^2 (\theta - \sin \theta)$. θ is the central angle which intercepts the arc. In what units must θ be measured? Find the area of a segment of a circle for the following values of r and θ:

(a) $r = 2$, $\theta = 1$. (b) $r = 2$, $\theta = 0.5$.
(c) $r = 10$, $\theta = 30°$. (d) $r = 5$, $\theta = 50°$.

10. A curve called the cycloid is determined by the equations $x = a(\phi - \sin \phi)$ and $y = a(1 - \cos \phi)$. If $a = 1$, find the values of x and y for the following values of ϕ:

(a) $\phi = 0.1$. (b) $\phi = 0.2$. (c) $\phi = 0.4$. (d) $\phi = 30°$.
(e) $\phi = 50°$.

11. A curve called the involute of a circle is determined by the equations $x = \cos \theta + \theta \sin \theta$ and $y = \sin \theta - \theta \cos \theta$. Find the values of x and y for

(a) $\theta = 0.1$. (b) $\theta = 0.2$. (c) $\theta = 0.4$. (d) $\theta = 30°$. (e) $\theta = 50°$.

12. The instantaneous voltage, e, for a 25-cycle electrical system, is given by the formula $e = 110 \sin 157t$, where t is measured in seconds. Find the voltage at the following times:

(a) $t = 0.002$ sec. (b) $t = 0.005$ sec. (c) $t = 0.01$ sec.

4-5. VALUES OF THE TRIGONOMETRIC FUNCTIONS OF ANY REAL NUMBER

Using a method similar to that employed in Art. 2-7, it may be shown that a reduction rule for real numbers may be stated as: any trigonometric function of any real number is *numerically* equal to the same trigonometric function of a *nonnegative* real number less than $\pi/2$ represented by the related arc of the given number. The algebraic sign of the trigonometric function is determined by the quadrant of the given real number. The *related arc* of a given real number is the nonnegative arc less than $\pi/2$ between the terminal point of the representative arc of the given real number and the X-axis.

Example 1. Find the values of the following trigonometric functions:

(a) $\sin \dfrac{5\pi}{6}$. (b) $\cos \dfrac{5\pi}{6}$. (c) $\tan 4.00$. (d) $\cot 8.50$. (e) $\sin (-5.25)$.

Solution: Sketch the representative arcs and determine the related arc.

(a) $\dfrac{5\pi}{6}$ is a second quadrant arc (Fig. 4-5-1), hence $\sin \dfrac{5\pi}{6}$ is positive.

The related arc is $\pi - \dfrac{5\pi}{6} = \dfrac{\pi}{6}$. Hence, $\sin \dfrac{5\pi}{6} = \sin \dfrac{\pi}{6} = \dfrac{1}{2}$.

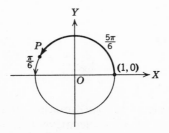

Figure 4-5-1

(b) $\cos \dfrac{5\pi}{6}$ will be negative. Hence, $\cos \dfrac{5\pi}{6} = -\cos \dfrac{\pi}{6} = -\dfrac{\sqrt{3}}{2}.$

(c) Since 4.00 is a third quadrant arc (Fig. 4-5-2), tan 4.00 is positive. The related arc is $4.00 - 3.14 = 0.86.$ Hence,

$$\tan 4.00 = \tan 0.86 = 1.162.$$

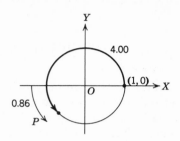

Figure 4-5-2

(d) Since $8.50 = 6.28 + 2.22$ it is a second quadrant arc (Fig. 4-5-3) and cot 8.50 is negative. Hence,

$$\cot 8.50 = -\cot 0.92 = -0.7615.$$

(e) Since $6.28 - 5.25 = 1.03,$ the related arc is 1.03 (Fig. 4-5-4). Hence, $\qquad \sin (-5.25) = \sin 1.03 = 0.8573.$

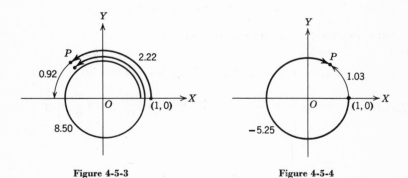

Figure 4-5-3   Figure 4-5-4

▶ EXERCISES

1. Express the trigonometric function in terms of the same trigonometric function of a nonnegative real number less than $\pi/2$. Recall that $\pi/2 = 1.57,$ $\pi = 3.14,$ and $2\pi = 6.28.$

(a) sin 2. (b) cos 3. (c) tan 4. (d) cot 6.
(e) sec 6.15. (f) csc 3.89. (g) sin 7. (h) tan 9.4.

2. Use Table II to evaluate the trigonometric functions:

(a) sin 2.30. (b) tan 1.76. (c) cos 4.0. (d) cot 3.25.
(e) sec 2.05. (f) csc 4.18. (g) sin 30. (h) cot 15.
(i) sin (− 1). (j) cos (− 0.8). (k) tan (− 2.6). (l) cot (− 3.7).

3. Complete the table with the exact value of the trigonometric function.

u	$\frac{2\pi}{3}$	$\frac{3\pi}{4}$	$\frac{5\pi}{6}$	π	$\frac{7\pi}{6}$	$\frac{5\pi}{4}$	$\frac{4\pi}{3}$	$\frac{3\pi}{2}$	$\frac{5\pi}{3}$	$\frac{7\pi}{4}$	$\frac{11\pi}{6}$	2π
sin u												
cos u												
tan u												
cot u												
sec u												
csc u												

4. Find the current, i, in an electric circuit at time, t sec, where $i = 8 \sin 377t$ for (a) $t = 0.01$, (b) $t = 0.1$, (c) $t = 1$.

5. Find the values of x and y for the following ϕ, where

$$x = 2(\phi - \sin \phi), \quad y = 2(1 - \cos \phi).$$

(a) $\phi = 60°$. (b) $90°$. (c) $135°$. (d) $180°$. (e) $225°$. (f) $270°$. (g) $315°$.

6. Given that $x = \frac{1}{10} \sin 10t - t \cos 10t$, find x when (a) $t = 1$, (b) $t = 1.5$, (c) $t = 2$.

Fundamental Identities

5-1. INTRODUCTION

The expression $(x - 2)(x + 2) = 0$ is true if and only if $x = 2$, or $x = -2$; whereas the expression $(x - 2)(x + 2) \equiv x^2 - 4$ is true for *every* value of x. Expressions of the first type are called *conditional equations* or usually just *equations*. Expressions of the latter type are called *identical equations* or usually just *identities*. To indicate an *identity*, we shall use the symbol $\equiv$, which is read "is identical to." Conditional equations are true for only particular values of the variable, while identities are true for *all* values of the *variable which are permissible*. Recall that division by zero is not allowed.

Example 1. $x^2 - x - 2 \equiv (x - 2)(x + 1)$ is true for all values of x.

Example 2. $\dfrac{1}{x - 2} + x \equiv \dfrac{1 + x^2 - 2x}{x - 2}$ is true for all values of x except $x = 2$. (Why?)

5-2. EIGHT FUNDAMENTAL IDENTITIES

There are eight fundamental identities of the trigonometric functions. These may be separated into three groups, namely: the *reciprocal, ratio,* and *squared* identities. They are fundamental for trigonometric analysis and they should be *memorized*. Of course, the relations are *true* only when the expressions involved *have meaning*. We will derive the identities, using the definitions of the trigonometric functions of real numbers. The identities are also true for the trigonometric functions of angles.

Reciprocal* Identities

$$(5\text{-}2\text{-}1) \qquad\qquad \sin u \csc u \equiv 1,$$

$$(5\text{-}2\text{-}2) \qquad\qquad \cos u \sec u \equiv 1,$$

$$(5\text{-}2\text{-}3) \qquad\qquad \tan u \cot u \equiv 1.$$

Ratio Identities

$$(5\text{-}2\text{-}4) \qquad\qquad \tan u \equiv \frac{\sin u}{\cos u},$$

$$(5\text{-}2\text{-}5) \qquad\qquad \cot u \equiv \frac{\cos u}{\sin u}.$$

Squared Identities

$$(5\text{-}2\text{-}6) \qquad\qquad \sin^2 u + \cos^2 u \equiv 1,$$

$$(5\text{-}2\text{-}7) \qquad\qquad 1 + \tan^2 u \equiv \sec^2 u,$$

$$(5\text{-}2\text{-}8) \qquad\qquad 1 + \cot^2 u \equiv \csc^2 u.$$

The proof of these identities may be obtained by applying the definitions of the trigonometric functions of real numbers. For example, $\sin u = y$, $\csc u = 1/y$ (if $y \neq 0$); hence, $\sin u \csc u \equiv 1$. The rest of the reciprocal and the ratio identities is left as an exercise for the student to verify.

The identity $\sin^2 u + \cos^2 u \equiv 1$ may be proved by substituting the values $y = \sin u$ and $x = \cos u$ in the equation of the unit circle $y^2 + x^2 = 1$. Thus, $(\sin u)^2 + (\cos u)^2 \equiv 1$, or

$$\sin^2 u + \cos^2 u \equiv 1.$$

---

* Two numbers are said to be *reciprocal numbers* when their product is one.

(The power to which a trigonometric function is raised is denoted by writing the exponent immediately after the abbreviation of the function.) The student can verify the identities 5-2-7 and 5-2-8 as exercises.

Recall that the symbols for the trigonometric functions represent numbers just as do the symbols a, x, y, t, etc. Thus, the algebraic processes for numbers can be applied to the trigonometric functions. Each of the above identities can be written in different ways; for example, $sin\ u \equiv \dfrac{1}{csc\ u}$ and $sin\ u \equiv \pm \sqrt{1 - cos^2\ u}$, where the sign is determined by the quadrant of u. Hence, any trigonometric expression can be written in terms of $sin\ u$ or any other trigonometric function.

Example. Reduce the expression $\dfrac{sec^2\ \theta - 1}{sin^2\ \theta}$ ($sin\ \theta \neq 0$) to one involving only $sin\ \theta$.

Solution:

$$\frac{sec^2\ \theta - 1}{sin^2\ \theta} \equiv \frac{\dfrac{1}{cos^2\ \theta} - 1}{sin^2\ \theta} \qquad \text{[Relation (5-2-2)]}.$$

$$\equiv \frac{1 - cos^2\ \theta}{sin^2\ \theta\ cos^2\ \theta}, \qquad \text{(Combining fractions)}.$$

$$\equiv \frac{sin^2\ \theta}{sin^2\ \theta\ cos^2\ \theta}, \qquad \text{[Relation (5-2-6)]}.$$

$$\equiv \frac{1}{cos^2\ \theta}, \qquad \text{(Dividing out } sin^2\ \theta\text{)}.$$

$$\frac{sec^2\ \theta - 1}{sin^2\ \theta} \equiv \frac{1}{1 - sin^2\ \theta}, \qquad \text{[Relation (5-2-6)]}.$$

▶ **EXERCISES**

1. Write out in words the eight fundamental identities.

2. Write each of the fundamental identities in two other ways. (For example, for equation 5-2-2 $cos\ u \equiv \dfrac{1}{sec\ u}$, and $sec\ u \equiv \dfrac{1}{cos\ u}$.

3. Verify the (a) reciprocal, (b) ratio, and (c) squared identities.

4. Reduce the following expressions to a single function of the given argument. (The denominators of the fractions are not zero.)

(a) $\dfrac{\tan u \csc^2 u}{1 + \tan^2 u}$.

(b) $\dfrac{\sec u}{\tan u + \cot u}$.

(c) $\dfrac{1 + \tan^2 A}{\csc^2 A}$.

(d) $\dfrac{\tan \beta \sin \beta}{\sec^2 \beta - 1}$.

(e) $\dfrac{1 + \tan^2 B}{\tan B \csc^2 B}$.

(f) $\dfrac{\sec^2 \theta - 1}{\sec \theta \sin^2 \theta}$.

(g) $\cos \alpha (1 + \tan^2 \alpha)$.

(h) $\dfrac{\sec^2 u + \csc^2 u}{\sec^2 u \csc u}$.

(i) $\tan v (\sin v + \cot v \cos v)$.

(j) $\dfrac{1}{\sin A \cos A} - \dfrac{\cos A}{\sin A}$.

(k) $1 + \dfrac{\tan^2 \theta}{1 + \sec \theta}$.

(l) $\dfrac{\sin B}{1 + \cos B} + \dfrac{1 + \cos B}{\sin B}$.

5. Derive the fundamental identities using the definitions of the trigonometric functions of an angle in standard position.

In problems 6 through 8, for simplicity, let a and b be nonnegative and u be in the first quadrant. The necessity for such restrictions will become evident after studying Chapter 10.

6. (a) Show that the expression $\sqrt{a^2 + b^2}$ may be written as $a \sec u$ where $\tan u = b/a$.

(b) Evaluate $\sqrt{100 + 25}$ by part a.

(c) Find the approximate value of $\sqrt{149}$.

(d) Find the approximate value of $\sqrt{80}$. [Hint: $80 = 64 + 16$.]

7. Many algebraic expressions can be simplified by making use of a suitable trigonometric substitution. Verify the following:

(a) $\sqrt{a^2 - x^2} = a \cos u$, when $x = a \sin u$.

(b) $\sqrt{a^2 + x^2} = a \sec u$, when $x = a \tan u$.

(c) $\sqrt{x^2 - a^2} = a \tan u$, when $x = a \sec u$.

(d) $\sqrt{25 + 4x^2} = 5 \sec u$, when $x = \frac{5}{2} \tan u$.

8. Using the suggested substitutions, reduce the given expressions to an expression involving only trigonometric functions.

(a) $(4 - x^2)^{3/2}$, let $x = 2 \sin u$.

(b) $(4 + x^2)^{3/2}$, let $x = 2 \tan u$.

(c) $\dfrac{\sqrt{x^2 - 4}}{x}$, let $x = 2 \sec u$.

(d) $\dfrac{x}{\sqrt{4 - 9x^2}}$, let $x = \frac{2}{3} \sin u$.

(e) $x^2 \sqrt{4 + 9x^2}$, let $x = \frac{2}{3} \tan u$.

5-3. ELEMENTARY IDENTITIES

The verification or proving of an identity means that the left-hand member may be reduced to the right-hand member or the right-hand member to the left-hand member, or each side may be separately reduced to the same form. The verification of identities is performed by using the fundamental relations and algebraic manipulations that are reversible, such as the addition of fractions, factoring, and multiplication. Division by zero and the introduction of radicals should be avoided.

Unfortunately, there is no one rule to be followed in proving an identity. Usually, the more complicated side is reduced to the simpler side by use of the fundamental relations and algebraic processes. The student should keep constantly in mind the expression at which he is trying to arrive. He should think of all the fundamental relations and pick out those to use that will steer him toward the final expression. As a last resort the writing of the identity in sines and cosines is sometimes useful. Practice and a thorough familiarity with the fundamental relations are necessities. A few examples follow.

The proving of identities helps a student to master the fundamental relations and also provides a usually much needed review of algebraic manipulations; the techniques learned will be extremely valuable in future courses.

Example 1. Prove the identity

$$\csc u \equiv \frac{\cot u}{\cos u}.$$

Solution: Here the right-hand side is the more complicated. The left-hand side immediately makes us think of $\sin u$. Hence, can we obtain $\sin u$ on the right-hand side?

Replace $\cot u$ by $\dfrac{\cos u}{\sin u}$ to obtain

$$\csc u \equiv \frac{\dfrac{\cos u}{\sin u}}{\cos u}.$$

Performing the division on the right-hand side, we have

$$\csc u \equiv \frac{\cos u}{\sin u} \cdot \frac{1}{\cos u} \equiv \frac{1}{\sin u}.$$

Thus, $\qquad\qquad$ **$\csc u \equiv \csc u.$**

Example 2. Prove the identity

$$\frac{\cos A}{1 + \sin A} + \frac{\cos A}{1 - \sin A} \equiv 2 \sec A.$$

Solution: Combine the left side to a single fraction.

$$\frac{\cos A(1 - \sin A) + \cos A(1 + \sin A)}{(1 + \sin A)(1 - \sin A)} \equiv 2 \sec A.$$

Multiplying and combining terms we have

$$\frac{\cos A - \cos A \sin A + \cos A + \cos A \sin A}{1 - \sin^2 A} \equiv 2 \sec A,$$

$$\frac{2 \cos A}{\cos^2 A} \equiv 2 \sec A,$$

$$\frac{2}{\cos A} \equiv 2 \sec A.$$

and thus $\qquad\qquad$ **$2 \sec A \equiv 2 \sec A.$**

Example 3. Verify the identity

$$\csc^4 u - \cot^4 u \equiv \csc^2 u + \cot^2 u.$$

Solution: The left-hand side suggests factoring.

Hence $\quad (\csc^2 u + \cot^2 u)(\csc^2 u - \cot^2 u) \equiv \csc^2 u + \cot^2 u.$

Since $\qquad \csc^2 u - \cot^2 u \equiv 1$ (see formula 5-2-8),

we have $\qquad$ **$\csc^2 u + \cot^2 u \equiv \csc^2 u + \cot^2 u.$**

Example 4. Verify the identity

$$\frac{1}{\csc \alpha + \cot \alpha} \equiv \frac{1 - \cos \alpha}{\sin \alpha}.$$

Solution: Multiply both numerator and denominator of the left side by $\csc \alpha - \cot \alpha$ and obtain

$$\frac{\csc \alpha - \cot \alpha}{\csc^2 \alpha - \cot^2 \alpha} \equiv \frac{1 - \cos \alpha}{\sin \alpha}.$$

Using the fundamental relation

$$1 + \cot^2 \alpha \equiv \csc^2 \alpha,$$

we have

$$\frac{\csc \alpha - \cot \alpha}{1} \equiv \frac{1 - \cos \alpha}{\sin \alpha}.$$

Rewrite the left side as

$$\frac{1}{\sin \alpha} - \frac{\cos \alpha}{\sin \alpha} \equiv \frac{1 - \cos \alpha}{\sin \alpha},$$

and thus

$$\frac{1 - \cos \alpha}{\sin \alpha} \equiv \frac{1 - \cos \alpha}{\sin \alpha}.$$

► **EXERCISES**

Verify the following identities for admissible values of the argument.

1. $\sin^2 u(1 + \cot^2 u) \equiv 1$.

2. $\cos^2 u(1 + \tan^2 u) \equiv 1$.

3. $\sec^2 A(1 - \sin^2 A) \equiv 1$.

4. $\dfrac{2 \sin B(1 - \sin^2 B)}{2 \sin B \cos B} \equiv \cos B$.

5. $\dfrac{\sec v + \tan v}{\cos v + \cot v} \equiv \sec v \tan v$.

6. $\dfrac{1 + \cot^2 w}{1 + \tan^2 w} \equiv \cot^2 w$.

7. $\dfrac{1}{1 - \cos u} + \dfrac{1}{1 + \cos u} \equiv 2 \csc^2 u$.

8. $\dfrac{2 - \tan^2 \theta}{\sec^2 \theta} - 1 + 2 \sin^2 \theta \equiv \cos^2 \theta$.

9. $\cot B + \tan B \equiv \sec B \csc B$.

10. $\dfrac{\sin \theta}{1 - \cos \theta} \equiv \dfrac{1 + \cos \theta}{\sin \theta}$.

11. $\dfrac{1 - \sin A}{\cos A} \equiv \dfrac{\cos A}{1 + \sin A}$.

12. $\dfrac{\sin \alpha}{1 - \cos \alpha} - \cot \alpha \equiv \csc \alpha$.

13. $\csc B - \dfrac{\sin B}{1 + \cos B} \equiv \cot B$.

14. $\sec \beta - \dfrac{\cos \beta}{1 + \sin \beta} \equiv \tan \beta$.

15. $\dfrac{\cos \alpha \tan \alpha + \sin \alpha}{\tan \alpha} \equiv 2 \cos \alpha$.

16. $\dfrac{\tan^2 \theta \sin^2 \theta}{\tan \theta - \sin \theta} \equiv \tan \theta + \sin \theta$.

17. $\csc^2 A + \sec^2 A \equiv \csc^2 A \sec^2 A$.

18. $\sec^2 A - \sin^3 A \sec^3 A \cot^3 A \equiv \tan^2 A$.

19. $\dfrac{\cos B}{\sin B + 1} - \dfrac{\cos B}{\sin B - 1} \equiv 2\sec B$.

20. $\dfrac{\tan^2 u \sin^2 u}{\tan u + \sin u} \equiv \tan u - \sin u$.

21. $\csc^2 u - \cos^3 u \csc^3 u \tan^3 u \equiv \cot^2 u$.

22. $\dfrac{\cos u \sec u}{1 + \tan^2 u} \equiv \cos^2 u$.

23. $(\sin^2 \theta - \cos^2 \theta) \dfrac{\tan \theta + \cot \theta}{\tan \theta - \cot \theta} \equiv 1$.

24. $\dfrac{2 + \sec A}{\csc A} - 2\sin A \equiv \tan A$.

25. $\dfrac{\tan \theta + \sin \theta}{\tan \theta - \sin \theta} - \dfrac{\sec \theta + 1}{\sec \theta - 1} \equiv 0$.

26. $2 \sin u + \tan u \equiv \dfrac{2 + \sec u}{\csc u}$.

27. $\sec B + 2\tan B \equiv \dfrac{\cot B + 2\cos B}{\csc B - \sin B}$.

28. $\cot \alpha + \dfrac{\sin \alpha}{1 + \cos \alpha} \equiv \csc \alpha$.

29. $\dfrac{\sin \alpha}{\csc \alpha \, (1 + \cot^2 \alpha)} \equiv (1 - \cos^2 \alpha)^2.$

30. $\dfrac{\cos \phi \, (1 + \tan^2 \phi)}{\sec \phi} \equiv 1.$

31. $\dfrac{\tan A + \cot A}{\tan A - \cot A} \equiv \dfrac{\sec^2 A}{\tan^2 A - 1}.$

32. $\sec \theta - \tan \theta \sin \theta \equiv \cos \theta.$

33. $\sin A \, (\sec A + \csc A) - \cos A \, (\sec A - \csc A) \equiv \sec A \csc A.$

34. $\cos^4 B - \sin^4 B + 1 \equiv 2 \cos^2 B.$

35. $(\sin \alpha + \cos \alpha)^2 + (\sin \alpha - \cos \alpha)^2 \equiv 2.$

36. $\dfrac{\sin \beta}{1 + \cos \beta} + \dfrac{1 + \cos \beta}{\sin \beta} \equiv 2 \csc \beta.$

37. $\dfrac{\cos \alpha}{1 - \tan \alpha} + \dfrac{\sin \alpha}{1 - \cot \alpha} \equiv \sin \alpha + \cos \alpha.$

38. $\cot^2 u - \cos^2 u \equiv \cot^2 u \cos^2 u.$

39. $1 - \tan^4 u \equiv 2 \sec^2 u - \sec^4 u.$

40. $\sin u \tan^2 u + \csc u \sec^2 u - 2 \tan u \sec u \equiv \csc u - \sin u.$

41. $\cos^3 u - \sin^3 u \equiv (\cos u - \sin u)(1 + \sin u \cos u).$

42. $\sin^6 A + \cos^6 A \equiv 1 - 3 \sin^2 A \cos^2 A.$

43. $1 - \sin \theta \equiv (1 + \sin \theta)(\sec \theta - \tan \theta)^2.$

44. $1 + \cos \theta \equiv (1 - \cos \theta)(\csc \theta + \cot \theta)^2.$

45. $(1 + \sin \alpha + \cos \alpha)^2 \equiv 2(1 + \sin \alpha)(1 + \cos \alpha).$

46. $(1 - \sin u - \cos u)^2(1 + \sin u + \cos u)^2 \equiv 4 \sin^2 u \cos^2 u.$

47. $\sin^3 u + \cos^3 u \equiv (\sin u + \cos u)(1 - \sin u \cos u).$

48. $\sin^6 \theta + \cos^6 \theta \equiv \sin^4 \theta + \cos^4 \theta - \sin^2 \theta \cos^2 \theta.$

49. $\sin^2 u \tan^2 u + \cos^2 u \cot^2 u \equiv \tan^2 u + \cot^2 u - 1.$

50. $(\sin^2 u + \cos^2 u)^2 \equiv 1.$

5-4. TRIGONOMETRIC ELIMINATION OF PARAMETERS

If x is a function of the variable t, and y is also a function of t, then the pair of equations

$$\begin{cases} x = f(t), \\ y = g(t) \end{cases}$$

are said to be *parametric equations* where t is called the **parameter**. Parametric equations are particularly useful in studying the position of a particle when its position is a function of the time. For instance, what is the position of a projectile at a particular time after it has been fired? To study the locus of parametric equations, it is often useful to eliminate the parameter and obtain an equation in terms of x and y. If the function of t is a trigonometric function, the use of trigonometric identities frequently helps in eliminating t. There are several methods of attacking such problems. A few of them are shown in the illustrative examples.

Example 1. Eliminate t from the parametric equations

$$\begin{cases} x = a \cos t, \\ y = a \sin t. \end{cases}$$

Solution: Noticing that the equations contain $\cos t$ and $\sin t$, we recall that $\cos^2 t + \sin^2 t \equiv 1$. Hence, divide by a to obtain

$$\frac{x}{a} = \cos t,$$

$$\frac{y}{a} = \sin t.$$

Square both equations
$$\frac{x^2}{a^2} = \cos^2 t,$$

$$\frac{y^2}{a^2} = \sin^2 t.$$

Add
$$\frac{x^2}{a^2} + \frac{y^2}{a^2} = \cos^2 t + \sin^2 t.$$

Since
$$\cos^2 t + \sin^2 t \equiv 1,$$

we have
$$\boldsymbol{x^2 + y^2 = a^2}.$$

Example 2. Eliminate t from the parametric equations

$$\begin{cases} x = 2 + 3 \sec t, \\ y = -1 + 2 \tan t. \end{cases}$$

Solution: Recall that $\sec^2 t - \tan^2 t \equiv 1$.

Rewrite the equations as
$$\frac{x - 2}{3} = \sec t,$$

$$\frac{y + 1}{2} = \tan t.$$

Square both equations $\quad \dfrac{(x-2)^2}{9} = \sec^2 t,$

$$\dfrac{(y+1)^2}{4} = \tan^2 t.$$

Subtract $\quad \dfrac{(x-2)^2}{9} - \dfrac{(y+1)^2}{4} = \sec^2 t - \tan^2 t.$

Hence, $\quad \dfrac{(x-2)^2}{9} - \dfrac{(y+1)^2}{4} = 1.$

This is the equation of a curve called the *hyperbola* which is studied in analytical geometry.

Example 3. Eliminate t from the parametric equations

$$\begin{cases} x = \cos t, \\ y = 2 \sin t \cos t. \end{cases}$$

Solution: From the fundamental relation $\cos^2 t + \sin^2 t \equiv 1$, we have $\quad \sin t \equiv \pm \sqrt{1 - \cos^2 t}.$

Replacing $\cos t$ by x, we have

$$\sin t = \pm \sqrt{1 - x^2}.$$

Hence, $\quad y = 2(\pm \sqrt{1 - x^2})(x).$

Thus, $\quad y^2 = 4(1 - x^2)(x^2),$

or $\quad y^2 = 4x^2 - 4x^4.$

▶ **EXERCISES**

Eliminate t from the following parametric equations to obtain one equation in x and y.

1. $\begin{cases} x = \cos t, \\ y = \sin t. \end{cases}$
2. $\begin{cases} x = 3 \sin t, \\ y = 2 \cos t. \end{cases}$

3. $\begin{cases} x = 2 \tan t, \\ y = 4 \sec t. \end{cases}$
4. $\begin{cases} x = a \cos^3 t, \\ y = a \sin^3 t. \end{cases}$

5. $\begin{cases} x = \sin t, \\ y = \cos^2 t - \sin^2 t. \end{cases}$
6. $\begin{cases} x = 2 \cos t, \\ y = \cos^2 t - \sin^2 t. \end{cases}$

7. $\begin{cases} x = h + a \cos t, \\ y = k + a \sin t. \end{cases}$
8. $\begin{cases} x = \csc t, \\ y = 2 - \cot t. \end{cases}$

9. $\begin{cases} x = 2 \sec t, \\ y = 2 \tan t. \end{cases}$

10. $\begin{cases} x = \cos t, \\ y = \sin t \cos t. \end{cases}$

11. $\begin{cases} x = 2 \sin t, \\ y = 2(1 - \cos t). \end{cases}$

12. $\begin{cases} x = 3 \cos^4 t, \\ y = 3 \sin^4 t. \end{cases}$

13. $\begin{cases} x = 2 \cot t, \\ y = 2 \sin^2 t. \end{cases}$

14. $\begin{cases} x = \sin t, \\ y = \tan t(1 + \sin t). \end{cases}$

15. $\begin{cases} x = \csc t - \sin t, \\ y = \sec t - \cos t. \end{cases}$

16. $\begin{cases} x = 2 \sin t + \cos t, \\ y = 2 \cos t - \sin t. \end{cases}$

17. The parametric equations

$$\begin{cases} x = a \cos\left(t\sqrt{\dfrac{k}{m}}\right), \\ y = v_0 \sqrt{\dfrac{m}{k}} \sin\left(t\sqrt{\dfrac{k}{m}}\right). \end{cases}$$

are the solutions of differential equations for a particle of mass m attracted toward the origin by a force proportional to the distance; a, v_0, k, and m are constants. Eliminate t and obtain one equation in x and y.

Variations and Graphs of the Trigonometric Functions

6-1. VARIATION OF sin θ AND cos θ

We have seen that for different angles the trigonometric functions take on different values. In this chapter we shall see how these values vary as the angle varies. This will be shown by considering a point P on the terminal side of any angle θ in standard position at a distance r from the origin. As θ goes from $0°$ to $360°$ the terminal side will make one complete revolution and the point P will trace out a circle of radius r. Since P can be any point on the terminal side of θ, let us choose $r = 1$ for convenience. We will then have a unit circle (Fig. 6-1-1).

The coordinates of P are ($\cos \theta$, $\sin \theta$). That is, $OM = \cos \theta$, and $MP = \sin \theta$.

Table 6-1 should be obvious as θ goes from $0°$ through $360°$ in a counterclockwise sense. In view of Art. 2-7 we need only consider one revolution.

TABLE 6-1

Variation of sin θ and cos θ

When θ increases from	sin θ	cos θ
0° to 90°	increases from 0 to 1,	decreases from 1 to 0.
90° to 180°	decreases from 1 to 0,	decreases from 0 to −1.
180° to 270°	decreases from 0 to −1,	increases from −1 to 0.
270° to 360°	increases from −1 to 0,	increases from 0 to 1.

As θ continues for one or more revolutions, sin θ and cos θ will repeat their values in the same order. A function having this property is said to be periodic. The sine and cosine functions are periodic with a period of 360° or 2π radians. If $f(x + p) = f(x)$ for all x, and p is the smallest positive number for which such a relation holds, then p is said to be the period of the function.

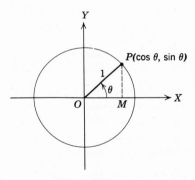

Figure 6-1-1

▶ EXERCISE

Discuss the variation of sin u and cos u as u varies from 0 to 2π. State clearly the maximum and minimum values of sin u and cos u.

6-2. THE GRAPH OF $y = \sin x$

The graph of $y = \sin x$ affords a pictorial representation of the variation of the function sin x. The argument x, a real number, will be the abscissa of any point on the graph. If we make use of the

circle, the ordinate of any point on the circumference will be
n by sin x.

To construct an appropriate scale for the abscissas, let us consider
the equation $S = rx$, Art. 1-5, where S is the arc length on the
circumference of a circle and x is the central angle. For the unit
circle, where $r = 1$, we have $S = x$, which tells us that the abscissas
will equal the arc length.

To construct the graph of $y = \sin x$, proceed as follows (see
Fig. 6-2-1):

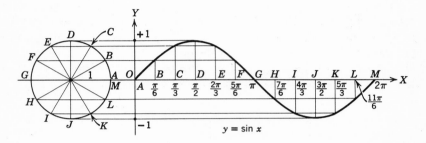

Figure 6-2-1

1. Draw a unit circle and a set of coordinate axes. Let the
horizontal or X-axis pass through the center of the circle and the
Y-axis be to the right of the circle.

2. Divide the circumference of the circle into 12 equal parts (for
convenience) and label them as shown.

3. Lay off a scale on the X-axis. Let $\overset{\frown}{ADG} = \pi$ on the unit circle
be represented by length $AG = \pi$ on the X-axis. Since $\pi = 3.14$,
AG will be 3.14 times as long as the radius of the circle. In a similar
manner, $\overset{\frown}{AB} = $ length $AB = \pi/6$, $\overset{\frown}{AD} = $ length $AD = \pi/2$, $\overset{\frown}{ADGJ}$
$= $ length $AJ = 3\pi/2$, and so forth. The scale on the Y-axis is
determined by the radius of the unit circle.

4. Draw a horizontal line from B on the circle until it intersects a
vertical line through B on the X-axis. The ordinate of this point
will represent $\sin (\pi/6)$. Do the same for the other points as shown.

5. Draw a smooth curve through the points located in step 4 to
obtain the graph of $y = \sin x$. This graph is called the *sine curve*.
This smooth curve approximates $\sin x$ for values of x between those
computed.

From Fig. 6-2-1, we see that the sine curve crosses the X-axis at

$x = 0$, $x = \pi$, and $x = 2\pi$. It reaches its highest point at $x = \pi/2$ and its lowest point at $x = 3\pi/2$.

Using the periodicity of the sine function we may extend the graph in both directions along the X-axis for as many cycles as we please. A *cycle* is the shortest segment of the graph which includes one period. In Fig. 6-2-2, the sine curve has been drawn for values of x from -3π to 3π.

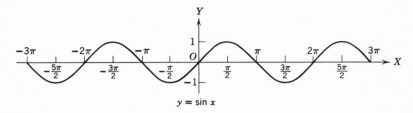

$y = \sin x$

Figure 6-2-2

The graph of $y = a \sin x$, where a is a positive constant, is readily drawn by comparing it to the sine curve. The constant a is called the **amplitude** of the function. The ordinates of $y = a \sin x$ are a times the ordinates of $y = \sin x$. When sin x reaches its maximum value of 1 at $x = \pi/2$, $y = a \sin x$ reaches its maximum value of a. When the graph of sin x crosses the X-axis, the value of $y = a \sin x$ will also be zero. When sin x reaches its lowest point, -1, at $x = 3\pi/2$, the graph of $y = a \sin x$ will obtain its least value of $-a$.

In Fig. 6-2-3 on the following page the graph of $y = 3 \, sin \, x$ is drawn. The dotted curve shows the graph of $y = \sin x$.

The graph of $y = \sin bx$, where b is a positive constant, can be drawn after a few preliminary observations. This curve is sinusoidal in nature. The angle in this function is bx. As x varies from 0 to $2\pi/b$, bx will vary from 0 to 2π. Thus sin bx will cover one complete period as x goes from 0 to $2\pi/b$. The graph of this function is called a sine curve with **period $2\pi/b$**. Considering one cycle, we find that the graph will cross the X-axis when

$$bx = 0, \; \pi, \text{ and } 2\pi,$$

or when
$$x = 0, \; \frac{\pi}{b}, \text{ and } \frac{2\pi}{b}.$$

The graph will reach its highest point when

$$bx = \frac{\pi}{2} \text{ or } x = \frac{\pi}{2b}.$$

It will reach its lowest point when

coeffcient of sin x is called the amplitude of the equation

$$bx = \frac{3\pi}{2} \text{ or } x = \frac{3\pi}{2b}.$$

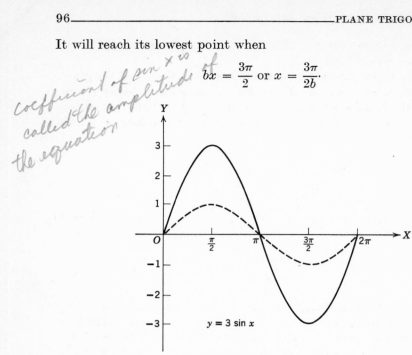

Figure 6-2-3

The graph of **y = a sin bx** can be drawn from the above considerations. It is sinusoidal in form and the graph of the function is called a sine curve with **amplitude a** and **period 2π/b**. It will be illustrated in the following example.

Example. Sketch the graph of $y = 2 \sin 3x$, for $(-2\pi/3) \leq x \leq (4\pi/3)$.

Solution: This function is sinusoidal in form with an amplitude of **2** and a period of **2π/3**. We shall sketch one period and then extend the graph to cover the required values of **x** (Fig. 6-2-4).

For one cycle, the graph crosses the X-axis when

$$3x = 0, \pi, \text{ and } 2\pi,$$

or when
$$x = 0, \frac{\pi}{3}, \text{ and } \frac{2\pi}{3}.$$

It reaches its highest value of 2 at

$$3x = \frac{\pi}{2}, \text{ or at } x = \frac{\pi}{6}.$$

It reaches its least value of -2 at

$$3x = \frac{3\pi}{2}, \text{ or at } x = \frac{\pi}{2}.$$

The darker portion of the curve is drawn first.

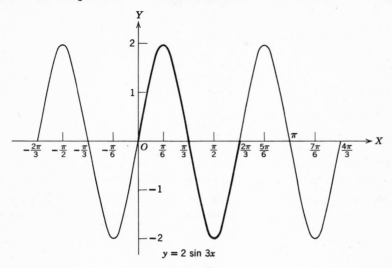

$$y = 2 \sin 3x$$

Figure 6-2-4

▶ **EXERCISES**

Sketch the graph for the required values of x. State the amplitude and period.

1. $y = \sin x,$ $-\pi \leqq x \leqq 2\pi.$

2. $y = 2 \sin x,$ $-\dfrac{\pi}{2} \leqq x \leqq 3\pi$

3. $y = \frac{1}{3} \sin x,$ $0 \leqq x \leqq 2\pi.$

4. $y = \sin 2x,$ $0 \leqq x \leqq 3\pi.$

5. $y = 2 \sin \frac{1}{2}x,$ $0 \leqq x \leqq 4\pi.$

6. $y = \sin \pi x,$ $0 \leqq x \leqq 2.$

7. $y = 3 \sin 3x,$ $-\pi \leqq x \leqq \pi.$

8. $y = -\sin x,$ $0 \leqq x \leqq 2\pi.$

9. $y = -2 \sin 2x,$ $-\pi \leqq x \leqq \pi.$

10. $y = -\frac{1}{2} \sin \frac{1}{3} x,$ $0 \leqq x \leqq 3\pi.$

11. $y = 3 \sin \dfrac{\pi}{2} x,$ $\qquad 0 \leq x \leq 4.$

12. $y = 4 \sin \tfrac{2}{3} x,$ $\qquad 0 \leq x \leq \dfrac{4\pi}{3}.$

13. $y = \tfrac{3}{2} \sin \tfrac{1}{6} x,$ $\qquad 0 \leq x \leq 12\pi.$

14. $y = 2 \sin 3x,$ $\qquad -\dfrac{\pi}{3} \leq x \leq \dfrac{\pi}{3}.$

15. $y = 4 \sin \dfrac{3x}{2},$ $\qquad -\pi \leq x \leq \pi.$

16. $y = 2 \sin \tfrac{2}{3} x,$ $\qquad 0 \leq x \leq 3\pi.$

17. $y = \sin \dfrac{\pi}{3} x,$ one period.

18. $y = \tfrac{1}{2} \sin 6x,$ one period.

19. The equation for an alternating voltage, e, is given as $e = 110 \sin 157\, t$. Sketch the voltage curve for several cycles.

20. If b is small in $y = \sin bx$, the resulting curve would approximate the waves of the ocean swell. Sketch several cycles of $y = \sin \dfrac{\pi}{15} x.$

6-3. THE GRAPH OF $y = a \sin (bx + \alpha)$

The graph of $y = a \sin (bx + \alpha)$, $\alpha \neq 0$, is similar to the graph of $y = a \sin bx$. α is called the **phase* angle**. α shifts the graph to the left or to the right depending on whether α is positive or negative. The amount of the shift is given by α/b. The graph will be illustrated by considering the following example.

Example. Sketch one cycle of the graph of $y = \tfrac{1}{2} \sin \left(2x + \dfrac{\pi}{4} \right).$

Solution: The amplitude is $\tfrac{1}{2}$ and the period is $2\pi/2 = \pi$. The graph (Fig. 6-3-1) crosses the X-axis when the angle $\left(2x + \dfrac{\pi}{4} \right)$ has the following values:

$$2x + \frac{\pi}{4} = 0, \quad \pi, \quad \text{and} \quad 2\pi,$$

or when $\qquad x = -\dfrac{\pi}{8}, \quad \dfrac{3\pi}{8}, \quad \text{and} \quad \dfrac{7\pi}{8}.$

_____

* The phase angle is often called the angle of _lead_ or _lag_.

The highest value is reached when

$$2x + \frac{\pi}{4} = \frac{\pi}{2},$$

or when

$$x = \frac{\pi}{8}.$$

The lowest point is reached when

$$2x + \frac{\pi}{4} = \frac{3\pi}{2},$$

or when

$$x = \frac{5\pi}{8}.$$

When $x = 0$, $\qquad y = \frac{1}{2} \sin \frac{\pi}{4} = 0.35.$

Figure 6-3-1 shows that this curve is shifted $\pi/8$ units to the left of the sine curve. The student should sketch the sine curve on the same axes for comparison.

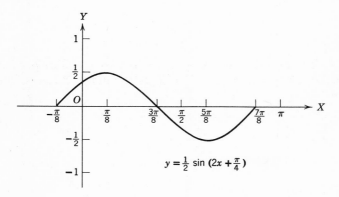

$$y = \frac{1}{2} \sin \left(2x + \frac{\pi}{4} \right)$$

Figure 6-3-1

6-4. THE GRAPH OF $y = \cos x$

From Art. 3-2 we have $\sin \left(x + \dfrac{\pi}{2} \right) = \cos x$ for x, an acute angle. It can be shown that this expression is also true for all angles. See

Chapter 7. Hence, the graph of $y = \cos x$ can be drawn by considering the graph of $y = \sin\left(x + \dfrac{\pi}{2}\right)$. In view of Art. 6-3, this curve is shifted $\pi/2$ units to the *left* of the sine curve. It has an amplitude of **1**, and a period of $\mathbf{2\pi/1 = 2\pi}$.

The graph (Fig. 6-4-1) crosses the X-axis when

$$x + \frac{\pi}{2} = 0, \quad \pi, \quad \text{and} \quad 2\pi.$$

or when
$$x = -\frac{\pi}{2}, \quad \frac{\pi}{2}, \quad \text{and} \quad \frac{3\pi}{2}.$$

It reaches its highest point when

$$x + \frac{\pi}{2} = \frac{\pi}{2},$$

or when
$$x = 0.$$

It reaches its lowest point when

$$x + \frac{\pi}{2} = \frac{3\pi}{2},$$

or when
$$x = \pi.$$

When $x = 0$, $\qquad\qquad y = \cos 0 = 1.$

The graph may be extended along the X-axis by use of its periodicity.

The heavy portion in Fig. 6-4-1 is usually referred to as *one cycle* of the cosine curve.

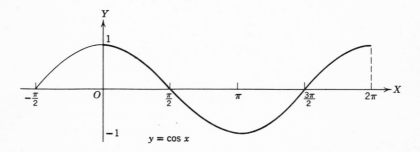

Figure 6-4-1

The graph of $y = a \cos bx$ will have an amplitude of a and a period of $2\pi/b$. It can be readily drawn by noting from Fig. 6-4-1 that the curve will cross the X-axis when the angle $bx = \pi/2$ and $3\pi/2$. The highest point will be reached when $bx = 0$ and 2π. The lowest point will occur at $bx = \pi$.

Example 1. Sketch one cycle of the curve $y = \cos \frac{1}{2}x$.

Solution: The amplitude is 1 and the period is 4π. The curve (Fig. 6-4-2) will cross the X-axis at

$$\frac{1}{2}x = \frac{\pi}{2} \quad \text{and} \quad \frac{3\pi}{2},$$

or at $\qquad\qquad x = \pi \quad \text{and} \quad 3\pi.$

The highest point occurs at

$$\tfrac{1}{2}x = 0 \quad \text{and} \quad 2\pi,$$

or at $\qquad\qquad x = 0 \quad \text{and} \quad 4\pi.$

The lowest point occurs at

$$\tfrac{1}{2}x = \pi,$$

or at $\qquad\qquad x = 2\pi.$

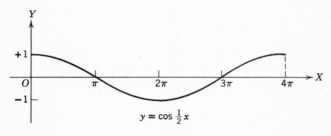

$$y = \cos \frac{1}{2}x$$

Figure 6-4-2

The graph of $y = a \sin bx + c \cos dx$ may be drawn by a process known as composition of ordinates. Let $y_1 = a \sin bx$ and $y_2 = c \cos dx$, then $y = y_1 + y_2$. Draw the curve $y_1 = a \sin bx$ and on the same axes draw the curve $y_2 = c \cos dx$. Obtain the curve for $y = a \sin bx + c \sin dx$ by adding the ordinates of y_1 and y_2.

Example 2. Sketch the graph of $y = \sin x + \cos x$.

Solution: Let $y_1 = \sin x$ and $y_2 = \cos x$; then $y = y_1 + y_2$. Sketch the graph of $y_1 = \sin x$ and of $y_2 = \cos x$ on the same set of axes. Then add the ordinates to obtain y. See Fig. 6-4-3.

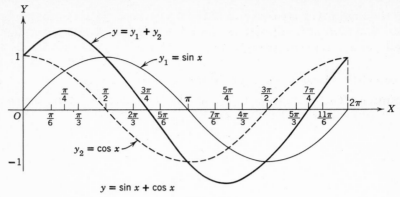

Figure 6-4-3

▶ **EXERCISES**

Sketch the graph for the required values of x. State the amplitude and the period.

1. $y = \cos x, \quad -\pi \leq x \leq 3\pi.$

2. $y = 2 \cos x, \quad -\dfrac{\pi}{2} \leq x \leq 2\pi.$

3. $y = \frac{1}{2} \cos x, \quad 0 \leq x \leq 2\pi.$

4. $y = \cos 2x, \quad -\pi \leq x \leq \pi.$

5. $y = 3 \cos \frac{1}{2}x, \quad -\pi \leq x \leq 5\pi.$

6. $y = 3 \cos \pi x, \quad 0 \leq x \leq 2.$

7. $y = \cos 3x, \quad -\pi \leq x \leq 2\pi.$

8. $y = 3 \cos \frac{1}{3}x, \quad 0 \leq x \leq 6\pi.$

Sketch one cycle of the graph for problems 9 through 16. State the amplitude, period, and phase shift.

9. $y = 5 \sin \left(x + \dfrac{\pi}{6} \right).$ **10.** $y = 3 \sin \left(2x - \dfrac{\pi}{2} \right).$

11. $y = 2 \sin \left(2x + \dfrac{\pi}{2} \right).$ **12.** $y = \cos \left(x - \dfrac{\pi}{3} \right).$

13. $y = \cos \left(x + \dfrac{\pi}{2} \right).$ **14.** $y = 2 \cos \left(3x + \dfrac{\pi}{2} \right).$

15. $y = \dfrac{1}{2} \sin \left(\dfrac{1}{2}x + \dfrac{\pi}{3} \right).$ **16.** $y = \dfrac{1}{3} \cos \left(\dfrac{1}{3}x - \dfrac{\pi}{6} \right).$

The graph of $y + d = a \sin (bx + \alpha)$ is merely the graph of $y = a \sin (bx + \alpha)$ oscillating about the line $y = -d$ instead of the X-axis. Sketch two cycles of the graph for problems 17 through 20.

17. $y - 2 = \sin x.$ **18.** $y + 1 = \cos x.$

19. $y + 3 = 2 \sin \left(2x + \dfrac{\pi}{3}\right).$ **20.** $y - 2 = 3 \sin \left(\dfrac{1}{2}x - \dfrac{\pi}{2}\right).$

Use the method of composition of ordinates to sketch two cycles of the graph of problems 21 to 25.

21. $y = 2 \sin x + \cos x.$ **22.** $y = \sin 2x + 2 \cos x.$

23. $y = \sin x + \cos 2x.$ **24.** $y = \sin 2x - 2 \sin x.$

25. $y = 2 \sin \tfrac{1}{2}x - \cos x.$

6-5. VARIATION OF tan θ

Consider the circle of unit radius in Fig. 6-5-1. If point $P'(x', y')$ is taken on the terminal side of θ such that $P'A$ is always tangent to the circle at point A, we have

$$\tan \theta = \frac{y'}{x'} = \frac{y'}{1} = y'.$$

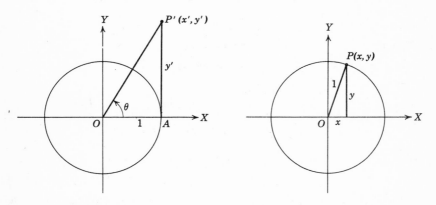

Figure 6-5-1   Figure 6-5-2

As θ increases from $0°$ to $90°$, tan θ, or y', will start at 0 and increase. As θ approaches $90°$ the line $P'A$ becomes very large. In Fig. 6-5-2, if P is on the circumference of the unit circle, y will approach 1 as x approaches 0. Hence $\tan \theta = y/x$ will become $1/0$ as the value for $\tan 90°$. This, of course, does not exist.

The fraction $1/h$ will increase numerically as h approaches 0 and can be made numerically larger than any given positive number by taking h small enough. Although the fraction $1/0$ does not exist, we say that the *limit* of $1/h$, as h **approaches** 0 through positive values of h, increases without bound. In symbols, this is expressed as

$\lim\limits_{h\to0^+} \dfrac{1}{h} = \infty$, where the symbol ∞ is called *infinity*. Thus, when the student uses the symbol ∞ he should think of a quantity that keeps increasing.

If h approaches 0 through negative values, we have $\lim\limits_{h\to0^-} \dfrac{1}{h} = -\infty$.

For $\tan \theta$, then, as θ approaches $90°$, y approaches 1, x approaches 0, and $\lim\limits_{\theta\to90°} \tan \theta = \pm \infty$, the sign depends on whether the approach is from QI or QII.

The above may be summarized by saying that as θ *increases from* $0°$ *to* $90°$, *tan* θ *takes on all of the positive numbers.*

As θ passes through $90°$, $\tan \theta$ becomes negative and as θ approaches $90°$ from values greater than $90°$, $\tan \theta$ approaches minus infinity. Hence, as θ increases from $90°$ to $180°$, $\tan \theta$ takes on all negative numbers from $-\infty$ to 0.

The student should investigate the variation of $\tan \theta$ in the third and fourth quadrant.

TABLE 6-5

Variation of tan θ

When θ increases from	$\tan \theta$
$0°$ to $90°$	increases from 0 to ∞.
$90°$ to $180°$	increases from $-\infty$ to 0.
$180°$ to $270°$	increases from 0 to ∞.
$270°$ to $360°$	increases from $-\infty$ to 0.

period of tan is π

From Table 6-5 we see that $\tan \theta$ is a periodic function with a period of $180°$ or π radians.

It would be well for the student to discuss the variation of *cot* θ, *sec* θ, and *csc* θ, considering them as reciprocals of *tan* θ, *cos* θ, and *sin* θ, respectively. He should also discuss the variation of *tan u*, *cot u*, *sec u*, and *csc u*, where u is a real number.

6-6. GRAPHS OF tan x, cot x, sec x, and csc x

The graphs of $y = \tan x$, $y = \cot x$, $y = \sec x$, and $y = \csc x$ are usually drawn by plotting points on the rectangular coordinate system. A table of values is given in Table 6-6. The curves are drawn in Fig. 6-6-1.

TABLE 6-6

x	$y = \tan x$	$y = \cot x$	$y = \sec x$	$y = \csc x$
0	0	does not exist	1	does not exist
$\dfrac{\pi}{6}$	0.6	1.7	1.2	2
$\dfrac{\pi}{3}$	1.7	0.6	2	1.2
$\dfrac{\pi}{2}$	does not exist	0	does not exist	1
$\dfrac{2\pi}{3}$	-1.7	-0.6	-2	1.2
$\dfrac{5\pi}{6}$	-0.6	-1.7	-1.2	2
π	0	does not exist	-1	does not exist
$\dfrac{7\pi}{6}$	0.6	1.7	-1.2	-2
$\dfrac{4\pi}{3}$	1.7	0.6	-2	-1.2
$\dfrac{3\pi}{2}$	does not exist	0	does not exist	-1
$\dfrac{5\pi}{3}$	-1.7	-0.6	2	-1.2
$\dfrac{11\pi}{6}$	-0.6	-1.7	1.2	-2
2π	0	does not exist	1	does not exist

The period of *tan x* is π, as mentioned in Art. 6-5. Since cot x is the reciprocal of *tan x*, its period is also π. Likewise *sec x* and *csc x* will have the same period as their reciprocals, namely 2π. Thus, in Fig. 6-6-1, the graphs of *tan x* and *cot x* covered two cycles, while those of *sec x* and *csc x* covered one cycle.

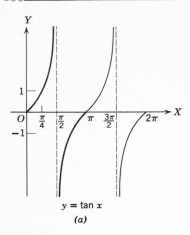

$y = \tan x$

(a)

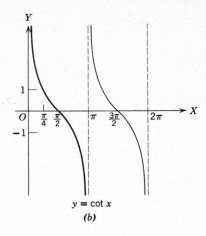

$y = \cot x$

(b)

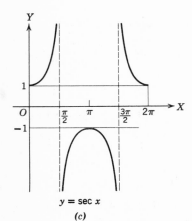

$y = \sec x$

(c)

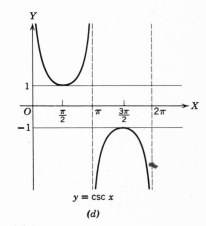

$y = \csc x$

(d)

Figure 6-6-1

The dotted lines in Fig. 6-6-1 are called *asymptotes*. They are lines which the graph approaches but never reaches and occur at the value of x for which the function does not exist.

The graphs of **$a \tan bx$**, **$a \cot bx$**, **$a \sec bx$**, and **$a \csc bx$** may be drawn by noting that the argument is **bx** and referring to Fig. 6-6-1. For **$\tan bx$** and **$\cot bx$**, the period is **π/b**, and for **$\sec bx$** and **$\csc bx$** the period is **$2\pi/b$**. The positive constant **a** increases or decreases the ordinates, depending on whether **a** is larger than **1** or less than **1**.

The graphs of $y = \sin x$ and $y = \cos x$ can also be drawn by plotting points.

▶ **EXERCISES**

1. On a piece of graph paper plot the points in the Table 6-6 and draw a smooth curve of (*a*) $y = \tan x$, (*b*) $y = \cot x$, (*c*) $y = \sec x$, (*d*) $y = \csc x$.

Draw two cycles of the graphs of the following functions, one on the positive side of the *X*-axis and one on the negative side. State the period.

2. $y = 2 \tan x$.   **3.** $y = \frac{1}{3} \tan x$.

4. $y = 3 \cot x$.   **5.** $y = \frac{1}{2} \cot x$.

6. $y = 4 \sec x$.   **7.** $y = \frac{1}{2} \csc x$.

8. $y = \tan 2x$.   **9.** $y = \cot \frac{1}{2}x$.

10. $y = 2 \tan \frac{1}{2}x$.   **11.** $y = 3 \cot 2x$.

12. $y = 2 \sec 3x$.

13. Sketch the graph of $y = \tan x$ by considering $\tan x$ as $\dfrac{\sin x}{\cos x}$.

14. Sketch the graph of $y = \sec x$ by considering the graph of $y = \cos x$.

15. Sketch the graph of $y = \csc x$ by considering the graph of $y = \sin x$.

Sketch the following curves for the indicated values of *x*.

16. $y = \frac{1}{2} \tan 3x$, $-\pi \leq x \leq \pi$.

17. $y = 2 \cot \frac{1}{3}x$, $-3\pi \leq x \leq 3\pi$.

18. $y = \frac{1}{2} \sec 2x$, $0 \leq x \leq 2\pi$.

19. $y = \sec \frac{1}{2}x$, $-2\pi \leq x \leq 2\pi$.

20. $y = 3 \csc 2x$, $-2\pi \leq x \leq \pi$.

quiz { graph a sin with phase angle or cos function

Trigonometric Functions (Composite Angles)

7-1. INTRODUCTION

In Art. 1-7, in the discussion of functions, we saw that the symbol *sin* $(u + v)$ was to be read as "the sine function of $(u + v)$" and **not** *times* $(u + v)$. Hence, the abbreviation of the trigonometric functions cannot be multiplied through parentheses, nor can a constant be factored out of an argument and placed before a trigonometric function. For example, $\cos(30° + 60°) = \cos 90° = 0$ is not equal to $\cos 30° + \cos 60° = \dfrac{\sqrt{3}}{2} + \dfrac{1}{2} = \dfrac{\sqrt{3} + 1}{2}$. Also $\sin(2 \cdot 30°) = \sin 60° = \dfrac{\sqrt{3}}{2}$ is not equal to $2 \sin 30° = 2 \cdot \frac{1}{2} = 1$.

In this chapter we will derive various expressions which will enable us to work with trigonometric functions of composite angles. The formulas which we shall derive will hold true for the trigonometric functions of real numbers as well as for angles.

108

7-2. THE COSINE OF THE DIFFERENCE AND SUM OF TWO ANGLES

Consider the unit circle of Fig. 7-2-1 where angles A and B are *any* two angles in standard position. Angles A and B automatically include the integral multiples of 2π. The following proof depends only on the *position* of the terminal side. Point P_1 on the terminal side of angle A has coordinates ($cos\ A$, $sin\ A$), and point P_2 on the terminal side of angle B has coordinates ($cos\ B$, $sin\ B$).

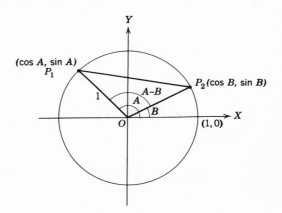

Figure 7-2-1

From the formula for the distance between two points,

$$P_1P_2 = \sqrt{(x_2 - x_1)^2 + (y_2 - y_1)^2},$$

we have from Fig. 7-2-1,

$$\overline{P_1P_2}^2 = (\cos B - \cos A)^2 + (\sin B - \sin A)^2.$$

Expanding and simplifying we obtain,

(7-2-1) $\qquad \overline{P_1P_2}^2 = 2 - 2 \cos B \cos A - 2 \sin B \sin A.$

Let us now rotate the circle in a clockwise direction with points P_1 and P_2 fixed on the circumference until point P_2 coincides with $(1, 0)$ (Fig. 7-2-2). The angle $(A - B)$ is now in standard position and point P_1 has the new coordinates $\left(cos\ (A - B), sin\ (A - B)\right)$. The square of the distance $\overline{P_1P_2}$ in this position is

$$\overline{P_1P_2}^2 = [1 - \cos (A - B)]^2 + [0 - \sin (A - B)]^2,$$

which upon squaring and simplifying becomes

(7-2-2) $$\overline{P_1P_2}^2 = 2 - 2 \cos (A - B).$$

Since the distance between points P_1 and P_2 remained constant throughout this rotation, we may equate equations 7-2-1 and 7-2-2 to obtain

(7-2-3) $\quad 2 - 2 \cos (A - B) = 2 - 2 \cos B \cos A - 2 \sin B \sin A,$

which upon simplifying and rewriting becomes

(7-2-4) $\qquad \cos (A - B) \equiv \cos A \cos B + \sin A \sin B.$

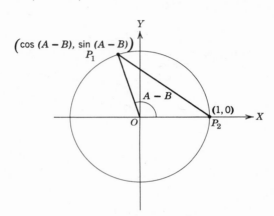

Figure 7-2-2

We may show that equation 7-2-4 holds true for *all* angles A and B by considering that angle P_2OP_1, in Figs. 7-2-1 and 7-2-2, is always equal to one of the angles

(7-2-5) $\quad (A - B), \quad (B - A), \quad [(A - B) \pm n \cdot 360°],$
$$[(B - A) \pm n \cdot 360°]$$

where n is any integer. In all of these cases

$$\cos \angle P_2OP_1 = \cos (A - B).$$

Thus, $\qquad \cos (B - A) = \cos [-(A - B)] = \cos (A - B),$

$$\cos [(A - B) \pm n \cdot 360°] = \cos (A - B),$$

and $\quad \cos [(B - A) \pm n \cdot 360°] = \cos (B - A) = \cos (A - B).$

Since equation 7-2-4 is true for all angles A and B, it is an *identity*. $\cos (A - B) \equiv \cos A \cos B + \sin A \sin B$ is known as the **cosine of the difference of two angles** and is one of the most basic formulas of trigonometry. It should be memorized in words thus: *the cosine of the difference of two angles is equal to the sum of the product of the cosines of the two angles and the product of the sines of the two angles.*

The Cosine of the Sum of Two Angles

The cosine of the sum of two angles may be obtained from the cosine of the difference of two angles by replacing angle B by $-B$. This may be done since formula 7-2-4 is an identity. That is,

$$\cos [A - (-B)] \equiv \cos A \cos (-B) + \sin A \sin (-B)$$

which becomes, by making use of the functions of negative angles,

$$(7\text{-}2\text{-}6) \qquad \cos (A + B) \equiv \cos A \cos B - \sin A \sin B.$$

The student should write out formula 7-2-6 in words. Identities 7-2-4 and 7-2-6 are called the addition formulas for the cosine function.

Example 1. Find the exact value of $\cos 75°$.

Solution: $\cos 75° = \cos (30° + 45°)$.

$$\cos (30° + 45°) = \cos 30° \cos 45° - \sin 30° \sin 45°,$$

$$= \frac{\sqrt{3}}{2} \cdot \frac{\sqrt{2}}{2} - \frac{1}{2} \cdot \frac{\sqrt{2}}{2}.$$

Thus, $\qquad \cos 75° = \dfrac{\sqrt{6} - \sqrt{2}}{4} = \dfrac{\sqrt{2}(\sqrt{3} - 1)}{4}.$

Example 2. Find the value of $\cos (A + B)$ given $\sin A = \frac{3}{5}$, A in QI, and $\cos B = -\frac{8}{17}$, B in QII.

Solution: From $\quad \sin A = \frac{3}{5}$, A in QI (Fig. 7-2-3),

we find $\qquad \cos A = \frac{4}{5}$.

From $\qquad \cos B = -\frac{8}{17}$, B in QII (Fig. 7-2-4),

we find $\quad \sin B = \frac{15}{17}$.

Hence $\qquad \cos (A + B) \equiv \cos A \cos B - \sin A \sin B$

$$= (\tfrac{4}{5})(-\tfrac{8}{17}) - (\tfrac{3}{5})(\tfrac{15}{17}), \qquad \frac{32}{45}$$

and $\qquad \cos (A + B) = -\frac{77}{85},$

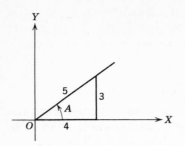

Figure 7-2-3   Figure 7-2-4

▶ EXERCISES

1. P_1 is a point on the terminal side of angle A in standard position, and P_2 is a point on the terminal side of angle B in standard position. Show that the angle P_2OP_1 may be expressed in one of the forms $(A - B)$, $(B - A)$, $[(A - B) \pm n \cdot 360°]$, and $[(B - A) \pm n \cdot 360°]$, with n an integer.

(a) $A = 30°$, $B = 150°$.   (b) $A = 10°$, $B = 70°$.
(c) $A = 25°$, $B = -205°$.   (d) $A = -40°$, $B = 170°$.
(e) $A = 210°$, $B = 70°$.   (f) $B = 300°$, $A = 100°$.
(g) $A = -150°$, $B = 500°$.   (h) $A = 470°$, $B = 380°$.

2. Using the exact values of the trigonometric functions at $30°$, $45°$, $60°$ and their integral multiples, find the exact value of:

(a) $\cos 15°$.   (b) $\cos 105°$.   (c) $\cos 90°$.
(d) $\cos 165°$.   (e) $\cos 195°$.   (f) $\cos 255°$.
                (g) $\cos 285°$.

3. Use equations 7-2-4 and 7-2-6 to show that the following formulas are true for any angle θ:

(a) $\cos (180° - \theta) \equiv -\cos \theta$.   (b) $\cos (180° + \theta) \equiv -\cos \theta$.
(c) $\cos (360° - \theta) \equiv \cos \theta$.   (d) $\cos (90° - \theta) \equiv \sin \theta$.
(e) $\cos (90° + \theta) \equiv -\sin \theta$.   (f) $\cos (270° - \theta) \equiv -\sin \theta$.
        (g) $\cos (270° + \theta) \equiv \sin \theta$.

4. Write the formulas of problem 3 in terms of real numbers.

5. If angles A and B are in the quadrant specified, find the value of $\cos (A + B)$ and $\cos (A - B)$, given that

(a) $\cos A = \frac{5}{13}$, $\sin B = \frac{4}{5}$, A and B in QI.
(b) $\sin A = -\frac{12}{13}$, A in QIII, $\tan B = \frac{5}{12}$, B in QI.

(c) $\sin A = -\frac{8}{17}$, A in QIV, $\sec B = \frac{5}{3}$, B in QIV.

(d) $\tan A = -\frac{24}{7}$, A in QII, $\csc B = \frac{17}{15}$, B in QII.

6. Verify the following:

(a) $\cos(60° - \theta) \equiv \dfrac{\cos\theta + \sqrt{3}\sin\theta}{2}$.

(b) $\cos\left(\phi + \dfrac{\pi}{4}\right) \equiv \dfrac{\cos\phi - \sin\phi}{\sqrt{2}}$.

(c) $\cos\left(\dfrac{\pi}{6} + A\right) - \cos(30° - A) \equiv -\sin A$.

(d) $\cos(45° + y) + \cos(45° - y) \equiv \sqrt{2}\cos y$.

(e) $\cos(\alpha + \beta)\cos(\alpha - \beta) \equiv \cos^2\alpha - \sin^2\beta$.

(f) $\cos(A + B) \equiv \dfrac{\csc A \csc B - \sec A \sec B}{\sec A \sec B \csc A \csc B}$.

7. Reduce the following to a single term:

(a) $\cos 7A \cos 3A + \sin 7A \sin 3A$.

(b) $\cos 3B \cos 5B - \sin 3B \sin 5B$.

(c) $\cos\left(\frac{2}{3}x\right)\cos\left(\frac{1}{3}x\right) - \sin\left(\frac{2}{3}x\right)\sin\left(\frac{1}{3}x\right)$.

(d) $\cos(A + B)\cos B + \sin(A + B)\sin B$.

8. Obtain an expression for $\cos(A + B + C)$ involving sines and cosines of A, B, and C. (Hint: Write the angle as $[(A + B) + C]$.)

9. A and B are both positive acute angles.

(a) Find $\sin A$, if $\cos(A + B) = \frac{33}{65}$ and $\sin B = \frac{3}{5}$.

(b) Find $\cos B$, if $\cos(A - B) = \frac{84}{85}$ and $\cos A = \frac{4}{5}$.

7-3. ADDITION FORMULAS FOR THE SINE AND TANGENT FUNCTIONS

In order to derive formulas for the sine of the sum and the difference of two angles, we need the identities $\cos(90° - B) \equiv \sin B$ and $\sin(90° - B) \equiv \cos B$.

In the identity $\cos(A - B) \equiv \cos A \cos B + \sin A \sin B$, let $A = 90°$ to obtain $\cos(90° - B) \equiv \cos 90° \cos B + \sin 90° \sin B$. Since $\cos 90° = 0$ and $\sin 90° = 1$, we have

(7-3-1) $\qquad \cos(90° - B) \equiv \sin B.$

In the identity of formula 7-3-1 we may replace B by $(90° - B)$ to obtain

$$\cos\left[90° - (90° - B)\right] \equiv \sin\left(90° - B\right),$$

which yields $\qquad\qquad \cos B \equiv \sin\left(90° - B\right),$

or rewritten as

(7-3-2) $\qquad\qquad$ **$\sin\left(90° - B\right) \equiv \cos B.$**

Identities 7-3-1 and 7-3-2 may be used with the fundamental identities of Chapter 5 to show that *cofunctions of complementary angles are equal.* For example, $100°$ and $-10°$ are complementary angles. Hence,

$$\cos\left(90° - 100°\right) = \cos\left(-10°\right) = \sin 100°.$$

Sine of the Sum of Two Angles

By use of identity 7-3-1 we have

$$\sin\left(A + B\right) \equiv \cos\left[90° - (A + B)\right].$$

We may write the right-hand side as $\cos\left[(90° - A) - B\right]$. Using the expression for the cosine of the difference of two angles, we obtain

$$\cos\left[(90° - A) - B\right] \equiv \cos\left(90° - A\right)\cos B + \sin\left(90° - A\right)\sin B.$$

Since

$$\cos\left(90° - A\right) \equiv \sin A \quad\text{and}\quad \sin\left(90° - A\right) \equiv \cos A,$$

we have

(7-3-3) $\qquad$ **$\sin\left(A + B\right) \equiv \sin A \cos B + \cos A \sin B.$**

Sine of the Difference of Two Angles

In identity 7-3-3 replace B by $(-B)$ to obtain

$$\sin\left[A + (-B)\right] \equiv \sin A \cos\left(-B\right) + \cos A \sin\left(-B\right).$$

Expressing the functions of the negative angles as functions of positive angles we obtain

(7-3-4) $\qquad$ **$\sin\left(A - B\right) \equiv \sin A \cos B - \cos A \sin B.$**

Tangent of the Sum of Two Angles

$$\tan\left(A + B\right) \equiv \frac{\sin\left(A + B\right)}{\cos\left(A + B\right)},$$

$$\equiv \frac{\sin A \cos B + \cos A \sin B}{\cos A \cos B - \sin A \sin B}.$$

If we divide the numerator and denominator by $\cos A \cos B$, we obtain

$$\tan (A + B) \equiv \dfrac{\dfrac{\sin A \cos B}{\cos A \cos B} + \dfrac{\cos A \sin B}{\cos A \cos B}}{\dfrac{\cos A \cos B}{\cos A \cos B} - \dfrac{\sin A \sin B}{\cos A \cos B}},$$

which reduces to

(7-3-5) $$\tan (A + B) \equiv \dfrac{\tan A + \tan B}{1 - \tan A \tan B}.$$

Tangent of the Difference of Two Angles

In the identity for $\tan (A + B)$ replace B by $- B$ to obtain

$$\tan [A + (- B)] \equiv \dfrac{\tan A + \tan (- B)}{1 - \tan A \tan (- B)}.$$

Recalling that $\tan (- B) \equiv - \tan B$, we have

(7-3-6) $$\tan (A - B) \equiv \dfrac{\tan A - \tan B}{1 + \tan A \tan B}.$$

Example. Show that for $a > 0$ and $b > 0$ the addition of the sine function $a \sin x$ to the cosine function $b \cos x$ will give a sine function.

Solution: $a \sin x + b \cos x$ may be written as

(7-3-7) $$\sqrt{a^2 + b^2}\left(\dfrac{a}{\sqrt{a^2 + b^2}} \sin x + \dfrac{b}{\sqrt{a^2 + b^2}} \cos x\right).$$

Let a and b form the two legs of a right triangle with the acute angle α, as in Fig. 7-3-1.

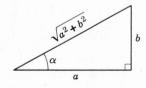

Figure 7-3-1

Then $$\dfrac{a}{\sqrt{a^2 + b^2}} = \cos \alpha \quad \text{and} \quad \dfrac{b}{\sqrt{a^2 + b^2}} = \sin \alpha.$$

Substituting these expressions in equation 7-3-7, we obtain

$$\sqrt{a^2 + b^2}\,(\sin x \cos \alpha + \cos x \sin \alpha)$$

which may be written as

$$\sqrt{a^2 + b^2}\,\sin (x + \alpha).$$

Thus

$$a \sin x + b \cos x = \sqrt{a^2 + b^2}\,\sin (x + \alpha),$$

where

$$\tan \alpha = \frac{b}{a}.$$

This method is extended in Art. 11-4 to include both positive and negative values of a and b.

▶ **EXERCISES**

1. Express in words the addition formulas for the sine and tangent functions.

2. Make use of identities 7-3-1 and 7-3-2 to show that cofunctions of complementary angles are equal.

3. Use the exact values of the trigonometric functions at $30°$, $45°$, $60°$ and their integral multiples to find the exact value of the sine and of the tangent at :

(a) $15°$. (b) $105°$. (c) $90°$. (d) $165°$. (e) $195°$. (f) $255°$. (g) $285°$.

4. Use identities 7-3-3, 7-3-4, 7-3-5, and 7-3-6 to show that the following identities are true for any angle θ :

(a) $\sin (180° - \theta) \equiv \sin \theta.$ (b) $\sin (180° + \theta) \equiv -\sin \theta.$
(c) $\sin (360° - \theta) \equiv -\sin \theta.$ (d) $\sin (90° + \theta) \equiv \cos \theta.$
(e) $\sin (270° - \theta) \equiv -\cos \theta.$ (f) $\sin (270° + \theta) \equiv -\cos \theta.$
(g) $\tan (180° - \theta) \equiv -\tan \theta.$ (h) $\tan (180° + \theta) \equiv \tan \theta.$
(i) $\tan (360° - \theta) \equiv -\tan \theta.$ (j) $\tan (90° + \theta) \equiv -\cot \theta.$
(k) $\tan (270° - \theta) \equiv \cot \theta.$ (l) $\tan (270° + \theta) \equiv -\cot \theta.$

5. Write the identities of problem 4 in terms of real numbers.

6. If $\sin A = -\frac{5}{13}$, A in QIII, and $\cos B = \frac{4}{5}$, B in QI, find :
(a) $\sin (A + B).$ (b) $\sin (A - B).$ (c) $\tan (A + B).$
(d) $\tan (A - B).$

7. If $\cot A = \frac{24}{7}$, $\cos A < 0$, and $\csc B = \frac{5}{4}$, $\sec B < 0$, find :
(a) $\sin (A + B).$ (b) $\sin (A - B).$ (c) $\tan (A + B).$
(d) $\tan (A - B).$

8. If $\cos A = \frac{8}{17}$, A in QI, and $\tan B = -\frac{12}{5}$, B in QIV, find:

(a) $\sin (A + B)$.　　(b) $\sin (A - B)$.　　(c) $\tan (A + B)$.

(d) $\tan (A - B)$.

9. Find $\sin A$, if $\sin (A + B) = \frac{63}{65}$, and $\sin B = \frac{5}{13}$, where A and B are both positive acute angles.

10. Verify the following:

(a) $\sin (x + 30°) \equiv \dfrac{\sqrt{3} \sin x + \cos x}{2}$.

(b) $\sin \left(\phi + \dfrac{\pi}{4} \right) \equiv \dfrac{\cos \phi + \sin \phi}{\sqrt{2}}$.

(c) $\sin (A + B) \sin (A - B) \equiv \sin^2 A - \sin^2 B$.

(d) $\tan \left(x - \dfrac{\pi}{3} \right) \equiv \dfrac{\tan x - \sqrt{3}}{1 + \sqrt{3} \tan x}$.

(e) $\tan (A + 45°) \equiv \dfrac{1 + \tan A}{1 - \tan A}$.

(f) $\tan \phi + \tan \theta \equiv \dfrac{\sin (\phi + \theta)}{\cos \phi \cos \theta}$.

11. Reduce to a single term:

(a) $\sin 3A \cos 5A + \cos 3A \sin 5A$.

(b) $\sin 4B \cos B - \cos 4B \sin B$.

(c) $\sin (\frac{1}{5}x) \cos (\frac{4}{5}x) + \cos (\frac{1}{5}x) \sin (\frac{4}{5}x)$.

(d) $\sin (A + B) \cos B + \cos (A + B) \sin B$.

(e) $\dfrac{\tan 2A + \tan 3A}{1 - \tan 2A \tan 3A}$.　　　　(f) $\dfrac{\tan 4A - \tan 7A}{\tan 4A \tan 7A + 1}$.

(g) $\dfrac{\tan (\frac{1}{3}A) + \tan (\frac{2}{3}A)}{1 - \tan (\frac{1}{3}A) + \tan(\frac{2}{3}A)}$.　　(h) $\dfrac{\tan (A + B) + \tan C}{1 - \tan (A + B) \tan C}$.

12. Obtain an expression for $\sin (A + B + C)$ involving sines and cosines of A, B, and C. (Hint: write $(A + B + C)$ as $[(A + B) + C]$).

13. Obtain an expression for $\tan (A + B + C)$ in terms of the tangents of A, B, and C.

14. Express as a sine function:

(a) $4 \sin x + 3 \cos x$.　　　　(b) $8 \sin t + 15 \cos t$.

(c) $\sqrt{3} \sin 2x + \cos 2x$.　　(d) $7 \cos 3t + 24 \sin 3t$.

15. Show that $A \sin x - B \cos x$ can be expressed as a sine function.

16. Will $A \sin (bt) + B \cos (ct)$ yield a sine function when b and c are not equal?

17. Show that $8 \sin (377t) + 6 \cos (377t)$ can be expressed as a sine function. (Expressions such as these arise in electricity.)

7-4. TRIGONOMETRIC FUNCTIONS OF THE DOUBLE-ANGLE

If we let $B = A$ in the identities for $\sin (A + B)$, $\cos (A + B)$, and $\tan (A + B)$, we will obtain identities for $\sin 2A$, $\cos 2A$, and $\tan 2A$. As an example, $\sin (A + A) \equiv \sin A \cos A + \cos A \sin A$, or

(7-4-1) $\qquad\qquad$ **$\sin 2A \equiv 2 \sin A \cos A.$**

Similarly, we can find

(7-4-2) $\qquad\qquad$ **$\cos 2A \equiv \cos^2 A - \sin^2 A,$**

or (7-4-3) $\qquad\qquad$ **$\cos 2A \equiv 1 - 2 \sin^2 A,$**

or (7-4-4) $\qquad\qquad$ **$\cos 2A \equiv 2 \cos^2 A - 1.$**

Also (7-4-5) $\qquad$ **$\tan 2A \equiv \dfrac{2 \tan A}{1 - \tan^2 A}.$**

(How are formulas 7-4-3 and 7-4-4 obtained?)

The student should note carefully that the argument on the left of each expression is *twice* (or double) the argument on the right. Hence, they are called the *double-angle* identities. The student should be able to express these identities in words.

Example. Find $\sin 2A$, given that $\sin A = \frac{8}{17}$, A in QII.

Solution: From the sketch (Fig. 7-4-1).

we find that $\qquad\qquad$ $\cos A = -\frac{15}{17}.$

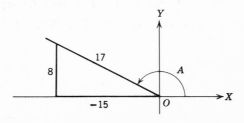

Figure 7-4-1

Hence,
$$\sin 2A = 2 \sin A \cos A,$$
$$= 2(\tfrac{8}{17})(-\tfrac{15}{17}).$$
$$\mathbf{\sin 2A} = -\tfrac{240}{289}.$$

▶ **EXERCISES**

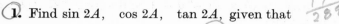

1. Find $\sin 2A$, $\cos 2A$, $\tan 2A$, given that

(a) $\sec A = \tfrac{25}{24}$, A in QI.   (b) $\tan A = -\tfrac{3}{4}$, A in QII.

(c) $\csc A = -\tfrac{13}{5}$, A in QIII.   (d) $\cos A = \tfrac{15}{17}$, A in QIV.

2. Reduce the following to a single term. The denominators are not equal to zero.

(a) $2 \sin 3x \cos 3x$.   (b) $\cos^2 5y - \sin^2 5y$.

(c) $\dfrac{2 \tan 3t}{1 - \tan^2 3t}$.   (d) $2 \cos^2 \dfrac{\phi}{2} - 1$.

(e) $\sin 4A \cos 4A$.   (f) $1 - 2 \sin^2 \left(\dfrac{x}{3}\right)$.

(g) $\dfrac{\tan 4t}{1 - \tan^2 4t}$.   (h) $2 \sin \left(\dfrac{A - B}{2}\right) \cos \left(\dfrac{A - B}{2}\right)$.

(i) $\cos^4 A - \sin^4 A$.

3. Obtain a formula in terms of A for:

(a) $\sin 3A$.   (b) $\cos 3A$.   (c) $\tan 3A$.

Prove the following:

4. $\dfrac{\sin 2x}{1 + \cos 2x} \equiv \tan x$.   5. $2 \csc 2x \equiv \sec x \csc x$.

6. $\dfrac{\csc^2 u}{\csc^2 u - 2} \equiv \sec 2u$.   7. $\dfrac{2 \tan u}{1 + \tan^2 u} \equiv \sin 2u$.

8. $\dfrac{1 - \tan^2 u}{1 + \tan^2 u} \equiv \cos 2u$.   9. $\tan u + \cot u \equiv 2 \csc 2u$.

10. $\cot u - \tan u \equiv 2 \cot 2u$.

7-5. TRIGONOMETRIC FUNCTIONS OF THE HALF-ANGLE

Solving for $\cos \theta$ in the identity $\cos 2\theta \equiv 1 - 2 \sin^2 \theta$, we obtain

$$\sin \theta \equiv \pm \sqrt{\dfrac{1 - \cos 2\theta}{2}}.$$

In order to emphasize that the *argument on the left side is* **one-half** *the argument on the right*, we shall replace θ by $A/2$.

Hence,

(7-5-1)
$$\sin \frac{A}{2} \equiv \pm \sqrt{\frac{1 - \cos A}{2}},$$

where the choice of sign is determined by the quadrant of $A/2$.

Using the identity $\cos 2\theta \equiv 2 \cos^2 \theta - 1$, and letting $\theta = A/2$, we find in a similar manner

(7-5-2)
$$\cos \frac{A}{2} \equiv \pm \sqrt{\frac{1 + \cos A}{2}},$$

where the choice of sign is determined by the quadrant of $A/2$.

An identity for $\tan (A/2)$ may be obtained by considering $\tan \frac{A}{2} \equiv \frac{\sin (A/2)}{\cos (A/2)}$ and multiplying the numerator and denominator of the right side by $2 \sin (A/2)$. Thus,

$$\tan \frac{A}{2} \equiv \frac{2 \sin^2 (A/2)}{2 \sin (A/2) \cos (A/2)}.$$

Applying identities 7-4-3 and 7-4-1 this reduces to

(7-5-3)
$$\tan \frac{A}{2} \equiv \frac{1 - \cos A}{\sin A}.$$

Similarly the student can show that

(7-5-4)
$$\tan \frac{A}{2} \equiv \frac{\sin A}{1 + \cos A}.$$

The student should be able to express the above identities in words.

▶ **EXERCISES**

1. Using the exact values of the trigonometric functions at $30°$, $45°$, $60°$ and their integral multiples, find the exact value of the following:

(a) $\sin 15°$.   (b) $\cos 15°$.   (c) $\tan 15°$.

(d) $\sin 22.5°$.   (e) $\cos 22.5°$.   (f) $\tan 22.5°$.

(g) $\sin 75°$.   (h) $\cos 75°$.   (i) $\tan 75°$.

(j) $\sin 67.5°$.   (k) $\cos 112.5°$.   (l) $\tan 157.5°$.

2. Find $\sin (A/2)$, $\cos (A/2)$, $\tan (A/2)$, given that

(a) $\sec A = \frac{25}{7}$, A in QI. (b) $\cot A = \frac{4}{3}$, A in QIII.

(c) $\sin A = \frac{5}{13}$, A in QII. (d) $\cos A = \frac{8}{17}$, A in QIV.

3. Reduce the following to a single term. The denominators are not equal to zero.

(a) $\sqrt{\dfrac{1 + \cos 4\alpha}{2}}$. (b) $\dfrac{1 - \cos 8A}{\sin 8A}$.

(c) $\sqrt{\dfrac{1 - \cos 3\alpha}{1 + \cos 3\alpha}}$. (d) $\dfrac{\sin 6B}{1 - \cos 6B}$.

(e) $\sqrt{\dfrac{4 - 4 \cos 12y}{2}}$.

4. Verify the following. The denominators are not equal to zero.

(a) $\cot 4y \equiv \dfrac{\sin 8y}{1 - \cos 8y}$. (b) $2 \cos^2 \dfrac{A}{2} \equiv \dfrac{1 + \sec A}{\sec A}$.

(c) $\dfrac{\cos t}{1 - \sin t} \equiv \dfrac{1 + \tan (t/2)}{1 - \tan (t/2)}$. (d) $\tan \dfrac{\theta}{2} \equiv \csc \theta - \cot \theta$.

(e) $\dfrac{\cos 2u}{1 + \sin 2u} \equiv \dfrac{1 - \tan u}{1 + \tan u}$.

7-6. PRODUCT AND SUM FORMULAS

In the more advanced courses of mathematics and science it is frequently desirable to be able to express the product of two trigonometric functions in terms of a sum or a difference, and vice versa.

If we add the formulas for $\sin (A + B)$ and $\sin (A - B)$, we obtain

$$\sin (A + B) \equiv \sin A \cos B + \cos A \sin B,$$
$$\dfrac{\sin (A - B) \equiv \sin A \cos B - \cos A \sin B}{\sin (A + B) + \sin (A - B) \equiv 2 \sin A \cos B},$$

or (7-6-1) $\sin A \cos B \equiv \frac{1}{2}[\sin (A + B) + \sin (A - B)]$.

Upon subtracting $\sin (A - B)$ from $\sin (A + B)$ and simplifying, we obtain

(7-6-2) $\cos A \sin B \equiv \frac{1}{2}[\sin (A + B) - \sin (A - B)]$.

Considering the formulas for $\cos (A + B)$ and $\cos (A - B)$, we obtain upon addition and simplifying

(7-6-3) $\cos A \cos B \equiv \frac{1}{2}[\cos (A + B) + \cos (A - B)]$.

Upon subtracting $\cos (A - B)$ from $\cos (A + B)$ and simplifying, we obtain

(7-6-4) $\sin A \sin B \equiv - \frac{1}{2} [\cos (A + B) - \cos (A - B)].$

Formulas for the sum of two trigonometric functions may be obtained from the above formulas by letting $u = A + B$ and $v = A - B$. Then, $A = \frac{1}{2}(u + v)$ and $B = \frac{1}{2}(u - v)$; upon rewriting, the above formulas become:

(7-6-5) $\sin u + \sin v \equiv 2 \sin \frac{1}{2}(u + v) \cos \frac{1}{2}(u - v).$

(7-6-6) $\sin u - \sin v \equiv 2 \cos \frac{1}{2}(u + v) \sin \frac{1}{2}(u - v).$

(7-6-7) $\cos u + \cos v \equiv 2 \cos \frac{1}{2}(u + v) \cos \frac{1}{2}(u - v).$

(7-6-8) $\cos u - \cos v \equiv -2 \sin \frac{1}{2}(u + v) \sin \frac{1}{2}(u - v).$

Example. In the Calculus, the derivative of the function $sin\ x$ involves the expression $\sin (x + \varDelta x) - \sin x$. Show that this expression may be written as a product.

Solution: In the formula

$$\sin u - \sin v \equiv 2 \cos \tfrac{1}{2}(u + v) \sin \tfrac{1}{2}(u - v)$$

let $u = x + \varDelta x$ and $v = x$. Then we have

$$\sin (x + \varDelta x) - \sin x \equiv 2 \cos \tfrac{1}{2}(2x + \varDelta x) \sin \tfrac{1}{2}(\varDelta x),$$

which is equivalent to

$$\sin (x + \Delta x) - \sin x \equiv 2 \cos \left(x + \frac{\Delta x}{2} \right) \sin \frac{\Delta x}{2}.$$

▶ **EXERCISES**

Verify the following:

1. $\sin 5x \cos 3x \equiv \frac{1}{2}(\sin 8x + \sin 2x).$

2. $\sin x \sin 3x \equiv \frac{1}{2} (\cos 2x - \cos 4x).$

3. $2 \sin x \cos y \equiv \sin (x + y) + \sin (x - y).$

4. $2 \sin 2u \cos 3v \equiv \sin (2u + 3v) + \sin (2u - 3v).$

5. $\sin 60° + \sin 30° \equiv 2 \sin 45° \cos 15°.$

6. $\sin 40° - \sin 10° \equiv 2 \cos 25° \sin 15°.$

7. $\sin 10\theta + \sin 6\theta \equiv 2 \sin 8\theta \cos 2\theta.$

8. $\sin 8x - \sin 4x \equiv 2 \cos 6x \sin 2x.$

9. $\sin 3\theta + \sin \theta \equiv 2 \sin 2\theta \cos \theta.$

10. $\sin 3\theta - \sin \theta \equiv 2 \cos 2\theta \sin \theta.$

11. $\sin 4\theta + \sin 2\theta \equiv 2 \sin 3\theta \cos \theta.$

12. $\dfrac{\sin x + \sin y}{\sin x - \sin y} \equiv \dfrac{\tan \frac{1}{2}(x + y)}{\tan \frac{1}{2}(x - y)}.$

13. $\dfrac{\sin u + \sin v}{\cos u + \cos v} \equiv \tan \frac{1}{2}(u + v).$

14. $\dfrac{\sin u + \sin v}{\cos u - \cos v} \equiv -\cot \frac{1}{2}(u - v).$

15. $\dfrac{\sin u - \sin v}{\cos u + \cos v} \equiv \tan \frac{1}{2}(u - v).$

16. $\dfrac{\sin u - \sin v}{\cos v - \cos u} \equiv \cot \frac{1}{2}(u + v).$

17. $\dfrac{\cos u + \cos v}{\cos v - \cos u} \equiv \cot \frac{1}{2}(u + v) \cot \frac{1}{2}(u - v).$

7-7. SUMMARY

Listed below is a summary of the formulas included in this chapter. The student should be able to express them in words.

Sum and Difference of Two Angles

(7-2-4) $\cos (A - B) \equiv \cos A \cos B + \sin A \sin B.$

(7-2-6) $\cos (A + B) \equiv \cos A \cos B - \sin A \sin B.$

(7-3-3) $\sin (A + B) \equiv \sin A \cos B + \cos A \sin B.$

(7-3-4) $\sin (A - B) \equiv \sin A \cos B - \cos A \sin B.$

(7-3-5) $\tan (A + B) \equiv \dfrac{\tan A + \tan B}{1 - \tan A \tan B}.$

(7-3-6) $\tan (A - B) \equiv \dfrac{\tan A - \tan B}{1 + \tan A \tan B}.$

Double-angles

(7-4-1) $\sin 2A \equiv 2 \sin A \cos A.$

(7-4-2) $\cos 2A \equiv \cos^2 A - \sin^2 A.$

(7-4-3) $\cos 2A \equiv 1 - 2 \sin^2 A.$

(7-4-4) $\cos 2A \equiv 2 \cos^2 A - 1.$

(7-4-5) $\tan 2A \equiv \dfrac{2 \tan A}{1 - \tan^2 A}.$

Half-angles

(7-5-1) $\sin \dfrac{A}{2} \equiv \pm \sqrt{\dfrac{1 - \cos A}{2}}.$

(7-5-2) $\cos \dfrac{A}{2} \equiv \pm \sqrt{\dfrac{1 + \cos A}{2}}.$

(7-5-3) $\tan \dfrac{A}{2} \equiv \dfrac{1 - \cos A}{\sin A}.$

(7-5-4) $\tan \dfrac{A}{2} \equiv \dfrac{\sin A}{1 + \cos A}$

Product and Sum of Two Functions

(7-6-1) $\sin A \cos B \equiv \tfrac{1}{2}[\sin (A + B) + \sin (A - B)].$

(7-6-2) $\cos A \sin B \equiv \tfrac{1}{2}[\sin (A + B) - \sin (A - B)].$

(7-6-3) $\cos A \cos B \equiv \tfrac{1}{2}[\cos (A + B) + \cos (A - B)].$

(7-6-4) $\sin A \sin B \equiv - \tfrac{1}{2}[\cos (A + B) - \cos (A - B)].$

(7-6-5) $\sin u + \sin v \equiv 2 \sin \tfrac{1}{2}(u + v) \cos \tfrac{1}{2}(u - v).$

(7-6-6) $\sin u - \sin v \equiv 2 \cos \tfrac{1}{2}(u + v) \sin \tfrac{1}{2}(u - v).$

(7-6-7) $\cos u + \cos v \equiv 2 \cos \tfrac{1}{2}(u + v) \cos \tfrac{1}{2}(u - v).$

(7-6-8) $\cos u - \cos v \equiv - 2 \sin \tfrac{1}{2}(u + v) \sin \tfrac{1}{2}(u - v).$

7-8. MISCELLANEOUS IDENTITIES

The fundamental identities of Art. 5-2 together with the formulas developed in this chapter enable us to verify many different identities. Facility in proving identities comes only with a mastery of the trigonometric identities and the algebraic manipulations.

Example. Verify the identity

$$\frac{\cos 2\theta + \cos \theta + 1}{\sin 2\theta + \sin \theta} \equiv \cot \theta.$$

Solution: Replace $\cos 2\theta$ by $2 \cos^2 \theta - 1$ and $\sin 2\theta$ by $2 \sin \theta \cos \theta$ to obtain

$$\frac{2 \cos^2 \theta - 1 + \cos \theta + 1}{2 \sin \theta \cos \theta + \sin \theta} \equiv \cot \theta.$$

This reduces to
$$\frac{\cos \theta (2 \cos \theta + 1)}{\sin \theta (2 \cos \theta + 1)} \equiv \cot \theta,$$

or
$$\frac{\cos \theta}{\sin \theta} \equiv \cot \theta,$$

and
$$\therefore \; \mathbf{\cot \theta \equiv \cot \theta.}$$

▶ **EXERCISES**

Verify the following identities. The denominators are not equal to zero.

1. $\dfrac{1 - \cos 2\theta}{\tan \theta} \equiv \sin 2\theta.$

2. $\dfrac{1 - \cos 2\theta}{\sin \theta} \equiv 2 \sin \theta.$

3. $2 \cos A - \sin 2A \csc A \equiv 0.$

4. $\cot A \sin 2A - 1 \equiv \cos 2A.$

5. $\cos 2A + \sin 2A \tan A \equiv 1.$

6. $\dfrac{2 \tan \theta}{1 + \tan^2 \theta} \equiv \sin 2\theta.$

7. $2 \cos \theta - 2 \cos^3 \theta \equiv \sin \theta \sin 2\theta.$

8. $\dfrac{2 \sin \alpha (1 - \sin^2 \alpha)}{\sin 2\alpha} \equiv \cos \alpha.$

9. $\dfrac{\sin 2\phi}{1 - \sin^2 \phi} - \tan \phi \equiv \tan \phi.$

10. $\dfrac{\sin 2\theta}{\sin \theta} - \dfrac{\cos 2\theta}{\cos \theta} \equiv \sec \theta.$

11. $\dfrac{\sin \alpha + \cos 2\alpha - 1}{\cos \alpha - \sin 2\alpha} \equiv \tan \alpha.$

12. $\cos 2\beta \equiv \dfrac{1 - \tan^2 \beta}{1 + \tan^2 \beta}.$

13. $\tan A + \cot A \equiv 2 \csc 2A.$

14. $1 + \tan 2A \tan A \equiv \sec 2A.$

15. $\dfrac{\sin (A + B)}{\sin (A - B)} \equiv \dfrac{\tan A + \tan B}{\tan A - \tan B}.$

16. $\dfrac{\tan (A - B) + \tan B}{1 - \tan (A - B) \tan B} \equiv \tan A.$

17. $\dfrac{\sin 2A}{1 + \cos 2A} \equiv \tan A.$

18. $\sin 3A \equiv 4 \sin A \sin \left(\dfrac{\pi}{3} + A\right) \sin \left(\dfrac{\pi}{3} - A\right).$

19. $\dfrac{\sin 4\alpha}{\sin 2\alpha} \equiv 2 \cos 2\alpha.$

20. $\dfrac{2 \cos 3A}{\sin 2A} + \dfrac{\sin 2A}{\cos A} \equiv \dfrac{\cos 2A}{\sin A}.$

21. $\sin \phi \equiv \dfrac{2 \tan \dfrac{\phi}{2}}{1 + \tan^2 \dfrac{\phi}{2}}.$

22. $\csc A - \cot A \equiv \tan \dfrac{A}{2}.$

23. $\dfrac{\sin 2x \cos x}{(1 + \cos 2x)(1 + \cos x)} \equiv \tan \dfrac{x}{2}.$

24. $\dfrac{2 \cot A}{\csc^2 A - 2} \equiv \tan 2A.$

25. $\dfrac{1 - \cos \alpha - \tan^2 \frac{1}{2}\alpha}{\sin^2 \frac{1}{2}\alpha} \equiv \dfrac{2 \cos \alpha}{1 + \cos \alpha}.$

26. $\dfrac{\sin A + \sin 2A}{\cos A + \cos 2A} \equiv \tan \dfrac{3}{2}A.$

27. $\dfrac{\cos 3A - \cos A}{\sin A - \sin 3A} \equiv \tan 2A.$

28. $\dfrac{\sin 5A - \sin 2A}{\cos 2A - \cos 5A} \equiv \cot \dfrac{7}{2}A.$

29. $\sin (A + B) \sin (A - B) \equiv \sin^2 A - \sin^2 B.$

30. $\sin (A + B) \sin (B - A) \equiv \cos^2 A - \cos^2 B.$

31. $\cos (A + B) \cos (A - B) \equiv \cos^2 A - \sin^2 B.$

32. $\dfrac{\cos 3x \sin 2x - \cos 4x \sin x}{\cos 5x \cos 2x - \cos 4x \cos 3x} \equiv -\cot 2x.$

33. $\cot u + \cot v \equiv \dfrac{\sin (u + v)}{\sin u \sin v}.$

34. $\cot u - \cot v \equiv \dfrac{\sin (v - u)}{\sin u \sin v}.$

35. $\cos 3x - \cos 7x \equiv 2 \sin 5x \sin 2x.$

36. $\dfrac{\sin 2\theta + \sin \theta}{\cos \theta + \cos 2\theta} \equiv \tan \dfrac{3\theta}{2}.$

37. $\cos \left(\dfrac{\pi}{3} + A\right) + \cos \left(\dfrac{\pi}{3} - A\right) \equiv \cos A.$

38. $\cos u + \cos 3u + \cos 5u + \cos 7u \equiv 4 \cos u \cos 2u \cos 4u.$

39. $\cot u + \tan v \equiv \dfrac{\cos (u - v)}{\sin u \cos v}.$

40. $\dfrac{\tan (x + y) - \tan y}{1 + \tan (x + y) \tan x} \equiv \tan x.$

Logarithms

8-1. LOGARITHMS

It is assumed that the student has worked with logarithms before. A brief review will be given in order to become reacquainted with them.

Definition: *The logarithm of a number, N, is the power, L, to which it is necessary to raise a given number, b, called the base, to produce the number N, where b and N are positive and $b \neq 1$.*

That is, if $$b^L = N$$

then $$L = \log_b N.$$

This last equation is read: L is the logarithm of N to the base b. The symbol *log* is the abbreviation for *logarithm*.

There are two numbers widely used for the base. One of them is

10 and the other is the transcendental number $2.71828\cdots$ which is denoted by the symbol e. Logarithms using 10 as the base are called *common* or *Brigg's* logarithms and are written as **log N**. Logarithms using e as the base are called *natural* logarithms and are written as $ln\ N$ or $\log_e N$. We shall consider only the common logarithms.

Three rules for computation with logarithms for M and N positive are given below:

Rule 1. The logarithm of a product is equal to the sum of the logarithms of the factors.

$$\log (MN) = \log M + \log N.$$

Rule 2. The logarithm of a quotient is equal to the logarithm of the numerator minus the logarithm of the denominator.

$$\log \left(\frac{M}{N}\right) = \log M - \log N.$$

Rule 3. The logarithm of a number raised to a power is equal to the power times the logarithm of the number.

$$\log M^p = p \log M.$$

These rules may be easily proved by using the definition of logarithms and the laws of exponents.

Since any number N can be written in the "standard" form of a number (Art. 3-3), we need only to be able to find logs of numbers between *1* and *10* and of powers of *10*. For example

(8-1-1) $$N = n \cdot 10^c,$$

where $1 \leq n < 10$ and c is an *integer*. Taking logarithms of both sides of equation 8-1-1 we obtain

$$\log N = \log n + \log 10^c,$$

or (8-1-2) $$\log N = \log n + c \log 10.$$

Consider the expressions

$$10^0 = 1 \quad \text{and} \quad 10^1 = 10.$$

Applying the definition of logarithms, we see that **log 1 = 0** and **log 10 = 1**. Thus equation 8-1-2 becomes

(8-1-3) $$\log N = \log n + c,$$

where $0 \leq \log n < 1$.

The expressions on the right-hand side of 8-1-3 are very important (in the use of tables) and are given special names; **log n** is called the

mantissa of *log N* and is denoted by *m*, *c* is called the **characteristic** of *log N*. Hence, we have

(8-1-4) $$\log N = m + c.$$

The values of *m*, the mantissa, are found in tables of logarithms and are always *positive* fractions less than one. The characteristic, *c*, may be found by writing the number in standard form, then the *power of 10 is c*.

Example 1. Find the characteristic of the logarithm of (*a*) 234. (*b*) 0.00234.

Solution: (*a*) $234 = 2.34 \times 10^2$, thus *c* = **2**.

(*b*) $0.00234 = 2.34 \times 10^{-3}$, thus $c = -3$.

For convenience in computing with logarithms, a negative characteristic is often changed in form by adding to it and subtracting from it a multiple of 10. Thus, if the characteristic of a logarithm is -3 and the mantissa is 0.2879, the log may be written as $7.2879 - 10$.

The **cologarithm** of a number is the logarithm of the reciprocal of that number.

Thus, $$\operatorname{colog} N = \log \frac{1}{N},$$

or $$\operatorname{colog} N = \log 1 - \log N.$$

Since $\log 1 = 0$, we have

$$\mathbf{colog}\, N = -\log N.$$

To avoid using negative logarithms, we may find the cologarithm of a number by subtracting the logarithm of the number from 10.———— $- 10$. For four place tables (four significant figures in the mantissa) we would subtract from $10.0000 - 10$.

Example 2. Find colog 323, given that $\log 323 = 2.5092$.

Solution: Subtract $\log 323 = 2.5092$ from $10.0000 - 10$. This may be done mentally by subtracting each digit, starting at the left, from 9 and the last nonzero digit from 10. Thus

$$
\begin{array}{r}
9.999\ 10 - 10 \\
\underline{\log 323 = 2.509\ \ 2} \\
\mathbf{colog\ 323 = 7.490\ \ 8 - 10.}
\end{array}
$$

From the definition of a cologarithm it follows that the effect of subtracting the logarithm of a number is equivalent to adding its cologarithm. That is,

$$\log \left(\frac{M}{N}\right) = \log M + \operatorname{colog} N.$$

8-2. LOG TABLES

Table III, *Four-Place Logarithms of Numbers from 1 to 10*, gives the mantissa of the logarithm to the base 10 accurate to four significant figures (called a four-place table). The logarithms of numbers containing no more than three significant figures may be read directly from the table. For numbers containing more than three significant figures interpolation must be used. (Refer to Art. 2-6.)

To find the logarithm of a number using four-place tables, first determine the characteristic as described in the last article. To find the mantissa, locate the first two digits in the left-hand column and locate the third digit in the top row. The mantissa is found at the intersection of the appropriate row and column.

Example 1. Find log 48.1.

Solution: Since $48.1 = 4.81 \times 10^1$, the characteristic is 1. Locate 48 in the left-hand column of the log table and 1 in the top row; at the intersection of row 48 and column 1 find the mantissa 0.6821.

Since the mantissa is a positive number less than one, we have

$$\log 48.1 = 1.6821.$$

Example 2. Find N, given that $\log N = 8.6937 - 10$.

Solution: The mantissa is given as 0.6937 and is called the tabular entry. It is located in the body of the table and corresponds to the number 494.

Since the characteristic is $8 - 10$ or -2, we have

$$N = 4.94 \times 10^{-2},$$

or $$N = 0.0494.$$

Example 3. Find log 47.36.

Solution: The characteristic is 1. Interpolation is required to find the mantissa.

$$
\begin{array}{cc}
N & m
\end{array}
$$

$$
10\left[6\begin{bmatrix}4730 & 0.6749 \\ 4736 \\ 4740 & 0.6758\end{bmatrix}x\right]9
$$

$$
\frac{6}{10} = \frac{x}{9}, \quad x = 5.4, \quad \text{round off to } x = 5.
$$

Hence,   **log 47.36 = 1.6754.**

Since trigonometric functions of angles are numbers, we may find logarithms of trigonometric functions. For example, log sin 30° = log 0.5 = 9.6990 − 10. Logarithms to the base 10 of the trigonometric functions of angles from 0° to 90° at 10′ intervals are given in Table IV, *Four-Place Logarithms of Trigonometric Functions. Angle θ in Degrees.*

The characteristic of the logarithm of a trigonometric function of an angle is not easily determined. Hence, Table IV includes the characteristic as well as the mantissa. For convenience in arranging the table, the − 10 part of the characteristic has been left off. To obtain the correct logarithm we must add − 10 to the tabular entry.

The value of the logarithm of the trigonometric function of an angle is on the same line as the angle. If the angle is listed at the *left* of the page, the column heading is at the *top* of the page. If the angle is listed at the *right* of the page, the column heading is at the *bottom* of the page. The logarithm of the trigonometric function of an angle is found at the intersection of the row for the angle and the column for the function. The logarithm for *sin θ* will be denoted by either *log sin θ* or *L sin θ*. Similar expressions are used for the logarithms of the other trigonometric functions.

Example 4. Find L tan 18°10′.

Solution: Since the angle is listed at the left of the page, the column heading is found at the top. Hence, we find

L tan 18°10′ = 9.5161 − 10.

Note: The − 10 is added to obtain the correct characteristic.

Example 5. Find θ for 0° < θ < 90°, if L sin θ = 9.9505 − 10.

Solution: Discard the − 10 and look for 9.9505 as a tabular entry in an *L sin θ* column. We find it in the column with the *L sin θ* heading at the *bottom*; hence, the angle is listed at the *right*.

Thus for $\qquad$ L sin $\theta = 9.9505 - 10,$

$$\theta = 63°10'.$$

Example 6. Find A for $0° < A < 90°$, if L cot $A = 10.4859 - 10$.
Solution:

$$10\left[x\left[\begin{array}{ll} A & \text{L cot } A \\ 18°00' & 10.4882 - 10 \\ 18°10' & 10.4859 - 10 \\ & 10.4839 - 10 \end{array}\right]23\right]43$$

$$\frac{x}{10} = \frac{23}{43}, \quad x = 5.3, \quad \text{round off to } x = 5.$$

Hence $\qquad$ $A = 18°05'.$

▶ **EXERCISES**

1. Find the following:

(a) log 204.
(b) log 0.03258.
(c) colog 16.2.
(d) colog 0.02549.
(e) colog 0.003038.
(f) L cos 32°10'.
(g) L tan 27°20'.
(h) L cot 2°30'.
(i) L csc 78°41'. 284
(j) L sec 43°31'.
(k) L sin 16°28'.
(l) L cos 64°07'.
(m) L tan 30°11'.
(n) L cot 25°19'.
(o) L csc 9°27'.
(p) L sec 77°22'.

2. Find the value of the number or the positive acute angle.

(a) log $M = 2.7482$.
(b) log $N = 8.8899 - 10$.
(c) log $M = 9.9802$.
(d) log $N = 6.9323$.
(e) log $N = 1.0467$.
(f) log $A = 3.2575$.
(g) L sin $A = 9.4269 - 10$.
(h) L cos $B = 9.6177 - 10$.
(i) L tan $\theta = 10.5535 - 10$.
(j) L cot $\theta = 9.0017 - 10$.
(k) L sec $A = 10.3652 - 10$.
(l) L sin $B = 9.7187 - 10$.
(m) L cos $A = 9.7332 - 10$.
(n) L tan $\alpha = 9.9887 - 10$.
(o) L cot $\alpha = 10.2352 - 10$.
(p) L cos $\beta = 9.9746 - 10$.

8-3. LOGARITHMIC COMPUTATION

The illustrative problems in this book are solved using the computational form in which any entry in a line refers to the first number at the left of the line. The logarithmic form is set up so that only *addition* of logarithms is required. This can always be accomplished by making use of cologarithms (abbreviated as *col*). The computational form should be set up before making any entries. This form will be illustrated below. In logarithmic computations it will be assumed that the accuracy of the data warrants an answer to four digits, except in the case of word problems where answers consistent with the data should be given. There are other good forms for logarithmic computation. Unless the instructor requires another form, the student should use the form illustrated.

Example 1. Use logarithms to find the value of

$$N = \frac{(3.14)(0.413)}{(6.12)(0.719)}.$$

Solution: Recalling that for products we add *logs* and for division we add *cologs*, we have

$$\log N = \log 3.14 + \log 0.413 + \text{col } 6.12 + \text{col } 0.719.$$

The log form follows :

$a = 3.14$	$\log a =$
$b = 0.413$	$\log b =$
$c = 6.12 \quad \log c =$	$\text{col } c =$
$d = 0.719 \log d =$	$\text{col } d =$
$\boxed{N =}$	$\overline{\log N =}$

Next the values are entered in the log form.

$a = 3.14$	$\log a = \quad 0.4969$
$b = 0.413$	$\log b = \quad 9.6160 - 10$
$c = 6.12 \quad \log c = 0.7868$	$\text{col } c = \quad 9.2132 - 10$
$d = 0.719 \log d = 9.8567 - 10$	$\text{col } d = \quad 0.1433$
$\boxed{N = 0.2947}$	$\overline{\log N = 19.4694 - 20}$

or $\boxed{N = \mathbf{0.295}}$ to three significant figures.

Example 2. Use logarithms to find the value of

$$N = \frac{(27.65)^{1/3}(3.160)}{(0.09876)(1.070)^4}.$$

Solution:

$$\log N = \tfrac{1}{3} \log 27.65 + \log 3.160 + \text{col } 0.09876 + 4 \text{ col } 1.070.$$

$a = 27.65$ $\log a = 1.4417$

$b = 3.160$

$c = 0.09876$ $\log c = 8.9946 - 10$

$d = 1.070$ $\log d = 0.0294$ $\text{col } d = 9.9706 - 10$

$\boxed{N = 73.80}$

$\tfrac{1}{3} \log a = 0.4806$

$\log b = 0.4997$

$\text{col } c = 1.0054$

$4 \text{ col } d = 39.8824 - 40$

$\log N = 41.8681 - 40$

Example 3. In spherical trigonometry the following formulas are used to solve a right triangle:

$$\cos c = \cos a \cos b, \quad \cot B = \sin a \cot b, \quad \cot A = \cot a \sin b.$$

Set up a log form for evaluating these formulas.

Solution:

$\text{L} \cos c = \text{L} \cos a + \text{L} \cos b, \qquad \text{L} \cot B = \text{L} \sin a + \text{L} \cot b,$
$\text{L} \cot A = \text{L} \cot a + \text{L} \sin b.$

$a =$ $\text{L} \cos a =$ $\text{L} \sin a =$ $\text{L} \cot a =$

$b =$ $\text{L} \cos b =$ $\text{L} \cot b =$ $\text{L} \sin b =$

$c =$ $\text{L} \cos c =$

$B =$ $\text{L} \cot B =$

$A =$ $\text{L} \cot A =$

▶ **EXERCISES**

1. Use four-place logarithmic tables to find the value of the following:

(a) $N = (908)(0.0539)(2.11)$

(b) $N = \dfrac{9.657}{2.973}$.

(c) $N = \dfrac{0.006784}{0.02904}$.

(d) $N = (7.682)^{0.38}$.

(e) $N = \dfrac{(35.87)(0.6020)}{(1.280)(3.056)}$.

(f) $N = \dfrac{(7.892)(2.350)^2}{(4.902)(1.005)^3}$.

(g) $N = \dfrac{(36.70)(874.3)}{(2.943)\sqrt{8.260}}$.

(h) $N = \dfrac{(212.1)(6.120)(2008)}{(365.0)(531.2)(2.576)}$.

(i) $N = \dfrac{(0.6235)^{3/5}}{(257.1)^{2/3}}$.

(j) $N = \sqrt{\dfrac{(36.37)^{1/7}(31.28)^2}{(0.1628)^2(0.03270)^{1/4}}}$.

2. The following problems require the use of five-place tables, if available:

(a) $N = (26.456)(3.2702)$.   (b) $N = \dfrac{9.8760}{19.004}$.

(c) $N = (0.82067)^{0.25}$.   (d) $N = \dfrac{(100.28)(26.027)}{(890.63)(1.0570)^2}$.

(e) $N = \sqrt{\dfrac{(28.704)^2(32.610)^{1/6}}{(0.16283)^2(0.032479)^{1/4}}}$.

3. Set up a log form for evaluating the following:

(a) $b = c \sin B$.   (b) $a = b \tan A$.

(c) $c = b \csc B$.   (d) $\tan B = \dfrac{b}{a}$, $c = b \csc B$.

(e) $c = a \csc A$, $b = a \cot A$. (f) $a = c \sin A \csc C$.

8-4. LOGARITHMIC SOLUTION OF RIGHT TRIANGLES

The method of solving a right triangle by means of logarithms consists of sketching the triangle approximately to scale, circling the given parts, writing the formulas for the unknown parts in terms of products of the given parts wherever possible, and evaluating these formulas by means of logarithms. The method will be shown in the following examples.

Example 1. Solve the right triangle ACB where $a = 27.92$ and $A = 31°22'$.

Solution: Sketch the triangle (Fig. 8-5-1). Write the formulas
$$B = 90° - A, \quad c = a \csc A, \quad b = a \cot A.$$
Set up the log scheme* and evaluate.
$$\log c = \log a + \text{L} \csc A, \quad \log b = \log a + \text{L} \cot A.$$

---

* If the letters and equal signs after each log symbol are omitted, then each entry in the log form is the value of the designated function of the first entry at the left of each line. This may be done to save writing time and space. The -10's may also be omitted for brevity. The computation form for Example 1 then becomes:

	(c)	(b)
$A = 31°22'$	L csc 10.2836	L cot 10.2149
$a = 27.92$	log 1.4459	log 1.4459
$c = \mathbf{53.64}$	log 11.7295	
$b = \mathbf{45.79}$		log 11.6608
$B = \mathbf{58°38'}$		

		(c)			(b)

$A = 31°22'$ $L \csc A = 10.2836 - 10$ | $L \cot A = 10.2149 - 10$
$a = 27.92$ $\log a = 1.4459$ | $\log a = 1.4459$

$\overline{c = 53.64}$ $\overline{\log c = 11.7295 - 10}$

$\overline{b = 45.79}$ $\log b = 11.6608 - 10$

$\overline{B = 58°38'}$

Note: The letters in parentheses at the top of the columns of logarithms indicate that part of the triangle is being solved for in that column.

For tables not having $L \csc \theta$ and $L \sec \theta$ tabulated, their values may be obtained by using colog $\sin \theta$ and colog $\cos \theta$ respectively.

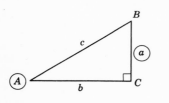

Figure 8-5-1

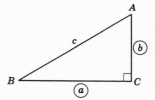

Figure 8-5-2

Example 2. Solve the right triangle ACB where $a = 345.4$, and $b = 216.2$.

Solution: Sketch the triangle (Fig. 8-5-2). Write the formulas

$$\tan B = \frac{b}{a}, \quad c = b \csc B, \quad A = 90° - B.$$

$$L \tan B = \log b + \operatorname{col} a, \qquad \log c = \log b + L \csc B.$$

		(B)	(c)
$b = 216.2$		$\log b = 2.3349$	$\log b = 2.3349$
$a = 345.4$	$\log a = 2.5383$	$\operatorname{col} a = 7.4617 - 10$	
$\overline{B = 32°03'}$		$\overline{L \tan B = 9.7966 - 10}$	$\overline{L \csc B = 10.2752 - 10}$
$\overline{c = 407.5}$			$\log c = 12.6101 - 10$
$\overline{A = 57°57'}$			

▶ **EXERCISES**

1. Solve the right triangles ACB by means of four-place logarithmic tables.

(a) $a = 79.30$, $A = 50°30'$. (b) $b = 23.51$, $B = 46°11'$.
(c) $a = 2.842$, $B = 63°07'$. (d) $b = 6190$, $A = 44°50'$.

(e) $a = 9.25$, $b = 2.34$.   (f) $b = 1.231$, $a = 1.160$.
(g) $A = 52°09'$, $c = 73.62$.   (h) $B = 49°46'$, $c = 28.94$.
(i) $a = 2.458$, $c = 17.93$.   (j) $c = 5.723$, $b = 5.630$.
(k) $a = 51.30$, $c = 150.0$.   (l) $b = 15.05$, $c = 17.82$.
(m) $c = 625.0$, $A = 44°00'$.   (n) $a = 40.27$, $A = 77°19'$.
(o) $b = 847.1$, $a = 769.4$.

2. Solve the right triangles ACB using five-place logarithmic tables if available.

(a) $a = 526.23$, $b = 414.75$. (b) $A = 35°16.3'$, $a = 388.26$.
(c) $A = 88°59.2'$, $b = 2.2349$. (d) $B = 64°00.6'$, $c = 73.000$.
(e) $c = 300.00$, $A = 52°10.0'$.

Oblique Triangles

9-1. INTRODUCTION

If we know three parts of a triangle, one of which must be a side, we can find the remaining three parts (*solve* the triangle) with the aid of certain formulas. We shall discuss in detail two of the many formulas, namely: the *Law of Sines* and the *Law of Cosines*.

From geometry we recall that triangles may be classified according to given information in the following way:

CASE 1. Two angles and one side.
CASE 2. Two sides and the angle opposite one of them.
CASE 3. Two sides and the included angle.
CASE 4. Three sides.

We shall denote the angles at the vertices of any triangle ABC by A, B, and C, respectively and the corresponding opposite sides by a, b, and c.

139

In this chapter most of the problems are to be solved with four-place log tables. If the slide rule is used, round the data off to three significant figures.

9-2. THE LAW OF SINES

In any triangle the sides are proportional to the sines of the opposite angles. That is, in any triangle ABC

$$\frac{a}{\sin A} = \frac{b}{\sin B} = \frac{c}{\sin C}.$$

Proof: Construct a coordinate system such that any angle of triangle ABC, say A, is in standard position. Fig. 9-2-1(a) shows A acute and Fig. 9-2-1(b) shows A obtuse. The coordinates of point C

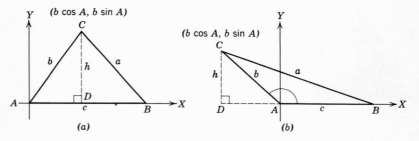

Figure 9-2-1

in either figure are $(b \cos A, b \sin A)$. The length, h, of the altitude of the triangle from C is equal to the ordinate of point C.

Hence,
$$h = b \sin A.$$

From right triangle BDC we also have
$$h = a \sin B.$$

Thus
$$b \sin A = a \sin B,$$

and dividing both sides by $\sin A \sin B$ we obtain

$$\frac{a}{\sin A} = \frac{b}{\sin B}.$$

By placing angle B in standard position we can find

$$\frac{b}{\sin B} = \frac{c}{\sin C}.$$

These last two equations may be written more compactly as

(9-2-1)
$$\frac{a}{\sin A} = \frac{b}{\sin B} = \frac{c}{\sin C}.$$

The Law of Sines provides us with a very simple proportion to use when the given parts of a triangle include a side and the opposite angle. It can be used in solving triangles of Case 1 and Case 2. There is one disadvantage in using the Law of Sines. That is, when solving for an angle we may not know in which quadrant the angle belongs, as the sine of an angle is positive in both the first and second quadrants. We may be able at times to choose the correct angle by knowing that the larger side of a triangle is opposite the larger angle. At other times we may have two values for the angle. This will be discussed in Case 2, the ambiguous case.

▶ **EXERCISES** $\quad \frac{a}{\sin A} = \frac{b}{\sin B} = \frac{c}{\sin C}$

1. For the given parts of $\triangle ABC$, use the Law of Sines to find the required part.

(a) $A = 30°$, $B = 45°$, $a = 4$, find b.
(b) $A = 120°$, $C = 30°$, $c = 5$, find a.
(c) $B = 30°$, $C = 135°$, $b = \sqrt{2}$, find c.
(d) $A = 120°$, $a = \sqrt{3}$, $b = 1$, find B.
(e) $B = 30°$, $b = 4$, $a = 4\sqrt{2}$, find A (two answers).

2. Show that in any triangle ABC, the area S is given by the formula $S = \frac{1}{2}bc \sin A$. (Hint: Drop a perpendicular from the vertex of angle C to the opposite side and use the formula; area of a triangle = $\frac{1}{2}$ base × height.)

3. Use the Law of Sines to show that the formula for the area of a triangle $S = \frac{1}{2}bc \sin A$ may be written as $S = \dfrac{b^2 \sin A \sin C}{2 \sin B}.$

4. Use the Law of Sines to deduce the expression

$$\frac{a + b}{b} = \frac{\sin A + \sin B}{\sin B}.$$

(Hint: Write Law of Sines as $\dfrac{a}{b} = \dfrac{\sin A}{\sin B}$ and add 1 to both sides.)

5. Use the Law of Sines to deduce the expression

$$\frac{a - b}{b} = \frac{\sin A - \sin B}{\sin B}.$$

6. Use the results of problems 4 and 5 and formulas 7-6-5 and 7-6-6 to show that

$$\frac{a + b}{a - b} = \frac{\tan \frac{1}{2}(A + B)}{\tan \frac{1}{2}(A - B)}.$$

7. Show that the relation $\dfrac{a + b}{c} = \dfrac{\cos \frac{1}{2}(A - B)}{\sin \frac{1}{2}C}$ is valid for a triangle ABC.

9-3. APPLICATION OF THE LAW OF SINES

Triangles in Case 1 and Case 2 may be solved by the Law of Sines as shown in the following examples.

CASE 1. LOGARITHMIC SOLUTION

Example. Solve the triangle ABC where $A = 104°14'$, $C = 27°09'$, and $c = 185.7$.

Solution: Sketch the triangle (Fig. 9-3-1).

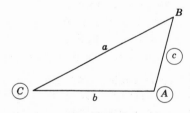

Figure 9-3-1

From $\qquad\qquad B = 180° - (A + C),$
we have $\qquad\qquad$ **$B = 48°37'$.**

From the Law of Sines we have,

$$\frac{a}{\sin A} = \frac{c}{\sin C} \quad \text{and} \quad \frac{b}{\sin B} = \frac{c}{\sin C}.$$

Hence $\qquad$ **$a = c \sin A \csc C$** and **$b = c \sin B \csc C.$**

Set up the log scheme and evaluate.

$\log a = \log c + \text{L} \sin A + \text{L} \csc C, \quad \log b = \log c + \text{L} \sin B + \text{L} \csc C.$

(a)

$$c = 185.7 \qquad \log c = 2.2688$$
$$A = 104°14' \quad \text{L} \sin A = 9.9865 - 10$$
$$C = 27°09' \quad \text{L} \csc C = 10.3408 - 10$$
$$B = 48°37'$$

$$\overline{a = 394.5} \quad \log a = 22.5961 - 20$$

$$\boxed{b = 305.4}$$

$$\boxed{B = 48°37'}$$

(b)

$$\log c = 2.2688$$
$$\text{L} \csc C = 10.3408 - 10$$
$$\text{L} \sin B = 9.8753 - 10$$

$$\log b = 22.4849 - 20$$

CASE 1. SLIDE RULE SOLUTION. For a slide rule solution it is convenient to write the Law of Sines as

$$\frac{\sin A}{a} = \frac{\sin B}{b} = \frac{\sin C}{c}.$$

Example. Solve the triangle ABC where $a = 47.5$, $B = 75°$, and $C = 45°$.

Solution: We may find angle A from the relation

$$A = 180° - (75° + 45°).$$
$$\mathbf{A = 60°.}$$

Since we now have an angle and an opposite side (Fig. 9-3-2), we may use the Law of Sines; thus

$$\frac{\sin 60°}{47.5} = \frac{\sin 75°}{b} = \frac{\sin 45°}{c}.$$

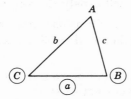

Figure 9-3-2

The setting on the slide rule is shown in Fig. 9-3-3.

Set **60°** on the S-scale opposite **47.5** on the D-scale. Then opposite **75°** on the S-scale, read $b = \mathbf{53.0}$ on the D-scale. Opposite **45°** on the S-scale, read $c = \mathbf{38.8}$ on the D-scale.

Thus, the solution of the triangle is

$$\mathbf{A = 60°,} \qquad \mathbf{b = 53.0,} \qquad \mathbf{c = 38.8}$$

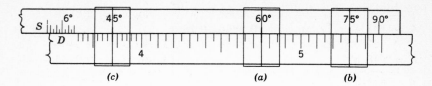

Figure 9-3-3

CASE 2. LOGARITHMIC SOLUTION. This case is known as the ambiguous case, for there may be two solutions, one solution, or no solution to the problem of computing the unknown parts of the triangle. The only triangle that may have two solutions is the type where the *given angle is acute* and the *opposite side is the smaller* of the two given sides.

The number of solutions is readily determined in the process of solving the triangle. Since the sine of an angle never exceeds one, its logarithm will not exceed zero. Consider the triangle ABC in which we are given a, b, and B, with $b < a$. Setting up the Law of Sines and solving for $sin\ A$ we have

$$\sin A = \frac{a \sin B}{b}.$$

If, upon taking logarithms, we find :

  (i) L sin $A < 0$; there will be *two* solutions.
        (sin A is positive in the first two quadrants; hence, two
        values of A will satisfy the expression.)

 (ii) L sin $A = 0$; there will be *one* solution.
        (sin $A = 1$; hence $A = 90°$, and the triangle is a right
        triangle.)

(iii) L sin $A > 0$; there will be *no* solution.
        (sin $A > 1$ does not exist.)

When two solutions are indicated, the student should be very careful to label properly the two triangles and keep their solutions separate.

Example. Solve the triangle ABC, given $b = 15.42$, $a = 21.76$, and $B = 28°15'$. Since $B < 90°$ and $b < a$, there may be two solutions.

Solution: The sketch of the triangle (Fig. 9-3-4) also shows the possibility of two solutions.

From the Law of Sines $\dfrac{\sin A}{a} = \dfrac{\sin B}{b}$, we find $\sin A = \dfrac{a \sin B}{b}$.

$C = 180° - (A + B)$. From $\dfrac{\sin C}{c} = \dfrac{\sin B}{b}$, we have

$$c = b \sin C \csc B.$$

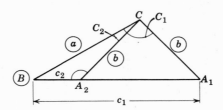

Figure 9-3-4

The logarithmic solution is on page 146. We solved for L sin A first to determine the number of solutions. Since L sin A was found to be less than zero, we knew there were two solutions.

CASE 2. SLIDE RULE SOLUTION. A slide rule method for determining the number of solutions for the ambiguous case is given in the following rule:

Rule: Let A represent the acute angle and its opposite side a be less than the other given side b. Then a rule for determining the number of solutions of the triangle is:

1. Set up the ratio $\dfrac{\sin A}{a}$. (A on the S-scale over a on the D-scale.)

2. Move the hairline to b on the D-scale.

3. Then, (i) if b is to the left of the 90° mark on the S-scale, there are **two** solutions.

(ii) if b is under the 90° mark on the S-scale there is **one** solution.

(iii) if b is to the right of the 90° mark on the S-scale there is **no** solution.

To show the validity of this rule consider the triangle ABC where A, a, and b, are given with $A < 90°$ and $a < b$. From the Law of Sines, we have

$$\frac{\sin A}{a} = \frac{\sin B}{b}.$$

Logarithmic solution for the example on page 144.

$$L \sin A = \log a + L \sin B + \operatorname{col} b, \quad \log c = \log b + L \sin C + L \csc B.$$

(A)

$$\begin{aligned}
\log a &= 1.3377 \\
\operatorname{col} b &= 8.8119\text{--}10 \\
L \sin B &= 9.6752\text{--}10 \\
\hline
L \sin A &= 19.8248\text{--}20
\end{aligned}$$

(c_1)

$$\begin{aligned}
\log b &= 1.1881 \\
L \csc B &= 10.3248\text{--}10 \\
L \sin C_1 &= 9.9734\text{--}10 \\
\hline
\log c_1 &= 21.4863\text{--}20
\end{aligned}$$

(c_2)

$$\begin{aligned}
\log b &= 1.1881 \\
L \csc B &= 10.3248\text{--}10 \\
L \sin C_2 &= 9.3734\text{--}10 \\
\hline
\log c_2 &= 20.8863\text{--}20
\end{aligned}$$

$a = 21.76$

$b = 15.42$

$B = 28°15'$

$A_1 = 41°55' \qquad A_2 = 138°05'$

$C_1 = 109°50'$

$C_2 = 13°40'$

$c_1 = 30.64$

$c_2 = 7.697$

Let b_1 represent the value of b when b is under the 90° mark of the S-scale. The Law of Sines then becomes

$$\frac{\sin A}{a} = \frac{\sin 90°}{b_1},$$

and we obtain $\qquad a = b_1 \sin A = p.$

We then have the right triangle of Fig. 9-3-5(a) and only one solution.

For the same values of A and a, but for $b > b_1$ (b to the right of the 90° mark), we have the triangle with the vertex of angle C at C_2. See Fig. 9-3-5(b). Clearly side a cannot intersect side AB and hence there will be no solution.

For the same values of A and a, but for $b < b_1$ (b to the left of the 90° mark), we have the triangle with the vertex of angle C at C_3. See Fig 9-3-5(c). In this triangle, side a may intersect side AB in two places and hence we have two solutions.

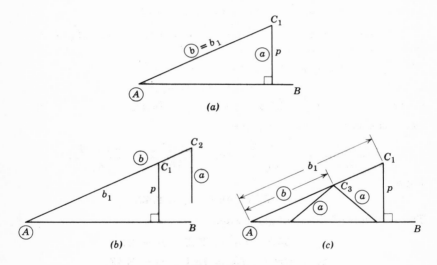

(a)

(b)   *(c)*

Figure 9-3-5

Example. Solve triangle ABC where $B = 37.2°$, $b = 16.4$, $a = 22.3$.

Solution: Since $B < 90°$ and $b < a$, we suspect two solutions. Setting up the Law of Sines on the slide rule, we have

$$\frac{\sin 37.2°}{16.4} = \frac{\sin A}{22.3}.$$

Since 22.3 is to the *left* of the 90° mark on the *S*-scale, we know that there will be *two solutions*. Draw the triangle as in Fig. 9-3-6.

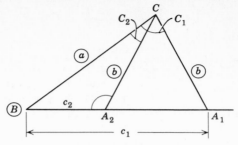

Figure 9-3-6

Recalling that $\sin A$ is positive in the first two quadrants, we will have two values of A, namely

$$A_1 = 55.3° \quad \text{and} \quad A_2 = 124.7°.$$

We now have two triangles to solve, the first with angle A_1 as A and the second with angle A_2 as A.

From the relations $\quad C_1 = 180° - (A_1 + B)$

and $\qquad\qquad\qquad C_2 = 180° - (A_2 + B),$

we find $\qquad C_1 = 87.5° \quad \text{and} \quad C_2 = 18.1°.$

From the Law of Sines we have,

$$\frac{\sin 37.2°}{16.4} = \frac{\sin 87.5°}{c_1} \quad \text{and} \quad \frac{\sin 37.2°}{16.4} = \frac{\sin 18.1°}{c_2}.$$

Thus,

$$c_1 = 27.1 \quad \text{and} \quad c_2 = 8.43.$$

The solution of the triangle is then

$$A_1 = 55.3°, \; C_1 = 87.5°, \; c_1 = 27.1,$$
$$A_2 = 124.7°, \; C_2 = 18.1°, \; c_2 = 8.43.$$

▶ **EXERCISES**

1. Solve the triangle ABC for each of the following:
   (a) $a = 6.22, \; A = 72°20', \; B = 55°30'$.
   (b) $b = 121.2, \; A = 36°23', \; C = 34°12'$.
   (c) $b = 0.5739, \; A = 41°20', \; B = 110°12'$.

(d) $C = 26°40'$, $B = 27°20'$, $a = 478.3$.

(e) $A = 69°59.2'$, $B = 11°25.3'$, $c = 22.568$. (Use five-place tables if available.)

(f) $B = 38°38.4'$, $C = 91°21.6'$, $a = 119.05$. (Use five-place tables if available.)

2. Sketch the following triangles ABC and determine the number of solutions for each. Let p represent the length of the perpendicular dropped from C to side AB.

(a) $A < 90°$, $a < b$, and $a < p$.

(b) $A < 90°$, $a < b$, and $a = p$.

(c) $A < 90°$, $a < b$, and $a > p$.

(d) $A < 90°$, $a > b$.

(e) $A > 90°$, $a > b$.

(f) $A > 90°$, $a < b$.

3. Solve the triangle ABC for each of the following:

(a) $a = 4.250$, $b = 7.580$, $A = 22°40'$.

(b) $c = 45.20$, $b = 32.91$, $C = 47°18'$.

(c) $b = 16.39$, $c = 20.11$, $B = 118°48'$.

(d) $b = 415.0$, $c = 673.1$, $B = 47°12'$.

(e) $C = 126°12.2'$, $a = 5132.0$, $c = 7713.3$. (Use five-place tables if available.)

(f) $A = 52°23.6'$, $a = 19.765$, $b = 23.523$. (Use five-place tables if available.)

4. Use the formulas of problem 3, page 141, to find the area of the following triangles:

(a) $a = 4342$, $b = 2160$, $C = 52°17'$.

(b) $c = 10.37$, $A = 21°09'$, $B = 103°43'$.

5. It is desired to establish point A due east of point B which is inaccessible by traveling due east. A point C is established such that $BC = 825.3$ ft in the direction S 21°42' E. The direction of CA is then N 51°20' E. How long is CA?

6. A building 52.72 ft high is at the top of a hill. From the top of the building the angle of depression of a car at the bottom of the hill is 55°18'. From the bottom of the building the angle of depression of the same car is 12°23'. How far is the car from the bottom of the building?

7. Two observers 1525 ft apart on a level plane saw at the same instant an object falling between them and reported the angles of elevation to be 32°22′ and 43°12′. How high was the object above the plane?

8. An old map claims that a treasure chest is buried at point C, which bears S 72°18′ E from a certain tree, T. To avoid a swamp between T and C, the map says to go 215.3 ft in the direction N 40°24′ E, then 140.0 ft to the buried chest. If the finder of the map has studied trigonometry, should he spend his time looking for the buried treasure? Why?

9. The navigator of a ship knows that two lights, A and B, on shore are 8.250 miles apart and that B bears 62°30′ from A. At 10 A.M. he finds that A bears 20°25′ and that B bears 35°42′. At 11 A.M., after the ship steamed on course 65°12′, he finds B to bear 325.0°. How far did the ship travel in that hour?

9-4. THE LAW OF COSINES

The square of any side of a triangle is equal to the sum of the squares of the other two sides minus twice the product of those two sides and the cosine of the angle between them. Thus for any triangle ABC we have

(9-4-1)
$$a^2 = b^2 + c^2 - 2bc \cos , A$$
$$b^2 = a^2 + c^2 - 2ac \cos B,$$
$$c^2 = a^2 + b^2 - 2ab \cos C.$$

Proof: Let any triangle ABC be placed on a set of rectangular coordinate axes X and Y as shown in Fig. 9-4-1. Since angle A was placed in standard position, the coordinates of the vertex of angle C

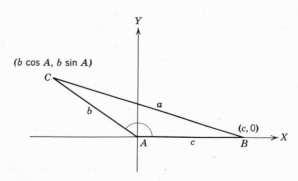

Figure 9-4-1

are ($b \cos A$, $b \sin A$). The coordinates of the vertex of angle B are (c, 0).

Applying the formula for the square of the distance between two points, we obtain

$$a^2 = (b \cos A - c)^2 + (b \sin A - 0)^2.$$

Upon squaring and combining terms we have,

$$a^2 = b^2 (\cos^2 A + \sin^2 A) + c^2 - 2\,bc \cos A.$$

Since $$\cos^2 A + \sin^2 A \equiv 1,$$

we have $$a^2 = b^2 + c^2 - 2bc \cos A.$$

Since the naming of the sides of the triangle is entirely arbitrary, the last two equations of 9-4-1 are readily established.

The Law of Cosines may be used to find the third side of a triangle if two sides and the included angle are known (Case 3). It may also be used to find an angle if three sides of a triangle are known (Case 4).

An advantage that the Law of Cosines has that the Law of Sines does not is that we know the quadrant of the angle from the sign of the cosine of the angle. That is, if $\cos A$ is *positive*, then A is in the *first quadrant*, and if $\cos A$ is *negative*, then A is in the *second quadrant*.

Example. Find angle C if in the triangle ABC, $a = 2$, $b = 3$, and $c = 4$.

Solution: From the formula $c^2 = a^2 + b^2 - 2ab \cos C$,

we find $$\cos C = \frac{a^2 + b^2 - c^2}{2ab}.$$

Substitute the given values

$$\cos C = \frac{(2)^2 + (3)^2 - (4)^2}{2(2)(3)},$$

$$\cos C = \frac{4 + 9 - 16}{12},$$

$$\cos C = -\tfrac{3}{12} = -0.25.$$

Since $\cos C$ is negative, C must be a second quadrant angle. From the tables of natural functions of angles we find, to the nearest degree,

$$C_r = 76° \ (C_r \text{ denotes the related angle to C}).$$

Hence $$C = 104°.$$

▶ EXERCISES

Use the Law of Cosines to find the indicated part of triangle ABC.

1. $a = 4$, $b = 5$, $C = 60°$, find c.

2. $a = 3$, $b = 5$, $c = 7$, find C.

3. $b = 6$, $c = 7$, $A = 90°$, find a.

4. $a = 12$, $c = 13$, $B = 120°$, find b.

5. Find a formula for the area of a triangle ABC given sides b, c, and angle A.

6. For the parallelogram shown (Fig. 9-4-2), show that the length of the diagonal d is

$$d^2 = a^2 + b^2 + 2ab \cos \theta.$$

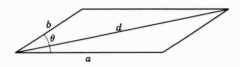

Figure 9-4-2

7. Show that in any triangle ABC

$$c^2 = (a - b)^2 + 4ab \sin^2 \tfrac{1}{2}C.$$

[Hint: Use the Law of Cosines and make use of formula 7-4-3.]

8. Show that for triangle ABC

$$\frac{a^2 + b^2 + c^2}{2abc} = \frac{\cos A}{a} + \frac{\cos B}{b} + \frac{\cos C}{c}.$$

9. Show that $2 \sin^2 \dfrac{A}{2} = \dfrac{(a + b - c)(a - b + c)}{2bc}$.

[Hint: Use Law of Cosines, formula 7-4-3, and factor.]

10. Show that $2 \cos^2 \dfrac{A}{2} = \dfrac{(a + b + c)(b + c - a)}{2bc}$.

[Hint: Use Law of Cosines, formula 7-4-4, and factor.]

11. Using the results of problems 9 and 10, show that

$$\tan \frac{A}{2} = \frac{1}{(s - a)} \sqrt{\frac{(s - a)(s - b)(s - c)}{s}},$$

where

$$s = \tfrac{1}{2}(a + b + c).$$

9-5. APPLICATION OF THE LAW OF COSINES

Triangles in Case 3 and Case 4 may be solved by the Law of Cosines as shown in the following examples.

CASE 3. LOGARITHMIC SOLUTION. Shown in the following example is a method of using logarithms with the Law of Cosines. The instructor, however, may prefer to have the student use the Law of Tangents which is given in the appendix.

Example. Solve the triangle ABC, given $a = 42.30$, $c = 76.40$, and $B = 32°17'$.

Solution: This triangle (Fig. 9-5-1) belongs to Case 3. The Law of Cosines is used. Writing the formulas for the unknown parts we have,

$$b^2 = a^2 + c^2 - 2ac \cos B,$$

$$\cos A = \frac{b^2 + c^2 - a^2}{2bc},$$

$$\cos C = \frac{a^2 + b^2 - c^2}{2ab}.$$

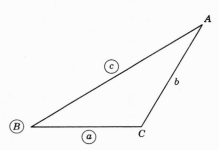

Figure 9-5-1

To find b use the following form.

	$(p = 2\,ac \cos B)$			(b^2)
$a = 42.30$	$\log a = \quad 1.6263$	$2 \log a = 3.2526$		$a^2 = 1789$
$c = 76.40$	$\log c = \quad 1.8831$	$2 \log c = 3.7662$		$c^2 = 5837$
2	$\log 2 = \quad 0.3010$			$a^2 + c^2 = 7626$
$B = 32°17'$	$\text{L} \cos B = \quad 9.9270{-}10$			
$p = 2\,ac \cos B$	$\log p = 13.7374{-}10$	$\longrightarrow$		$2\,ac \cos B = 5462\;(-)$
$\boxed{b = 46.51}$	$\log b = \quad 1.6676$	$2 \log b = 3.3353$	$\longleftarrow$	$b^2 = 2164$

Note 1. In the log form used here the squares of the sides are located in the right-hand column. To emphasize that these numbers are not the same as the numbers in the left column of each line a double vertical line has been drawn before the last column; b^2 is found by subtraction in the last column, and b is then found by going from the right-hand column to the left.

To find A and C make separate forms.

$$(A)$$

$q = b^2 + c^2 - a^2 = 6212$	$\log q =$	3.7932
2	col $2 =$	$9.6990{-}10$
$b = 46.51$	col $b =$	$8.3324{-}10$
$c = 76.40$	col $c =$	$8.1169{-}10$
$\boxed{A = 29°04'}$	L cos $A =$	$29.9415{-}30$

$$(C)$$

$r = a^2 + b^2 - c^2 = -1884$	$\log r = (-)$	3.2751
2	col $2 =$	$9.6990{-}10$
$b = 46.51$	col $b =$	$8.3324{-}10$
$a = 42.30$	col $a =$	$8.3737{-}10$
$\boxed{C = 118°37'}$	L cos $C =$	$(-)29.6802{-}30$

Check: $A + B + C = 29°04' + 32°17' + 118°37' = 179°58'$.

Note 2. The minus signs used in the column for the solution of C indicate that r is negative, cos C is negative, and hence C is a *second quadrant* angle. (L cos C is never positive.)

CASE 3. SLIDE RULE SOLUTION. Before attempting to solve triangles by the Law of Cosines with the aid of a slide rule, the student should review the process of finding the squares and square roots of numbers on the slide rule.

Example. In triangle ABC, $a = 5.32$, $b = 3.07$, $C = 122°$, find side c.

Solution: Since the triangle (Fig. 9-5-2) has two sides and the included angle known, we use the Law of Cosines.

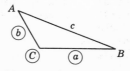

Figure 9-5-2

Hence $\qquad$ $c^2 = a^2 + b^2 - 2\,ab\cos C.$

Substituting the given values we obtain,

$$c^2 = (5.32)^2 + (3.07)^2 - 2(5.32)(3.07)\cos 122°.$$

By squaring the first two terms, multiplying out the coefficient of $\cos 122°$, and recalling that $\cos 122° = -\cos 58°$,

we may write $\qquad$ $c^2 = 28.3 + 9.42 + 32.7\cos 58°,$

$$c^2 = 28.3 + 9.42 + 17.3.$$

Hence $\qquad$ $c^2 = 55.02$

and $\qquad$ **$c = 7.42.$**

CASE 4. LOGARITHMIC SOLUTION. In solving the triangle when three sides are known we shall first use the Law of Cosines to find the largest angle; and next use the Law of Sines to solve for the other two angles. The finding of the largest angle by the Law of Cosines avoids any ambiguity when using the Law of Sines. Shown here is a method using logarithms with the Law of Cosines. Some instructors, however, may prefer to have their students solve this case using the half-angle formulas discussed in the appendix.

Example. Solve the triangle ABC, given $a = 46.10$, $b = 71.43$, and $c = 61.40$.

Solution: Since three sides are given, the triangle (Fig. 9-5-3)

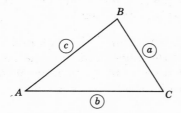

Figure 9-5-3

belongs to Case 4. Since b is the largest side, we shall solve for B first. One of the formulas necessary is:

$$\cos B = \frac{a^2 + c^2 - b^2}{2ac};$$

after B is found we may use the Law of Sines. Hence, we also need

$$\sin A = \frac{a \sin B}{b} \quad \text{and} \quad \sin C = \frac{c \sin B}{b}.$$

$$(a^2 + c^2 - b^2)$$

$a = 46.10$	$\log a = 1.6637$	$2 \log a = 3.3274$	$a^2 = 2125$
$c = 61.40$	$\log c = 1.7882$	$2 \log c = 3.5764$	$c^2 = 3771$
			$a^2 + c^2 = 5896$
$b = 71.43$	$\log b = 1.8539$	$2 \log b = 3.7078$	$b^2 = 5102$
			$a^2 + c^2 - b^2 = 794$

$$(B)$$

$q = a^2 + c^2 - b^2 = 794$		$\log q = 2.8998$
2		$\text{col } 2 = 9.6990{-}10$
$a = 46.10$		$\text{col } a = 8.3363{-}10$
$c = 61.40$		$\text{col } c = 8.2118{-}10$
$\boxed{B = 81°56'}$		$L \cos B = 29.1469{-}30$

<table>
<tr><td> </td><td>(A)</td><td>(C)</td></tr>
<tr><td>$B = 81°56'$</td><td>$L \sin B = 9.9957{-}10$</td><td>$L \sin B = 9.9957{-}10$</td></tr>
<tr><td>$b = 71.43$</td><td>$\text{col } b = 8.1461{-}10$</td><td>$\text{col } b = 8.1461{-}10$</td></tr>
<tr><td>$a = 46.10$</td><td>$\log a = 1.6637$</td><td></td></tr>
<tr><td>$\boxed{A = 39°43'}$</td><td>$L \sin A = 19.8055{-}20$</td><td></td></tr>
<tr><td>$c = 61.40$</td><td></td><td>$\log c = 1.7882$</td></tr>
<tr><td>$\boxed{C = 58°20'}$</td><td></td><td>$L \sin C = 19.9300{-}20$</td></tr>
</table>

Check: $A + B + C = 179°59'$ (which is allowable due to the rounding off process in interpolation).

Since the largest angle, B, was found first, the other two angles, A and C, must be first quadrant angles.

CASE 4. SLIDE RULE SOLUTION. We shall first employ the Law of Cosines to find one of the angles and then the Law of Sines to complete the solution. To avoid ambiguity in the quadrant of the angles, it is advisable to solve for the largest angle first.

Example. Solve the triangle ABC where $a = 25.3$, $b = 32.7$, and $c = 52.5$.

Solution: Since c is the larger side (Fig. 9-5-4), we shall find angle C first from the Law of Cosines.

From the formula $c^2 = a^2 + b^2 - 2ab \cos C$, we find

$$\cos C = \frac{a^2 + b^2 - c^2}{2ab}.$$

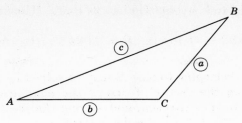

Figure 9-5-4

Substituting the values for a, b, c,

we have $\qquad \cos C = \dfrac{(25.3)^2 + (32.7)^2 - (52.5)^2}{(2)(25.3)(32.7)}$,

$\qquad\qquad \cos C = \dfrac{640 + 1070 - 2760}{1655}$,

$\qquad \cos C = -0.634.$

Since $\cos C$ is negative, we know that C must be a second quadrant angle. We find $C_r = 50.6°$ (the related angle).

Hence $\qquad\qquad\qquad\qquad C = 129.4°.$

We may now apply the Law of Sines to find A and B.

Thus $\qquad\qquad \dfrac{\sin 129.4°}{52.5} = \dfrac{\sin A}{25.3} = \dfrac{\sin B}{32.7}$,

or $\qquad\qquad \dfrac{\sin 50.6°}{52.5} = \dfrac{\sin A}{25.3} = \dfrac{\sin B}{32.7}$,

and $\qquad\qquad A = 21.8°, \quad B = 28.8°.$

Therefore, the solution is

$\qquad A = 21.8°, \quad B = 28.8°, \quad$ and $\quad C = 129.4°.$

▶ **EXERCISES**

1. Solve triangle ABC.

(a) $b = 53.70$, $c = 51.70$, $A = 71°10'$.

(b) $c = 6.750$, $a = 1.058$, $B = 128°31'$.

(c) $a = 478.5$, $b = 275.9$, $C = 27°48'$.

(d) $B = 28°06'$, $c = 11.51$, $a = 11.48$.

(e) $a = 221.34$, $b = 149.07$, $C = 30°40.6'$. (Use five-place tables if available.)

(f) $a = 109.03$, $c = 102.12$, $B = 33°23.9'$. (Use five-place tables if available.)

2. Triangles belonging to Case B may be solved by drawing a perpendicular from the vertex of one of the unknown angles to its opposite side, or its extension, and solving the resulting two right triangles. For Fig. 9-5-5 and right $\triangle BDA$,

$$p = c \sin B \quad \text{and} \quad x = c \cos B.$$

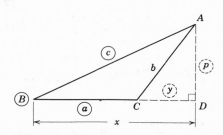

Figure 9-5-5

For right $\triangle CDA$,

$$y = x - a, \quad \tan \angle ACD = \frac{p}{y}, \quad b = p \csc \angle ACD.$$

Thus, $\qquad C = 180° - \angle ACD \quad \text{and} \quad A = 180° - (B + C).$

Solve the following triangles by this method.

(a) $a = 252.0$, $\qquad b = 229.0$, $\qquad C = 15°11'$.
(b) $a = 5132$, $\qquad b = 3476$, $\qquad C = 126°12'$.
(c) $B = 57°20'$, $\qquad a = 20.71$, $\qquad c = 18.41$.
(d) $b = 6.390$, $\qquad c = 2.690$, $\qquad A = 136°16'$.
(e) $a = 3184$, $\qquad b = 917.0$, $\qquad C = 34°09'$.

3. Solve triangle ABC.

(a) $a = 894.0$, $b = 802.3$, $c = 847.0$.
(b) $a = 98.41$, $b = 73.59$, $c = 49.81$.
(c) $a = 5.377$, $b = 6.211$, $c = 5.168$.
(d) $a = 28.40$, $b = 42.51$, $c = 23.70$.
(e) $a = 509.17$, $b = 221.36$, $c = 480.79$. (Use five-place tables if available.)

(f) $a = 5134.2$, $b = 7268.7$, $c = 9313.4$. (Use five-place tables if available.)

4. A surveyor at B sights two points A and C on the opposite sides of a lake. If $BA = 231.7$ ft, $BC = 342.2$ ft, and angle $ABC = 126°41'$, find the distance AC.

5. A force triangle consists of three forces $F_1 = 35.07$ lbs, $F_2 = 22.60$ lbs, and $F_3 = 41.72$ lbs. Find the angle between F_1 and F_2.

6. The adjacent sides of a parallelogram are 10.62 in. and 14.73 in. If the longest diagonal is 22.04 in., find the length of the shortest diagonal.

7. The sides of a triangular lot are 1532 ft, 1357 ft, and 1073 ft. The longer side bears $35°12'$. Find the bearing of the other sides.

8. An airplane leaves airport A at 10 A.M. and flies on course $32°51'$ at a speed of 315.0 mph. At the same time another airplane leaves airport B, 525.0 miles east of A, and flies at a speed of 280.0 mph. Find the course of the second airplane if it is to meet the first airplane at noontime.

9. A patrol boat steamed 27.80 miles on course $031.3°$ and then steamed 18.30 miles on course $136.7°$. Find the course to be set and the distance to be traversed in order to return to its starting point by the shortest route.

10. Ship A sails from point P on a course of $53°36'$ at 8.30 knots. Three quarters of an hour later ship B sails from P on course $22°42'$ at 10.30 knots. Find the distance between the ships two hours after B departs. (One knot is 1 nautical mile per hour.)

Inverse
Trigonometric Functions

10-1. INVERSE FUNCTIONS

In Art. 1-7, we stated that a function assigned one and only one image to each element of the domain. If the function also has the property that each image in the range corresponds to only one element of the domain, such a function is said to set up a one-to-one correspondence between the elements of the domain and the images of the range. When functions establish such a one-to-one correspondence, we can define a new function which is the inverse of the original function where the domain of the new function is the range of the original function, and the range of the new function is the domain of the original function. Each function is said to be the inverse of the other.

Definition: If f is a function such that $f(c) \neq f(d)$, *where c and d are two different elements in the domain, and if* $f(a) = b$, *then the inverse function of* f, *sometimes denoted by* f⁻¹, *is the function which assigns* a *as the image of* b. *The domain of* f⁻¹ *is the range of* f.

This definition tells us that if $f(a) = b$, then $f^{-1}(b) = a$.

The " − 1 " after the symbol f is not to be treated as an exponent; it is merely a symbol to denote the inverse function.

10-2. INVERSE TRIGONOMETRIC FUNCTIONS

The graph of $f(x) = \sin x$, Fig. 10-2-1, clearly shows that for each element x in the domain there corresponds only one image. The line l, representing any one image, intersects the curve in many places. Thus, there is not a one-to-one correspondence between the images

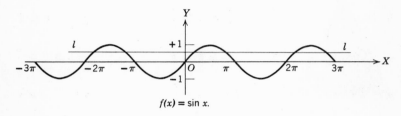

$f(x) = \sin x.$

Figure 10-2-1

of the range and the elements of the domain for the function *sin x*. Similar statements may be made about the other trigonometric functions. Thus, the trigonometric functions, strictly speaking, do not have inverses. However, we may get around this difficulty by *restricting* the domain so that there will be a one-to-one correspondence between the elements of the restricted domain and the range. Let us denote the trigonometric functions *with* this *restricted domain* by writing the first letters of the trigonometric functions as capital letters, thus *Sin x, Cos x, Tan x, Cot x, Sec x. Csc x*. (Read as "Cap-Sine of *x*," etc.) We then write their inverse functions as *Sin⁻¹x, Cos⁻¹x, Tan⁻¹x, Cot⁻¹x, Sec⁻¹x*, and *Csc⁻¹x*, respectively, which are read as "inverse Cap-Sine of *x*, etc." Another common symbol used to denote the inverse sine of *x* is *arc Sin x*, which is read as "arc Cap-Sine of *x*." Similar expressions are used for the other inverse trigonometric functions.

If the domain of the trigonometric functions consists of angles, then the range of the inverse trigonometric functions consists of angles. That is, if $y = \text{Sin } x$, x an angle, then its inverse, $Sin^{-1}x$, is said to be "an angle whose Sine is x."

It should be clear from the definition of inverse functions that *if* **$y = \text{Sin } \theta$**, *then* **$\theta = \text{Sin}^{-1}y$**. Thus for $\theta = Sin^{-1}(\frac{1}{2})$, we may write $Sin\ \theta = \frac{1}{2}$.

In the Table 10-2-1 we have listed the restricted domains of the trigonometric functions of angles measured in radians, or of real numbers.

TABLE 10-2-1

Function	Domain	Range
$y = \text{Sin } x$.	$-\dfrac{\pi}{2} \leqq x \leqq \dfrac{\pi}{2}$.	$-1 \leqq y \leqq 1$.
$y = \text{Cos } x$.	$0 \leqq x \leqq \pi$.	$-1 \leqq y \leqq 1$.
$y = \text{Tan } x$.	$-\dfrac{\pi}{2} < x < \dfrac{\pi}{2}$.	All real numbers.
$y = \text{Cot } x$.	$0 < x < \pi$.	All real numbers.
$y = \text{Sec } x$.	$0 \leqq x < \dfrac{\pi}{2}$, or	$y \geqq 1$,
	$-\pi \leqq x < -\dfrac{\pi}{2}$.	$y \leqq -1$.
$y = \text{Csc } x$.	$0 < x \leqq \dfrac{\pi}{2}$, or	$y \geqq 1$,
	$-\pi < x \leqq -\dfrac{\pi}{2}$.	$y \leqq -1$.

In the Table 10-2-2 we have listed the definitions of the inverse trigonometric functions. There is no universal agreement among mathematicians as to the range of the inverse trigonometric functions. The listed ranges are quite common.

TABLE 10-2-2

Function	Domain	Range
$y = $ arc Sin x.	$-1 \leq x \leq 1$.	$-\dfrac{\pi}{2} \leq y \leq \dfrac{\pi}{2}$,
$y = $ arc Cos x.	$-1 \leq x \leq 1$.	$0 \leq y \leq \pi$.
$y = $ arc Tan x.	All real numbers.	$-\dfrac{\pi}{2} < y < \dfrac{\pi}{2}$.
$y = $ arc Cot x.	All real numbers.	$0 < y < \pi$.
$y = $ arc Sec x.	$x \geq 1$, or	$0 \leq y < \dfrac{\pi}{2}$,
	$x \leq -1$.	$-\pi \leq y < -\dfrac{\pi}{2}$.
$y = $ arc Csc x	$x \geq 1$, or	$0 < y \leq \dfrac{\pi}{2}$,
	$x \leq -1$.	$-\pi < y \leq -\dfrac{\pi}{2}$.

The values in the range of each of the inverse trigonometric functions listed in Table 10-2-2 are sometimes called the *principal values* of that function.

Example 1. Find the exact value of arc Cos $(-\frac{1}{2})$.

Solution: Let $\qquad \theta = $ arc Cos $(-\frac{1}{2})$,

then $\qquad\qquad$ Cos $\theta = -\frac{1}{2}$.

We must find an angle whose cosine is $-\frac{1}{2}$. There are many such angles, e.g. $(2\pi/3) \pm 2n\pi$ and $(4\pi/3) \pm 2n\pi$, n an integer. However, the *range* of arc Cos x tells us that $0 \leq \theta \leq \pi$, hence

$$\theta = \frac{2\pi}{3}.$$

Example 2. Find $\quad$ cos [arc Tan $(-\frac{3}{4})$].

Solution: If we let $\theta = $ arc Tan $(-\frac{3}{4})$, then we are to find the value of cos θ.

$$\theta = \text{arc Tan } (-\tfrac{3}{4}) \text{ implies that Tan } \theta = -\tfrac{3}{4}.$$

The range of the inverse tangent tells us that θ must be a fourth quadrant angle. Hence, from the sketch (Fig. 10-2-2), we have

$$\cos \theta = \tfrac{4}{5}.$$

Thus, $\qquad\qquad$ **cos [arc Tan $(-\frac{3}{4})$] $= \frac{4}{5}$.**

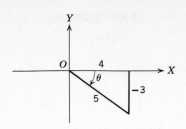

Figure 10-2-2

▶ **EXERCISES**

1. Make a table listing the restricted domains and the ranges of the trigonometric functions if their argument is an angle measured in degrees. Also state the inverses of these functions.

2. Write the inverse of the given function:

(a) $\text{Sin}^{-1} u$. (b) $\text{Cos}^{-1} v$. (c) $3 \text{Sin}^{-1} x$.

(d) $\text{Cos}^{-1} 2x$. (e) $\text{Tan}^{-1} (u + v)$. (f) $\text{Sec}^{-1} (1 + x^2)$.

(g) arc $\text{Cos} (\sqrt{1 + x^2})$.

3. Find the exact value of the angle expressed as an inverse function:

(a) $\text{Sin}^{-1} (\frac{1}{2})$. (b) $\text{Sin}^{-1} \left(-\frac{\sqrt{3}}{2}\right)$. (c) $\text{Cos}^{-1} 1$.

(d) arc $\text{Cos} (-\frac{1}{2})$. (e) arc $\text{Sin} (-1)$. (f) arc $\text{Sin} \frac{\sqrt{3}}{2}$.

(g) $\text{Tan}^{-1} (-1)$. (h) $\text{Tan}^{-1} \sqrt{3}$. (i) arc $\text{Tan} \left(-\frac{\sqrt{3}}{3}\right)$.

(j) arc $\text{Cot} (-\sqrt{3})$. (k) $\text{Cot}^{-1} (-1)$. (l) $\text{Cot}^{-1} 0$.

4. Use tables or the slide rule to find the value of the real number:

(a) $\text{Sin}^{-1} (0.743)$. (b) arc $\text{Sin} (-0.129)$. (c) arc $\text{Cos} (-0.352)$.

(d) $\text{Cos}^{-1} (0.416)$. (e) $\text{Tan}^{-1} (-1.46)$. (f) arc $\text{Tan} (0.754)$.

5. Find the exact value of the following:

(a) $\sin [\text{Tan}^{-1} (\frac{5}{12})]$. (b) $\sin [\text{Sin}^{-1} (\frac{1}{2})]$.

(c) $\text{Sin}^{-1} [\sin (\frac{1}{2})]$. (d) $\cos [\text{arc Sin} (-\frac{8}{17})]$.

(e) $\cos [\text{arc Tan} (\frac{7}{24})]$. (f) $\cos [2 \text{Sin}^{-1} (\frac{15}{17})]$.

(g) $\tan [\text{arc Cos} (-\frac{3}{5})]$. (h) $\tan [2 \text{arc Tan} (\frac{4}{3})]$.

(i) $\tan [\text{Cot}^{-1} (-\frac{24}{7})]$. (j) $\cot [\text{Sin}^{-1} (-\frac{5}{13})]$.

(k) $\cot [\text{arc Tan} (\frac{8}{15})]$. (l) $\cot [\text{arc Cos} (-\frac{24}{25})]$.

10-3. RELATIONS INVOLVING INVERSE TRIGONOMETRIC FUNCTIONS

The following examples will show a few methods of obtaining some relations among inverse trigonometric functions.

Example 1. Express $\text{Cos}^{-1} y$ in terms of an inverse sine.

Solution: Let $\theta = \text{Cos}^{-1} y$, then $y = \text{Cos } \theta$. From the fundamental identity $\text{Sin}^2 \theta + \text{Cos}^2 \theta \equiv 1$, we have

$$\text{Sin } \theta \equiv \pm \sqrt{1 - \text{Cos}^2 \theta}.$$

For $\text{Cos } \theta$, $\qquad 0 \leqq \theta \leqq \pi$, hence $\text{Sin } \theta > 0$.

Thus $\qquad\qquad \text{Sin } \theta = \sqrt{1 - y^2}$,

or $\qquad\qquad\qquad \theta = \text{Sin}^{-1} \sqrt{1 - y^2}$.

Hence, $\qquad\qquad \mathbf{Cos^{-1} \, y = Sin^{-1} \sqrt{1 - y^2}}.$

Example 2. Find the value of $\sin (2 \text{ arc Tan } x)$, for $x > 0$.

Solution: Let $\theta = \text{arc Tan } x$, then $\text{Tan } \theta = x$; we wish to find $\sin 2\theta \equiv 2 \sin \theta \cos \theta$. For $x > 0$, $0 < \theta < \pi/2$. (Why?)
From Fig. 10-3-1, we find

$$\sin 2\theta = 2 \left(\frac{x}{\sqrt{1 + x^2}}\right)\left(\frac{1}{\sqrt{1 + x^2}}\right).$$

Thus, $\qquad\qquad \mathbf{sin \, (2 \text{ arc Tan } x) = \dfrac{2x}{1 + x^2}}.$

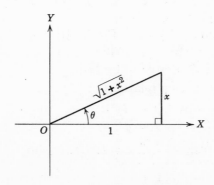

Figure 10-3-1

Example 3. Find the value of tan $[\text{Sin}^{-1} \frac{3}{5} - \text{Cos}^{-1}(-\frac{4}{5})]$.

Solution: Let $A = \text{Sin}^{-1} \frac{3}{5}$ and $B = \text{Cos}^{-1}(-\frac{4}{5})$.

Then $\qquad\qquad\qquad$ Sin $A = \frac{3}{5}$ and Cos $B = -\frac{4}{5}$.

From the sketches (Fig. 10-3-2),

we have $\qquad\qquad$ tan $A = \frac{3}{4}$ and tan $B = -\frac{3}{4}$.

Since $\qquad\qquad$ tan $(A - B) \equiv \dfrac{\tan A - \tan B}{1 + \tan A \tan B}$,

we have $\quad$ **tan** $[\textbf{Sin}^{-1} \frac{3}{5} - \textbf{Cos}^{-1}(-\frac{4}{5})] = \dfrac{\frac{3}{4} - (-\frac{3}{4})}{1 + (\frac{3}{4})(-\frac{3}{4})} = \dfrac{\textbf{24}}{\textbf{7}}.$

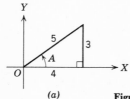 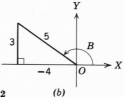

(a) $\qquad$ **Figure 10-3-2** $\qquad$ (b)

▶ **EXERCISES**

1. Find the value of the trigonometric functions:

(a) sin $(\text{Sin}^{-1} 2x)$, $x > 0$. $\qquad$ (b) cos $(\text{Cos}^{-1} u)$, $u > 0$.

(c) tan $(\text{arc Sin } y)$, $y < 0$. $\qquad$ (d) sin $(\text{arc Sin } v)$, $v < 0$.

(e) cos $(2 \text{ Sin}^{-1} u)$, $u < 0$. $\qquad$ (f) cos $(2 \text{ arc Cos } x)$, $x > 0$.

(g) sin $(2 \text{ arc Tan } v)$, $v < 0$. $\qquad$ (h) sin $(2 \text{ Cos}^{-1} y)$, $y < 0$.

(i) cos $[\text{Sin}^{-1} \frac{4}{5} + \text{Cos}^{-1} \frac{12}{13}]$. $\qquad$ (j) tan $[\text{Cos}^{-1} \frac{4}{5} + \text{Tan}^{-1} \frac{1}{2}]$.

(k) sin $[\text{Sin}^{-1} \frac{12}{13} + \text{Cos}^{-1} \frac{3}{5}]$.

(l) tan $[\text{arc Tan}(-\frac{8}{15}) - \text{arc Cos}(-\frac{3}{5})]$.

(m) sin $[\text{arc Cot}(-\frac{24}{7}) - \text{arc Sin}(-\frac{5}{13})]$.

(n) cos $[\text{arc Sin} \frac{15}{17} + \text{arc Cos}(-\frac{12}{13})]$.

2. Prove the following relations:

(a) $2 \text{ Sin}^{-1} x = \text{Cos}^{-1}(1 - 2x^2)$.

(b) $\text{Sin}^{-1} y = \text{Cos}^{-1} \sqrt{1 - y^2}$.

(c) $\text{Sin}^{-1} u = \text{Tan}^{-1} \dfrac{u}{\sqrt{1 - u^2}}$, $(1 - u^2 \neq 0)$.

(d) $2 \text{ Cot}^{-1} x = \text{Csc}^{-1} \dfrac{1 + x^2}{2x}$, $(x \neq 0)$.

(e) $\text{Tan}^{-1} u + \text{Tan}^{-1} v = \text{Tan}^{-1} \dfrac{u + v}{1 - uv}.$

(f) $\sin (2 \text{Sin}^{-1} u) = 2u \sqrt{1 - u^2}.$

(g) $2 \text{Tan}^{-1} u = \text{Tan}^{-1} \dfrac{2u}{1 - u^2}.$

(h) $\text{Tan}^{-1} \dfrac{5}{7} + \text{Tan}^{-1} \dfrac{1}{6} = \dfrac{\pi}{4}.$

(i) $\text{Cos}^{-1} \dfrac{1}{2} + 2 \text{Sin}^{-1} \dfrac{1}{2} = \dfrac{2\pi}{3}.$

(j) $\text{Cot}^{-1} 3 + \text{Csc}^{-1} \sqrt{5} = \dfrac{\pi}{4}.$

(k) $3 \text{Sin}^{-1} u = \text{Sin}^{-1} (3u - 4u^3).$

10-4. GRAPHS OF THE INVERSE TRIGONOMETRIC FUNCTIONS

The graphs of the inverse trigonometric functions can be drawn quite easily by comparing them with the graphs of their inverses. Since $y = \text{Sin } x$ is a restricted branch of the sine curve which oscillates about the X-axis, and $y = \text{Sin}^{-1} x$ can be written as $x = \text{Sin } y$, it is clear that the graph of $y = \text{Sin}^{-1} x$ is a branch of the sine curve which oscillates about the Y-axis. The graphs of $y = \text{Sin}^{-1} x$, $y = \text{Cos}^{-1} x$, and $y = \text{Tan}^{-1} x$ are shown in Fig. 10-4-1. The dotted lines represent the graphs of $y = \text{Sin } x$, $y = \text{Cos } x$, and $y = \text{Tan } x$.

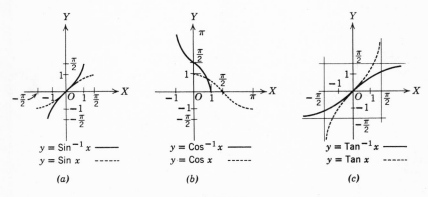

$y = \text{Sin}^{-1} x$ ——
$y = \text{Sin } x$ - - - - - -

(a)

$y = \text{Cos}^{-1} x$ ——
$y = \text{Cos } x$ - - - - - -

(b)

$y = \text{Tan}^{-1} x$ ——
$y = \text{Tan } x$ - - - - - -

(c)

Figure 10-4-1

▶ **EXERCISES**

1. Sketch the graph of:

(a) $y = \text{Cot}^{-1} x$.　　　(b) $y = \text{Sec}^{-1} x$.　　　(c) $y = \text{Csc}^{-1} x$.

(d) $y = \text{Cot } x$.　　　(e) $y = \text{Sec } x$.　　　(f) $y = \text{Csc } x$.

2. In Fig. 10-4-1, draw a straight line through the origin making an angle of 45° with the positive X-axis. What conclusion, with respect to this line, can you draw concerning the graphs of the restricted trigonometric functions and their inverses?

3. Sketch the graph of the following:

(a) $y = \text{Sin}^{-1} 2x$.　　　　　　(b) $y = \text{arc Cos } 2x$.

(c) $y = \text{Tan}^{-1} 2x$.　　　　　　(d) $y = 2 \text{ Sin}^{-1} x$.

(e) $y = \frac{1}{2} \text{Cos}^{-1} 2x$.　　　　　(f) $y = 3 \text{ arc Tan } \frac{1}{2}x$.

(g) $y - \dfrac{\pi}{2} = \text{Sin}^{-1} x$.　　　　(h) $y = \frac{1}{3} \text{Cos}^{-1} 3x$.

(i) $y = 2 \text{ Sin}^{-1} (\frac{1}{2}x)$.

11 Trigonometric Equations

11-1. INTRODUCTION

A trigonometric equation is an equation that contains trigonometric functions of angles or real numbers. It is unlike a trigonometric identity in that not all values of the angle or real number will satisfy it. A solution of a trigonometric equation consists of finding all of the angles or real numbers that will satisfy the equation. Since coterminal angles have the same trigonometric function values, $\theta \pm n \cdot 360°$, $n = 0, 1, 2, \cdots$ is a solution whenever θ is a solution. For convenience we shall restrict our solutions to values of the angle that are *positive or zero and less than 360°*. This is noted by the symbol $0° \leqq \theta < 360°$. For real numbers, u, the solutions will be restricted to values for $0 \leqq u < 2\pi$. There is no one general method of solving all trigonometric equations.

169

11-2. EQUATIONS INVOLVING SIMPLE ALGEBRAIC OPERATIONS

If we can solve an equation for one or more trigonometric functions, we can then find the corresponding values of the angle. Methods of solution are partly algebraic and partly trigonometric. If we take the square root of both sides of an equation or divide by a factor, we must be careful not to lose a root. If we square both sides of an equation, or multiply by a variable factor, we must check to see if we have introduced extraneous roots. This may be done by substituting all of the found roots into the original equation and discarding those that do not satisfy it.

The following examples will illustrate a few techniques of solving trigonometric equations.

Example 1. Solve the equation

$$2 \sin \theta \cos \theta = \sin \theta \quad \text{for} \quad 0° \leq \theta < 360°.$$

Solution: Transposing $sin \theta$ and factoring, we have

$$\sin \theta(2 \cos \theta - 1) = 0.$$

Setting each factor equal to zero and simplifying, we have

$$\sin \theta = 0, \quad \text{and} \quad \cos \theta = \tfrac{1}{2}.$$

Hence $\qquad \theta = 0°, \ 180°, \ \text{and} \ \theta = 60°, \ 300°.$

Thus the solutions are

$$\boldsymbol{\theta = 0°, \ 60°, \ 180°, \ 300°.}$$

These values may be checked by substituting them in the given equation.

Example 2. Solve the equation $2 \sin^4 u - 9 \sin^2 u + 4 = 0$, for $0 \leq u < 2\pi$.

Solution: This equation may be factored as

$$(2 \sin^2 u - 1)(\sin^2 u - 4) = 0.$$

Equating each factor to zero and simplifying we obtain,

$$\sin^2 u = \tfrac{1}{2}, \quad \text{and} \quad \sin^2 u = 4.$$

Upon taking the square roots, we have

$$\sin u = \pm \frac{1}{\sqrt{2}}, \quad \text{and} \quad \sin u = \pm 2.$$

From the first expression we find

$$u = \pi/4, \quad 3\pi/4, \quad 5\pi/4, \quad 7\pi/4.$$

The second expression has *no solution* as the numerical value of sin u *cannot* exceed 1.

Example 3. Solve the equation

$$3 \tan^2 \theta + 4 \tan \theta - 1 = 0 \quad \text{for} \quad 0° \leq \theta < 360°.$$

Solution: As this equation is not readily factorable, we may apply the quadratic formula using *tan θ* as the variable.

Thus, $\quad \tan \theta = \dfrac{-4 \pm \sqrt{16 - (4)(3)(-1)}}{2(3)} = \dfrac{-4 \pm \sqrt{28}}{6}.$

Hence $\quad\quad \tan \theta = 0.215 \quad \text{and} \quad \tan \theta = -1.55.$
Using the tables or slide rule, we find

$$\theta = 12°10', \; 192°10', \quad \text{and} \quad \theta = 122°50', \; 302°50'.$$

Thus the solutions are

$$\theta = 12°10', \; 122°50', \; 192°10', \; 302°50'.$$

▶ **EXERCISES**

Solve the following equations for $0° \leq \theta < 360°$, or for $0 \leq u < 2\pi$.

1. $\tan \theta + \sqrt{3} = 0.$

2. $\tan \theta + 1 = 0.$

3. $\sin u - 2 \sin^2 u = 0.$

4. $\tan^2 u + \tan u = 0.$

5. $3 \cos \theta - 4 \cos^2 \theta = 0.$

6. $2 \sin \theta - 1 = 0.$

7. $\cos u - \cos u \tan u = 0.$

8. $4 \sin^2 u \cos u - \cos u = 0.$

9. $\sin \theta - 2 \cos \theta \sin \theta = 0.$

10. $2 \sin \theta \cos \theta - \cos \theta = 0.$

11. $2 \sin^2 u - \sin u - 1 = 0.$

12. $3 \sin^2 u + \sin u - 2 = 0.$

13. $\tan^2 \theta - 2 \tan \theta - 3 = 0.$

14. $\cos^2 \theta - 2 \cos \theta - 1 = 0.$

15. $2 \cos^2 u + 3 \cos u + 1 = 0.$

16. $2 \sqrt{2} \sin u \cos u - \sqrt{6} \cos u + \sqrt{3} - 2 \sin u = 0.$

17. $\cot^2 \theta \sin \theta - 3 \sin \theta + \cot^2 \theta - 3 = 0.$

18. $\tan^2 \theta - 5 \tan \theta + 6 = 0.$

19. $2 \sec^2 u + 11 \sec u + 15 = 0.$

20. $21 \sin^2 u - 5 \sin u - 6 = 0.$

21. $\tan^2 \theta - 2 \tan \theta - 1 = 0.$

22. $9 \cos^2 \theta - 12 \cos \theta - 1 = 0.$

23. $2 \sin^2 u + \sin u - 5 = 0$.   **24.** $\sin^2 u - 2 \sin u - 1 = 0$.

25. $2 \cos^4 \theta - 9 \cos^2 \theta + 4 = 0$.

26. $6 \tan^4 \theta + 13 \tan^2 \theta + 5 = 0$.

27. $\cot^4 u - 5 \cot^2 u + 4 = 0$.

28. $15 \sin^4 u - 22 \sin^2 u + 8 = 0$.

29. $\sin^4 \theta - 2 \sin^2 \theta - 1 = 0$.   **30.** $\cot^4 \theta - 2 \cot^2 \theta - 1 = 0$.

11-3. EQUATIONS INVOLVING TRIGONOMETRIC REDUCTIONS

If an equation consists of different trigonometric functions or trigonometric functions of multiple angles, they may often be reduced to simpler forms by using trigonometric identities. It is best to avoid the use of radicals whenever possible.

Example 1. Solve the equation
$$\cos 2\theta - \sin \theta = 0 \text{ for } 0° \leqq \theta < 360°.$$
Solution: Since $\cos 2\theta \equiv 1 - 2 \sin^2 \theta$, we may write the given equation as $1 - 2 \sin^2 \theta - \sin \theta = 0$.

Rearranging and factoring, we have
$$(2 \sin \theta - 1)(\sin \theta + 1) = 0.$$
Equating each factor to zero, we obtain
$$\sin \theta = \tfrac{1}{2}, \quad \text{and} \quad \sin \theta = -1.$$
Thus, we find   **$\theta = 30°$, $150°$, and $270°$.**

Example 2. Solve the equation $-2 \sin u + 3 \cos u = 1$ for $0 \leqq u < 2\pi$.

Solution: Transposing $3 \cos u$ and then squaring both sides, we
have $4 \sin^2 u = 1 - 6 \cos u + 9 \cos^2 u$
which simplifies to $13 \cos^2 u - 6 \cos u - 3 = 0$.

Solving by the quadratic formula, we obtain
$$\cos u = \frac{6 \pm \sqrt{192}}{26} = \frac{6 \pm 13.86}{26},$$
or $\cos u = 0.764$ and $\cos u = -0.302$.

Using Table II, we find
$$u = \mathbf{0.701, \ 5.58,} \quad \text{and} \quad u = \mathbf{1.88, \ 4.41.}$$

Since we squared both sides of the equation in the process of solving, we must check for extraneous roots. Substituting the values of u in the original equation, we find that $u = 5.58$ and $u = 1.88$ do not satisfy the equation. Hence the solutions are

$$u = \mathbf{0.701} \text{ and } u = \mathbf{4.41}.$$

Sometimes it is easier to solve for a multiple angle like 2θ, 3θ, $\frac{1}{2}\theta$, etc., first rather than for θ. When this is done, we must be careful to solve for angles in the desired range. That is, if θ is to lie between $0°$ and $360°$, 2θ must lie between $0°$ and $720°$ and $\frac{1}{2}\theta$ between $0°$ and $180°$.

Example 3. Solve the equation $\sin\theta\cos\theta = -\dfrac{\sqrt{3}}{4}$ for

$$0° \leqq \theta < 360°.$$

Solution: Let $\sin\theta\cos\theta$ be replaced by $\frac{1}{2}\sin 2\theta$.

Then

$$\frac{1}{2}\sin 2\theta = -\frac{\sqrt{3}}{4},$$

and

$$\sin 2\theta = -\frac{\sqrt{3}}{2}.$$

Since θ is in the range $0° \leqq \theta < 360°$, 2θ is in the range

$$0° \leqq 2\theta < 720°.$$

We thus have $\quad 2\theta = 240°,\ 300°,\ 600°,\ 660°,$

and the solutions are $\quad \boldsymbol{\theta = 120°,\ 150°,\ 300°,\ 330°.}$

▶ **EXERCISES**

Solve the following equations for $0° \leqq \theta < 360°$, or for $0 \leqq u < 2\pi$.

1. $\sin 2\theta \cos\theta - \sin\theta = 0.$ **2.** $\sin 2\theta \sin\theta - \cos\theta = 0.$

3. $\cos 2u + \cos u + 1 = 0.$ **4.** $\cos 2u - \sin u - 1 = 0.$

5. $\sin 2\theta + \cos\theta = 0.$ **6.** $\sin 2\theta - \sin\theta = 0.$

7. $2\cos^2 u - \sin u - 1 = 0.$ **8.** $3\sin u - 2\cos^2 u = 0.$

9. $\sin^2\theta + 2\cos\theta + 1 = 0.$ **10.** $2\sin\theta = \tan\theta.$

11. $\cos 2u + 2\cos u + 1 = 0.$ **12.** $\tan^2 u - 2\sec^2 u + 5 = 0.$

13. $2\sin\theta - 3\cot\theta = 0.$ **14.** $\sec^2\theta - 4\tan\theta = 0.$

15. $\sin^2 u - \cos^2 u = 0$.

16. $\cos u \sin 2u + 3 \sin^2 u - 3 \sin u = 0$.

17. $\cos \theta - \sin^2 \theta - 1 = 0$.   **18.** $3 \sin \theta - \cos^2 \theta + 3 = 0$.

19. $\cos^2 u + 4 \sin u - 4 = 0$.   **20.** $3 \cos u - \sin^2 u - 3 = 0$.

21. $\cos^2 \theta - \sin^2 \theta = \frac{1}{2}$.   **22.** $\cos^2 \theta - \sin^2 \theta = -\frac{1}{2}$.

23. $\cos 2u \sec u + \sec u + 1 = 0$.

24. $\cos 2u = \cos^2 u$.   **25.** $4 \sin \theta \cos \theta = 2$.

26. $\sin^2 3\theta = \frac{1}{2}$.   **27.** $\cos \frac{1}{2} u = 1 + \cos u$.

28. $4 \cos u + 3 \sin u = 5$.   **29.** $\sin \theta + \cos \theta = \sqrt{2}$.

30. $\sin \theta + 2 \cos \theta = 1$.

11-4. EQUATIONS OF THE FORM $a \sin \theta + b \cos \theta = c$

Certain types of trigonometric equations may be solved by special methods. The equation

(11-4-1) $a \sin \theta + b \cos \theta = c,$

where a, b, and c are *nonzero* constants and $c \leq \sqrt{a^2 + b^2}$, may be solved by a method similar to the problem of adding a sine and a cosine function as in the example of Art. 7-3. If $c = 0$, the equation reduces to the form $\tan \theta = -b/a$.

Let $a = r \cos \alpha$ and $b = r \sin \alpha,$

where r and α are constants with $r > 0$.

Equation 11-4-1 then becomes

$$r \cos \alpha \sin \theta + r \sin \alpha \cos \theta = c.$$

This may be rewritten as

$$r (\sin \theta \cos \alpha + \cos \theta \sin \alpha) = c.$$

Recalling that $\sin (\theta + \alpha) \equiv \sin \theta \cos \alpha + \cos \theta \sin \alpha$, we immediately have

$$r \sin (\theta + \alpha) = c,$$

from which we obtain $\sin (\theta + \alpha) = \dfrac{c}{r},$

where r and α may be determined from the given relations

$$a = r \cos \alpha \quad \text{and} \quad b = r \sin \alpha.$$

This method of solution will be illustrated in the following example.

Example. Solve the equation $-2 \sin \theta + 3 \cos \theta = 1$ for

$$0° \leq \theta < 360°.$$

Solution: The solution will be of the form

$$\sin (\theta + \alpha) = \frac{c}{r}.$$

From the relations $-2 = r \cos \alpha$ and $3 = r \sin \alpha$, we may sketch (Fig. 11-4-1) angle α in standard position and find the values of r and α by using the tables or slide rule to solve a right triangle with two legs given. We thus find $r = 3.61$ and $\alpha = 123°40'$.

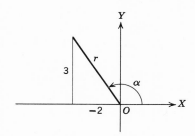

Figure 11-4-1

Hence $\qquad \sin (\theta + 123°40') = \dfrac{1}{3.61} = 0.277,$

and $\qquad \theta + 123°40' = 16°05'$ and $163°55'.$

Thus $\qquad\qquad \theta = -107°35'$ and $40°15'.$

Since θ was to be positive, we have $\boldsymbol{\theta = 40°15'}$ and $\boldsymbol{252°25'}$.

▶ **EXERCISES**

Solve the following equations for $0° \leq \theta < 360°$.

1. $\sqrt{3} \sin \theta + \cos \theta = 1.$ **2.** $-\sin \theta + \sqrt{3} \cos \theta = 1.$

3. $-\sqrt{3} \sin \theta - \cos \theta = 1.$ **4.** $\sin \theta - \sqrt{3} \cos \theta = 1.$

5. $13 \sin \theta + 3 \cos \theta = 5.$ **6.** $-3 \sin \theta + 13 \cos \theta = 5.$

7. $-15 \cos \theta + 24 \sin \theta = 22.$ **8.** $-8 \sin \theta - 11 \cos \theta = 7.$

9. $7 \sin \theta - 15 \cos \theta = 12.$ **10.** $8 \sin \theta - 5 \cos \theta = 2.$

11. $-5 \sin \theta - 3 \cos \theta = 4.$ **12.** $6 \sin \theta + 10 \cos \theta = -7.$

13. $2.86 \sin \theta - 4.13 \cos \theta = 1.68.$

14. $0.956 \sin \theta + 1.17 \cos \theta = -1.21.$

Solve the following equations for $0 \leqq u < 2\pi.$

15. $2 \sin u + 2 \cos u = \sqrt{2}.$ **16.** $\sqrt{3} \sin u - \cos u = \sqrt{2}.$

17. $\sin u + \sqrt{3} \cos u = 1.$ **18.** $2 \sin u + 5 \cos u = 2.$

19. $3 \cos u - 8 \sin u = 3.$ **20.** $4 \sin u - 15 \cos u = 4.$

Vectors
and Complex Numbers

12-1. VECTORS

In Art. 3-5 we defined a vector as a line segment which has both *magnitude* and *direction*, where the magnitude is represented by the length of the line segment and its direction is indicated by an arrow at one end of the line segment. Here, we shall briefly discuss some properties of plane vectors, i.e. vectors which lie in the same plane.

In this book we shall denote vectors by drawing an arrow above a letter; thus $\vec{v}$ denotes a vector and is read "**the vector v**." Since a vector is determined by a magnitude and a direction, we can denote a vector by a length and an angle. The symbol $[r, \boldsymbol{\theta}]$ will denote the *polar* form of a vector; r represents the *length* and θ the *direction*; r is always considered to be *positive*; θ is an angle measured from the positive X-direction. Figure 12-1-1 shows several vectors.

Consider the directed line segment AB (Fig. 12-1-2). Drop perpendiculars from A and B to line L meeting L at M and N. The

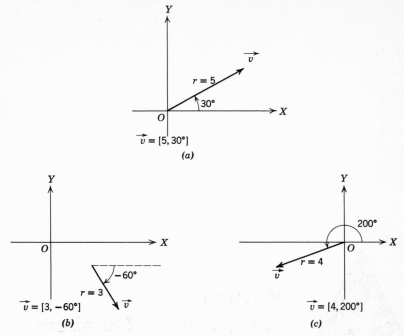

$$\overrightarrow{v} = [5, 30°]$$

(a)

$$\overrightarrow{v} = [3, -60°]$$

(b)

$$\overrightarrow{v} = [4, 200°]$$

(c)

Figure 12-1-1

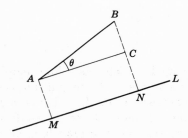

Figure 12-1-2

directed line segment MN is called the *projection of line segment AB on line L*. It is denoted symbolically as **$\text{proj}_L AB$**. Its directed distance is given as $AB \cos \theta$, where θ is the angle between the positive sense of L (or a line parallel to L) and AB.

Thus,   **$\text{proj}_L AB = AB \cos \theta.$**

The projections of $\overrightarrow{v}$, on the X- and Y-axes are called the *rect-*

angular components of the vector and are denoted as $\vec{v}_x$ and $\vec{v}_y$. The *numbers* v_x and v_y are called the *scalar components* of $\vec{v}$ and are given by the formulas

(12-1-1) $$v_x = v \cos \theta,$$

(12-1-2) $$v_y = v \sin \theta.$$

In Fig. 12-1-3, A is called the *initial* point and B is called the *terminal* point of $\overrightarrow{AB}$.

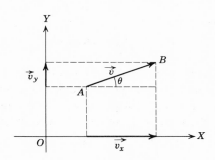

Figure 12-1-3

If v_x and v_y are known, $\vec{v}$ is easily determined by solving a right triangle. Another expression for a vector is $\vec{v} = [v_x, v_y]$. This symbol is called the *rectangular* form of a vector. Notice carefully that **square brackets** around an ordered pair of numbers represent a **vector**, whereas **parentheses** around an ordered pair of numbers represent a **point**. The student should be careful not to confuse these two symbols.

Example 1. Draw $\vec{v} = [5, 120°]$ with the initial point at $(-2, 3)$ and express $\vec{v}$ in rectangular form.

Solution: The vector is shown in Fig. 12-1-4.

$$v_x = 5 \cos 120° = -5 \cos 60° = -\frac{5}{2},$$

$$v_y = 5 \sin 120° = 5 \sin 60° = \frac{5\sqrt{3}}{2}.$$

Thus $$\vec{v} = \left[-\frac{5}{2}, \frac{5\sqrt{3}}{2}\right].$$

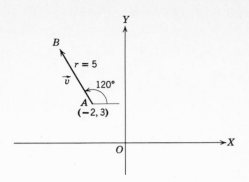

Figure 12-1-4

Example 2. Draw $\vec{v} = [-2, -3]$ and express it in polar form.

Solution: The initial point is not specified; for convenience let it be the origin (Fig. 12-1-5). Draw $v_x = 2$ units in the *negative X-*direction, and then $v_y = 3$ units in the *negative Y-*direction. Draw $\overrightarrow{OP}$.

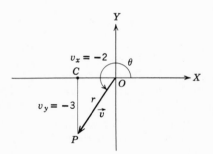

Figure 12-1-5

Solve the right triangle OCP to find $r = 3.6$ and $\measuredangle COP = 56.3°$. Thus $\theta = 180° + \measuredangle COP = 236.3°$ and $\vec{v} = [\mathbf{3.6}, \quad \mathbf{236.3°}]$.

To deal with vectors algebraically a few definitions are needed.

Definition 1: *Two vectors are equal if and only if their scalar components are equal. Thus if* $\vec{u} = [u_x, u_y]$ *and* $\vec{v} = [v_x, v_y]$, $\vec{u} = \vec{v}$ if and only if $u_x = v_x$ and $u_y = v_y$.

Definition 2: *The sum of two vectors is a vector whose scalar com-*

ponents are equal to the sum of the respective scalar components of the two vectors. Thus if $\vec{u} = [u_x, u_y]$ and $\vec{v} = [v_x, v_y]$, then

$$\vec{u} + \vec{v} = [u_x + v_x, u_y + v_y].$$

Definition 3: *The product of a constant and a vector is a vector whose scalar components are multiplied by the constant.* Thus if $\vec{v} = [v_x, v_y]$ and k is a constant, then

$$k\vec{v} = k[v_x, v_y] = [kv_x, kv_y].$$

Definition 4: *The difference of two vectors is a vector whose scalar components are equal to the difference of the respective scalar components of the two vectors.* Thus if $\vec{u} = [u_x, u_y]$ and $\vec{v} = [v_x, v_y]$, then

$$\vec{u} - \vec{v} = [u_x - v_x, u_y - v_y].$$

Definition 5: *The scalar product of two vectors is a number equal to the sum of the products of the respective scalar components of the two vectors.* It is also called the *dot* product and is represented by the symbol $\vec{u} \cdot \vec{v}$. If $\vec{u} = [u_x, u_y]$ and $\vec{v} = [v_x, v_y]$, then

$$\vec{u} \cdot \vec{v} = u_x v_x + u_y v_y.$$

Definition 6: *If $\vec{u} = [u_x, u_y]$ and $\vec{v} = [v_x, v_y]$, then the alternating product of two vectors is a number equal to $u_x v_y - v_x u_y$.* It is called the *bar* product by some writers* and is denoted by the symbol $\vec{u} \mid \vec{v}$. Thus

$$\vec{u} \mid \vec{v} = u_x v_y - v_x u_y.$$

Example 3. Given $\vec{u} = [-1, 3]$, $\vec{v} = [4, -5]$, find: (a) $\vec{u} + \vec{v}$, (b) $7\vec{u}$, (c) $\vec{u} - \vec{v}$, (d) $\vec{u} \cdot \vec{v}$, (e) $\vec{u} \mid \vec{v}$.

Solution: Apply the definitions:

$$(a) \quad \vec{u} + \vec{v} = [-1 + 4, 3 - 5],$$
$$\vec{u} + \vec{v} = [\mathbf{3, -2}].$$
$$(b) \quad 7\vec{u} = 7[-1, 3],$$
$$7\vec{u} = [\mathbf{-7, 21}].$$

---

* See *Analytic Geometry* by W. K. Morrill, published by International Textbook Co.

(c) $\vec{u} - \vec{v} = [-1 - 4,\ 3 - (-5)]$,

$\vec{u} - \vec{v} = [-5,\ 8]$.

(d) $\vec{u} \cdot \vec{v} = (-1)(4) + (3)(-5)$,

$\vec{u} \cdot \vec{v} = -4 - 15$,

$\vec{u} \cdot \vec{v} = -19$.

(e) $\vec{u} \mid \vec{v} = (-1)(-5) - (3)(4)$,

$\vec{u} \mid \vec{v} = 5 - 12$,

$\vec{u} \mid \vec{v} = -7$.

Example 4. Show that $\vec{u} \cdot \vec{v} = uv \cos \theta$, where θ is the angle between $\vec{u}$ and $\vec{v}$.

Solution: Let $\vec{u} = [u,\ \alpha]$ and $\vec{v} = [v,\ \beta]$ (Fig. 12-1-6) so that $u_x = u \cos \alpha$, $u_y = u \sin \alpha$, $v_x = v \cos \beta$, and $v_y = v \sin \beta$.

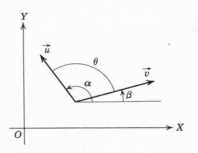

Figure 12-1-6

Then $\vec{u} \cdot \vec{v} = u_x v_x + u_y v_y$,

$= (u \cos \alpha)(v \cos \beta) + (u \sin \alpha)(v \sin \beta)$,

$= uv(\cos \alpha \cos \beta + \sin \alpha \sin \beta)$,

$= uv \cos (\alpha - \beta)$.

Since $(\alpha - \beta)$ or $(\beta - \alpha)$ is equal to θ, we have

$$\vec{u} \cdot \vec{v} = uv \cos \theta.$$

As an immediate consequence of Example 4, we see that if $\vec{u} \perp \vec{v}$, then $\cos \theta = 0$, and $\vec{u} \cdot \vec{v} = 0$. That is, if two vectors are *perpendicular, their dot product is zero*. The converse is also true for two nonzero vectors. That is, if the dot product of two nonzero vectors is zero, then the vectors are perpendicular.

▶ **EXERCISES**

1. Write the following vectors in rectangular form. Draw each vector.

(a) $[5, 45°]$.   (b) $[2, 270°]$.   (c) $[3, 135°]$.
(d) $[5, 200°]$.   (e) $[2, 310°]$.

2. Write the following vectors in polar form. Draw each vector.

(a) $[0, 5]$.   (b) $[12, 5]$.   (c) $[-7, 24]$.
(d) $[-3, -1]$.   (e) $[2, -3]$.   (f) $[16.7, 22.1]$.
(g) $[-72.3, 50.5]$.   (h) $[-17.7, -9.8]$.   (i) $[2.62, -10.7]$.

3. Show that in general for $\vec{v} = [v_x, v_y] = [v, \theta]$,

$$v^2 = v_x{}^2 + v_y{}^2, \quad \text{and} \quad \tan \theta = \frac{v_y}{v_x}.$$

4. Perform the following operations. Express the answer as a single vector in rectangular form.

(a) $[4, 3] + [-3, 7]$.   (b) $3[2, -3]$.
(c) $[-5, -1] - [0, 5]$.   (d) $5[6, -3] - 2[-1, 3]$.
(e) $3[2, -1] + [2, 30°]$.   (f) $[-1, 1] + 3[1, 60°]$.
(g) $3[2.5, -3.2] - 2[3, 90°]$.
(h) $[3, 100°] - 2[5, 40°] + 3[-2, 7]$.

5. Show that two vectors $\vec{u}$ and $\vec{v}$ can be added graphically by placing the initial point of the second vector at the terminal point of the first vector and drawing the resultant vector from the initial point of the first vector to the terminal point of the second vector. Also show that $\vec{u} + \vec{v}$ is the diagonal of a parallelogram which has $\vec{u}$ and $\vec{v}$ as adjacent sides. (Hint: Let $\vec{w} = \vec{u} + \vec{v}$. Show that $w_x = u_x + v_x$ and $w_y = u_y + v_y$.)

6. Find the scalar product of the following pairs of vectors:

(a) $[2, 3], [4, -2]$.   (b) $[12, -5], [-24, -7]$.
(c) $[3, 45°], [2, 315°]$.   (d) $[6, 270°], [3, 0°]$.
(e) $[1, 3], [2, 30°]$.   (f) $[5, 100°], [-3, 1]$.
(g) $[4, -2], [1, 2]$.   (h) $[5, 50°], [3, -40°]$.

7. Find the alternating product of the pairs of vectors of problem 6.

8. Show that the following pairs of vectors are perpendicular:

(a) $[1, 3], [-3, 1]$.   (b) $[-2, 5], [5, 2]$.
(c) $[-3, -4], [-8, 6]$.   (d) $[a, b], [b, -a]$.

9. Find the angle between the pairs of vectors:

(a) [2, 3], [4, − 2].   (b) [1, − 3], [2, 5].
(c) [6, − 1], [2, − 5].   (d) [1, 8], [− 12, − 9].

10. An airplane is headed on course 100° with an airspeed of 300 mph. If the wind is blowing from the southwest at 20 mph, find the true course of the plane and its groundspeed. (Hint: Find the vector sum of the air velocity of the plane and the velocity of the wind.)

11. In physics it is shown that a resultant force acting on a body is the vector sum of all the forces acting on the body. Find the resultant force of the forces acting on each body shown in Fig. 12-1-7.

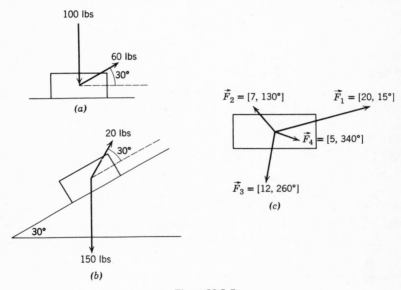

Figure 12-1-7

12. The alternating product of two vectors may be expressed as $\vec{u} \mid \vec{v} = uv \sin \theta$ where θ is the angle between the two vectors measured positively from $\vec{u}$ to $\vec{v}$. Show that this is true. (Hint: Let $\vec{u} = [u, \alpha]$ and $\vec{v} = [v, \beta]$ and use the definition of the alternating product.)

13. The area of a triangle formed with two vectors $\vec{u}$ and $\vec{v}$ as adjacent sides (Fig. 12-1-8) is given as $A = \frac{1}{2}\vec{u} \mid \vec{v}$, or $A = \frac{1}{2} uv \sin \theta$ (see problem 12). Show that this is true.

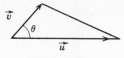

Figure 12-1-8

14. Using the formula of problem 13, find the area of the triangle formed with the following pairs of vectors as adjacent sides:

(a) [2, 3], [4, − 2].   (b) [− 24, − 7], [12, − 5].
(c) [15, 5], [− 2, 3].   (d) [− 5, 4], [− 8, 1].

15. Any point $P(x, y)$ in the rectangular coordinate system may be considered as the terminal point of a vector from the origin to point $P(x, y)$ (Fig. 12-1-9). Such a vector is called the **position vector** of point P.

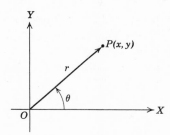

Figure 12-1-9

Locate the points whose position vectors are:

(a) [3, 30°].   (b) [5, − 150°].   (c) [2, 100°].   (d) [4, 320°].

12-2. COMPLEX NUMBERS

In an algebra course the student has seen the symbol $a + bi$. This symbol is called a *complex number* if a and b are real numbers and i has the property $i^2 = -1$. A complex number consists of two parts: the real part a and the imaginary part b. If $a \neq 0$ and $b = 0$, the complex number reduces to the real number a. If $a = 0$ and $b \neq 0$, the complex number reduces to a *pure imaginary* number. If two complex numbers differ only in the signs of their imaginary parts, they are said to be *conjugate*. For example, $3 - 2i$ and $3 + 2i$ are conjugate numbers. Each is the conjugate of the other. A complex number written in the form $a + bi$ is said to be in *rectangular form*.

Example 1. Write the numbers (a) 4 and (b) $-3i$ as complex numbers in rectangular form.

Solution: (a) $4 = 4 + 0i$;   (b) $-3i = 0 - 3i.$

Definition 1: Two complex numbers are equal if and only if their real parts are equal and their imaginary parts are equal.

Example 2. $a + bi = c + di$, if $a = c$ and $b =$ d.
This implies that $a + bi = 0$, if and only if $a = 0$ and $b = 0.$

Definition 2: If a, b, c, and d are real
$$(a + bi) + (c + di) = (a + c) + (b + d)i.$$

Example 3. (a) $(2 + 3i) + (-5 + 4i) = -3 + 7i.$
(b) $(3 - 4i) - (-1 - i) = 4 - 3i.$

Multiplication and division of two complex numbers in rectangular form may be treated by the rules of ordinary algebra if i^2 is always replaced by -1.   However, multiplication and division of two complex numbers are more conveniently treated if they are written in the polar form which is discussed in the next article.

▶ **EXERCISES**

1. Show that $i^3 = -i$, $i^4 = +1$, $i^6 = -1$.   Show that any integral power of i may be written in one of the four forms i, $-i$, 1, -1.

2. Perform the indicated operations and write the answer in the form $a + bi$.

(a) $(3 + 2i) + (-1 + 5i)$.
(b) $(-4 - 3i) + (7 - 2i)$.
(c) $(2 + 2i) + (-5 - 3i) + (4 + 7i)$.
(d) $(-3 + i) - (-2 + 3i)$.
(e) $(2 - i) - (5 - 3i) - (-1 - i)$.
(f) $(5 + 3i)(-2 - i)$.
(g) $(-3 + i)(i)(1 - 2i)$.
(h) $(1 + \sqrt{-4})(2 + \sqrt{-9})$.   (Hint: $\sqrt{-P} = i\sqrt{P}$, for $P > 0$.)
(i) $(2 - \sqrt{-7})(-3 + \sqrt{-2})$.
(j) $\dfrac{3 + 7i}{2 - 5i}.$ (Hint: Multiply numerator and denominator by the conjugate of the denominator.)
(k) $\dfrac{2 - 3i}{1 + i}.$ (l) $\dfrac{1 - \sqrt{-9}}{2 + \sqrt{-4}}.$ (m) $\dfrac{3 + \sqrt{-25}}{\sqrt{-16}}.$

3. Solve the following for x and y, where x and y are real.

(a) $3x + 16i = 6 - yi$. (b) $-5 - 11i = x + 3yi$.
(c) $(2x + 4) + (-y - 3)i = 0$. (d) $x - 2i + 3 + yi = 0$.

12-3. POLAR FORM OF COMPLEX NUMBERS

A complex number can be given a graphical interpretation if we let the number $a + bi$ or $a + ib$ be represented by the point P whose coordinates are (a, b). See Fig. 12-3-1. For this representation the *X-axis* is called the *axis of real numbers* and the *Y-axis* is called the *axis of imaginary numbers*. In Fig. 12-3-1 points A and B represent the complex numbers $3 + 2i$ and $-3i$, respectively.

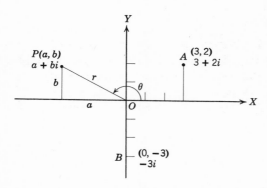

Figure 12-3-1

Let us join the origin to the point P by a straight line OP of length r, and let the **angle** between the positive X-axis and OP be denoted as θ. See Fig. 12-3-1. Then we have $a = r \cos \theta$ and $b = r \sin \theta$, and we may write the complex number $a + ib$ as

(12-3-1) $a + ib = r \cos \theta + ir \sin \theta = r (\cos \theta + i \sin \theta)$.

The right-hand side of equation 12-3-1 is called the **polar form** of the complex number. The number, r, of the polar form is called the *absolute value* or the *modulus* of the complex number, and is *defined* to be *positive*. The angle θ is called the *argument* or the *amplitude*. The values of r and θ may be found from the relations

(12-3-2) $r = \sqrt{a^2 + b^2}$ and $\tan \theta = \dfrac{b}{a}$.

The amplitude may be any angle whose initial side is the positive X-axis and whose terminal side coincides with OP. This, of course, implies that the amplitude is not unique. Usually θ is taken in the range $0° \leq \theta < 360°$.

Theorem: *Two complex numbers in polar form are equal if their moduli are equal* and *if their arguments are equal or differ by an integral multiple of 360°.*

The student may prove this theorem by using Definition 1 in Art. 12-2.

To write the number $a + bi$ in polar form:

1. Plot the point P (a, b) representing $a + bi$.

2. Draw the modulus and a perpendicular from P to the X-axis.

3. Solve the resulting right triangle (usually easiest by means of the slide rule).

4. Find θ by noticing the proper quadrant.

Example 1. Write $-7 + 11i$ in polar form.

Solution: Plot the point P $(-7, 11)$ and construct the right triangle as shown in Fig. 12-3-2. Solving the right triangle, we find $\alpha = 57.5°$ and $r = 13$. Noticing that θ is in QII, we find $\theta = 122.5°$. Thus, we have $-7 + 11i = 13$ **(cos 122.5° + i sin 122.5°)**.

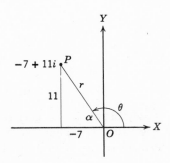

Figure 12-3-2

To write r ($cos\ \theta + i\ sin\ \theta$) in *rectangular form*, **multiply** through by r and evaluate.

Example 2. Write $3.5(\cos 212° + i \sin 212°)$ in rectangular form.

Solution: $3.5(\cos 212° + i \sin 212°) = 3.5 \cos 212° + i(3.5 \sin 212°)$. Evaluating, we find

$$3.5(\cos 212° + i\ \sin 212°) = -2.97 - 1.85i.$$

A vector whose initial point is at the origin may be used to represent a complex number if we associate the real part of the complex number with the X-component of the vector and the imaginary part with the Y-component of the vector. This vector may be called the *position vector* of the complex number (see problem 15, page 185). If we denote the position vector by $\vec{r}$, its rectangular form is $[a, b]$ and its polar form is $[r, \theta]$. See Fig. 12-3-3.

For example, the position vector for the complex number $-3 + 2i$ is $\vec{r} = [-3, 2]$.

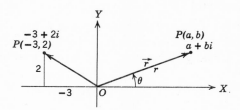

Figure 12-3-3

Let $r_1 = [a, b]$ be the position vector for the complex number $a + bi$, and $\vec{r_2} = [c, d]$ be the position vector for the complex number $c + di$; then $\vec{r_1} + \vec{r_2} = [a + c, b + d]$.

▶ **EXERCISES**

1. Represent the complex numbers as a point in the rectangular coordinate system and write them in polar form.

(a) $\sqrt{3} + i$.   (b) $-\sqrt{3} + i$.   (c) $1 - i$.

(d) $-1 + i$.   (e) $2i$.   (f) $-5i$.

(g) 4.   (h) -8.   (i) $-7 - 11i$.

(j) $-8 + 11i$.   (k) $-14.1 - 5.13i$.   (l) $6.92 - 4i$.

(m) $10 + 17.3i$.   (n) $3 - 5i$.   (o) $-1.025 + 2.82i$.

2. Express the following in rectangular form.

(a) $5(\cos 30° + i \sin 30°)$.   (b) $\cos 0° + i \sin 0°$.

(c) $(\cos 240° + i \sin 240°)$.   (d) $2(\cos 45° + i \sin 45°)$.

(e) $2(\cos 90° + i \sin 90°)$.   (f) $4(\cos (-30°) + i \sin (-30°))$.

(g) $3(\cos 180° + i \sin 180°)$.

(h) $3(\cos (-240°) + i \sin (-240°))$.

(i) $13(\cos 57.5° + i \sin 57.5°)$.   (j) $3(\cos 110° + i \sin 110°)$.

(*k*) 13(cos 302.5° + *i* sin 302.5°).

(*l*) 13(cos 67.4° + *i* sin 67.4°).   (*m*) 15(cos 200° + *i* sin 200°).

(*n*) 89(cos 424° + *i* sin 424°).

(*o*) 65(cos 120.5° + *i* sin 120.5°).

(*p*) 5(cos 162.3° + *i* sin 162.3°).

3. Add the following complex numbers.

(*a*) 2(cos 60° + *i* sin 60°) + 3(cos 30° + *i* sin 30°).

(*b*) 5(cos 200° + *i* sin 200°) + 4(cos 15° + *i* sin 15°).

4. Let $\vec{r}_1$ and $\vec{r}_2$ be the position vectors of the complex numbers $a + bi$ and $c + di$, respectively. Form a parallelogram with $\vec{r}_1$ and $\vec{r}_2$ as adjacent sides. Show that the diagonal (from O) of the parallelogram represents the sum of the complex numbers $a + bi$ and $c + di$.

5. Show graphically the sum of the following complex numbers:

(*a*) $(2 + i) + (-1 + 2i)$.   (*b*) $(-7 - 11i) + (8 + 7i)$.

(*c*) $(2i) + (3i)$.   (*d*) $(10 - 6i) + (-3 + 2i)$.

12-4. MULTIPLICATION, INTEGRAL POWERS, AND DIVISION OF COMPLEX NUMBERS

For convenience in the following we may simplify the notation $r(\cos\theta + i\sin\theta)$ by using **r cis θ**.

Multiplication: The product of two complex numbers in polar form is a complex number in polar form whose modulus is the product of the moduli and whose amplitude is the sum of the amplitudes.   That is,

$$r_1 \text{ cis } \theta_1 \cdot r_2 \text{ cis } \theta_2 = r_1 r_2 \text{ cis }(\theta_1 + \theta_2).$$

To show this consider the following:

$$r_1 \text{ cis } \theta_1 \cdot r_2 \text{ cis } \theta_2 = r_1 r_2 \text{ cis } \theta_1 \cdot \text{cis } \theta_2,$$
$$= r_1 r_2(\cos\theta_1 + i\sin\theta_1)(\cos\theta_2 + i\sin\theta_2).$$

Expanding the right-hand side, we obtain

$$r_1 r_2(\cos\theta_1\cos\theta_2 + i\cos\theta_1\sin\theta_2 + i\sin\theta_1\cos\theta_2 + i^2\sin\theta_1\sin\theta_2)$$

which combines to

$$r_1 r_2[(\cos\theta_1\cos\theta_2 - \sin\theta_1\sin\theta_2) + i(\cos\theta_1\sin\theta_2 + \sin\theta_1\cos\theta_2)].$$

Applying the appropriate addition formulas of trigonometry to the above expression, we have

$$r_1 \text{ cis } \theta_1 \cdot r_2 \text{ cis } \theta_2 = r_1 r_2 [\cos(\theta_1 + \theta_2) + i\sin(\theta_1 + \theta_2)],$$

which may be written as

(12-4-1) $r_1 \text{ cis } \theta_1 \cdot r_2 \text{ cis } \theta_2 = r_1 r_2 \text{ cis } (\theta_1 + \theta_2)$.

This process may be extended to the product of any number of complex numbers. Thus the product of three complex numbers is

$$r_1 \text{ cis } \theta_1 \cdot r_2 \text{ cis } \theta_2 \cdot r_3 \text{ cis } \theta_3 = r_1 \, r_2 \, r_3 \text{ cis } (\theta_1 + \theta_2 + \theta_3).$$

Example 1. $3 \text{ cis } 15° \cdot 2 \text{ cis } 100° = 6 \text{ cis } 115°$.

Integral Powers: Since the integral power of a number is the repeated product of the number, we have

(12-4-2) $(r \text{ cis } \theta)^n = r^n \text{ cis } n\theta$,   for n a positive integer.

This relation is also true for real values of n, but the proof will not be given in this book. This is known as *De Moivre's Theorem*.

Example 2. $(2 \text{ cis } 30°)^4 = 2^4 \text{ cis } (4 \cdot 30°) = 16 \text{ cis } 120°$.

Division: *The quotient of two complex numbers in polar form is a complex number in polar form whose modulus is the modulus of the numerator divided by the modulus of the denominator and whose amplitude is the amplitude of the numerator minus the amplitude of the denominator.* That is,

$$\frac{r_1 \text{ cis } \theta_1}{r_2 \text{ cis } \theta_2} = \frac{r_1}{r_2} \text{ cis } (\theta_1 - \theta_2).$$

To show this consider the fraction

$$\frac{r_1 \text{ cis } \theta_1}{r_2 \text{ cis } \theta_2}, \quad (r_2 \text{ cis } \theta_2 \neq 0).$$

If we multiply both numerator and denominator by $r_2 \text{ cis}(-\theta_2)$, we have

$$\frac{r_1 \text{ cis } \theta_1}{r_2 \text{ cis } \theta_2} = \frac{r_1 \text{ cis } \theta_1}{r_2 \text{ cis } \theta_2} \cdot \frac{r_2 \text{ cis } (-\theta_2)}{r_2 \text{ cis } (-\theta_2)} = \frac{r_1 \, r_2 \text{ cis } (\theta_1 - \theta_2)}{r_2 \, r_2 \text{ cis } 0}.$$

Since $\text{cis } 0 = 1$, we obtain

(12-4-3) $\dfrac{r_1 \text{ cis } \theta_1}{r_2 \text{ cis } \theta_2} = \dfrac{r_1}{r_2} \text{ cis } (\theta_1 - \theta_2), \quad (r_2 \text{ cis } \theta_2 \neq 0)$.

Example 3. $\dfrac{6 \text{ cis } 80°}{2 \text{ cis } 35°} = 3 \text{ cis } 45°$.

▶ **EXERCISES**

1. Perform the indicated operations:

(a) $3 \operatorname{cis} 30° \cdot 2 \operatorname{cis} 30°$. (b) $4 \operatorname{cis} 10° \cdot 5 \operatorname{cis} 140°$.

(c) $2 \operatorname{cis} 225° \cdot 3 \operatorname{cis} 180°$.

(d) $4 \operatorname{cis} 120° \cdot 2 \operatorname{cis} 15° \cdot 3 \operatorname{cis} 135°$.

(e) $(2 \operatorname{cis} 45°)^2$. (f) $(3 \operatorname{cis} 130°)^3$.

(g) $(2 \operatorname{cis} 225°)^2$. (h) $(4 \operatorname{cis} 25°)^4$.

(i) $\dfrac{6 \operatorname{cis} 150°}{2 \operatorname{cis} 30°}$. (j) $\dfrac{15 \operatorname{cis} 45°}{5 \operatorname{cis} 135°}$.

(k) $\dfrac{12 \operatorname{cis} (-30°)}{24 \operatorname{cis} (-150°)}$. (l) $\dfrac{36 \operatorname{cis} 450°}{3 \operatorname{cis} 120°}$.

2. Perform the indicated operations by making use of the polar form. The use of the slide rule is recommended.

(a) $(3 + 4i)(5 + 12i)$. (b) $(-8 + 15i)(24 - 7i)$.

(c) $(4 + 3i)(-4 - 3i)$. (d) $(8 + 5i)(3 - 2i)(-2 - 3i)$.

(e) $(3 + 2i)^2$. (f) $(-1.732 + i)^3$.

(g) $(-4 - 3i)^3$. (h) $(4 - 3i)^4$.

(i) $\dfrac{6.4 - 3.5i}{-3.5 + 6.4i}$. (j) $\dfrac{-1 + 3i}{2 - 4i}$.

(k) $\dfrac{3 + 2i}{1 + 2i}$. (l) $\dfrac{(7 + 4i)(-2 + 2i)}{8 + 15i}$.

3. Obtain an expression for $\cos 2\theta$ and $\sin 2\theta$ in terms of θ by making use of De Moivre's Theorem. (Hint: Use $(\operatorname{cis} \theta)^2 \equiv \operatorname{cis} 2\theta$. Expand the left-hand side by squaring. Then consider the equality of two complex numbers.)

4. Obtain an expression for $\cos 3\theta$ and $\sin 3\theta$ in terms of θ.

5. Prove the identity $\sin \theta \equiv \dfrac{i}{2}[\operatorname{cis}(-\theta) - \operatorname{cis} \theta]$.

12-5. ROOTS OF COMPLEX NUMBERS

Let us recall that the amplitude of a complex number is not unique. That is, if a complex number can be represented by $r \operatorname{cis} \theta$ it can also be represented by $r \operatorname{cis} (\theta + n \cdot 360°)$ where n is any integer.

We shall show the process of obtaining the roots of complex numbers in the following example.

Example. Find the cube roots of $8i$.

Solution: Write $8i$ in the polar form $8 \text{ cis } 90°$ (Fig. 12-5-1). Assume one of the cube roots to be of the form $r \text{ cis } \theta$, where we are to find the values of r and θ. Using the definition of the nth root of a number, that is, a number which when raised to the nth power produces the given number, we may write

$$(r \text{ cis } \theta)^3 = 8 \text{ cis } 90°.$$

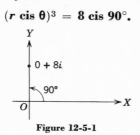

Figure 12-5-1

From De Moivre's Theorem, we have

$$r^3 \text{ cis } 3\theta = 8 \text{ cis } 90°.$$

From the equality of two complex numbers we obtain

$$r^3 = 8, \text{ and } 3\theta = 90° + n \cdot 360°, \ n \text{ an integer.}$$

Thus we find

$$r = 2 \text{ and } \theta = 30° + n \cdot 120°.$$

On letting n have the values 0, 1, 2 we have for

$$n = 0, \quad \theta = 30°,$$
$$n = 1, \quad \theta = 30° + 1 \cdot 120° = 150°,$$
$$n = 2, \quad \theta = 30° + 2 \cdot 120° = 270°.$$

For other integral values of n, we find that θ will be an angle coterminal with one of these three angles. (The student should try a few such values of n.) Hence, these are the only three distinct values of θ and the cube roots are thus

$$2 \text{ cis } 30°, \quad 2 \text{ cis } 150°, \quad \text{and} \quad 2 \text{ cis } 270°;$$

in rectangular form they are

$$\sqrt{3} + i, \quad -\sqrt{3} + i, \quad \text{and} \quad -2i.$$

Theorem: *If $r \text{ cis } \alpha$ is a qth root of a complex number $R \text{ cis } \theta$, then there are exactly q distinct roots of $R \text{ cis } \theta$.*

Proof: If $r \text{ cis } \alpha$ is a qth root, then

$$(r \text{ cis } \alpha)^q = R \text{ cis } \theta.$$

By De Moivre's Theorem, we have

$$r^q \operatorname{cis} q\,\alpha = R \operatorname{cis} \theta,$$

and from the equality of two complex numbers, we find

$$r^q = R, \quad \text{and} \quad q\alpha = \theta + n \cdot 360°, \quad n \text{ an integer,}$$

or $\qquad r = R^{1/q} \quad \text{and} \quad \alpha = \dfrac{\theta}{q} + \dfrac{n \cdot 360°}{q}, \quad n \text{ an integer.}$

By knowing the real q^{th} root of R we know r.

To find α let n take on different integral values. For $n = 0$, $\alpha = \dfrac{\theta}{q}$ and one of the roots is $R^{1/q} \operatorname{cis} \dfrac{\theta}{q}$. For $n = 1$, $\alpha = \dfrac{\theta}{q} + \dfrac{360°}{q}$ and another root is $R^{1/q} \operatorname{cis} \left(\dfrac{\theta}{q} + \dfrac{360°}{q}\right)$. The roots for $n = 0$ and $n = 1$ are two distinct roots of $R \operatorname{cis} \theta$. By letting n take on other integral values from 2 to $q - 1$, we will obtain $q - 2$ more distinct roots of $R \operatorname{cis} \theta$.

Now, if we let $n = q$, we find $\alpha = \dfrac{\theta}{q} + q \cdot \dfrac{360°}{q} = \dfrac{\theta}{q} + 360°$, and we obtain a root $R^{1/q} \operatorname{cis}\left(\dfrac{\theta}{q} + 360°\right) = R^{1/q} \operatorname{cis}\left(\dfrac{\theta}{q}\right)$, which is the same root we found for $n = 0$. Hence there are exactly q distinct q^{th} roots of any complex number $R \operatorname{cis} \theta$.

▶ **EXERCISES**

1. Find the cube roots of the following. Leave the answer in polar form.

(a) 8 cis 120°.   (b) 64 cis 240°.   (c) 64 cis 300°.
(d) 8 cis 150°.   (e) 27 cis 210°.   (f) 125 cis 30°.

2. Find the indicated roots of the following. Write the answer in the form in which the problem is given.

(a) cube roots of $-8i$.   (b) square roots of $7 + 24i$.
(c) square roots of $5 + 12i$.   (d) fourth roots of 81 cis 0°.
(e) cube roots of $-75 + 100i$.   (f) square roots of 169 cis 67.4°.
(g) cube roots of 125 cis 249.4°.   (h) fourth roots of 16 cis 0°.
(i) cube roots of 1.   (j) fourth roots of -1.

3. Find all of the roots of the following equations:

(a) $x^5 - 1 = 0$.   (b) $x^3 + 64 = 0$.   (c) $x^4 = 16$.   (d) $x^3 - 27 = 0$.

Appendix

A-1. THE MIL

The Armed Forces of the United States employ the *mil* as an important unit of angular measure in the adjustment of gunfire. The **mil** is *defined as the measure of an angle whose vertex is at the center of a circle and which intercepts an arc equal in length to 1/6400 of the circumference.*

From the definition of a mil we immediately find that

$$6400 \text{ mils} = 360°,$$

and since we know that 2π radians $= 360°$,

we find that 6400 mils $= 2\pi$ radians,

or **1 mil $=$ 0.000982** radian.

The length of arc S, of a circle of radius r, is given by $S = r\theta$, θ measured in radians.

If the mil is used as the unit of measurement for θ, this formula becomes $\qquad S = 0.000982\ r\theta,$

or approximately $\qquad S = 0.001\ r\theta,$

which may be written as $\quad S = \dfrac{r\theta}{1000},\quad \theta$ in mils.

This last formula tells us that at a distance of **1000 units** an angle of **one mil** intercepts an arc approximately equal to **one unit** in length. It is this fact that makes the mil an important unit for rapid calculation.

Example: How much correction should be applied to a gun firing at a range of 10,000 yds, if it is missing its target by 50 yds?

Solution: Using the formula $S = \dfrac{r}{1000}\ \theta,$

we have $\qquad\qquad 50 = \dfrac{10,000}{1000}\ \theta,$

or $\qquad\qquad\qquad \boldsymbol{\theta = 5\ \text{mils.}}$

▶ **EXERCISES**

1. Show that the following relations exist between degrees, radians, and mils.

(a) $90° = \dfrac{\pi}{2}$ radians $= 1600$ mils.

(b) $1° = 0.01745$ radian $= 17.778$ mils.

(c) 1 radian $= 57°17.75' = 1018.6$ mils.

(d) 1 mil. $= 0.05625° = 0.000982$ radian.

2. Change the following angle measure into mils.

(a) 10°. $\qquad$ (b) 25°. $\qquad$ (c) 120°. $\qquad$ (d) 47°26.5′.
(e) 1.5 radians. $\quad$ (f) 0.6 radian. $\quad$ (g) 0.01 radian. (h) 3.14 radians.

3. Change the following angle measure into degrees and minutes.

(a) 10 mils. $\qquad$ (b) 32 mils. $\qquad$ (c) 100 mils. $\qquad$ (d) 275 mils.
$\qquad\qquad\qquad\qquad$ (e) 2000 mils.

4. Change the following angle measure into radians.

(a) 235 mils. $\qquad$ (b) 520 mils. $\qquad$ (c) 800 mils. $\qquad$ (d) 1000 mils.

5. A wall 2000 yds distant subtends an angle of 5 mils. How high is the wall?

6. Find the length of a building, 5000 ft distant, if it subtends an angle of 10 mils.

7. A ship 325 ft long subtends an angle of 15 mils. How far is it from the observer?

8. A gun has a range of 20,000 yds. If it can be traversed through an angle of 2500 mils, what length of arc can it keep under fire?

9. An antiaircraft battery notes that an airplane is flying at 420 mph in a direction perpendicular to its line of fire. In 5 sec, it is then observed that the plane has flown a distance that subtends an angle of 500 mils. How far is the plane from the antiaircraft battery?

A-2. THE LAW OF TANGENTS

The Law of Tangents may be used to solve an oblique triangle given two sides and the included angle. For a triangle ABC this law is:

(A-2-1)
$$\frac{\tan\frac{1}{2}(A - B)}{\tan\frac{1}{2}(A + B)} = \frac{a - b}{a + b},$$

$$\frac{\tan\frac{1}{2}(A - C)}{\tan\frac{1}{2}(A + C)} = \frac{a - c}{a + c},$$

$$\frac{\tan\frac{1}{2}(B - C)}{\tan\frac{1}{2}(B + C)} = \frac{b - c}{b + c}.$$

The first formula of A-2-1 was derived in problems 4, 5, and 6 on page 141. The other two formulas may be established in a similar manner.

In using the Law of Tangents to solve a triangle given two sides a and b and the included angle C, it is necessary to note that the quantities $a - b$, $a + b$, and $\frac{1}{2}(A + B)$ are easily computed. The latter quantity may be found from noting that $A + B = 180° - C$ for any triangle. Then the quantity $\frac{1}{2}(A - B)$ may be computed. The values of A and B can then be determined by noting that

$$\frac{1}{2}(A + B) + \frac{1}{2}(A - B) = A \quad \text{and} \quad \frac{1}{2}(A + B) - \frac{1}{2}(A - B) = B.$$

The Law of Sines may then be used to find side c.

Note: If $b > a$, then write the Law of Tangents as

$$\frac{\tan\frac{1}{2}(B - A)}{\tan\frac{1}{2}(B + A)} = \frac{b - a}{b + a} \quad \text{to avoid negative quantities.}$$

Example: Solve the triangle ABC given $a = 42.32$, $c = 76.40$, and $B = 32°17'$.

Solution: Sketch the triangle (Fig. A-2-1). Noting that $c > a$, the formulas to be used are

$$\frac{\tan \frac{1}{2}(C - A)}{\tan \frac{1}{2}(C + A)} = \frac{c - a}{c + a}, \quad \text{or}$$

$$\boldsymbol{\tan \tfrac{1}{2}(C - A) = \frac{c - a}{c + a} \tan \tfrac{1}{2}(C + A);}$$

$$\boldsymbol{C + A = 180° - B;}$$

and

$$\frac{b}{\sin B} = \frac{a}{\sin A}, \quad \text{or}$$

$$\boldsymbol{b = a \sin B \csc A.}$$

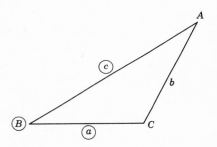

Figure A-2-1

The logarithmic computation follows:

		$\frac{1}{2}(C - A)$	(b)
$c =$	76.40		
$a =$	42.32		$\log a = 1.6265$
$c - a =$	34.08	$\log (c - a) = 1.5325$	
$c + a =$	118.72	$\text{col} (c + a) = 7.9255{-}10$	
$B =$	$32°17'$		$\text{L} \sin B = 9.7276{-}10$
$C + A =$	$147°43'$		
$\frac{1}{2}(C + A) =$	$73°52'$	$\text{L} \tan \frac{1}{2}(C + A) = 10.5387{-}10$	
$\frac{1}{2}(C - A) =$	$44°47'$	$\text{L} \tan \frac{1}{2}(C - A) = 19.9967{-}20$	
$A =$	$\boldsymbol{29°05'}$		$\text{L} \csc A = 10.3133{-}10$
$C =$	$\boldsymbol{118°39'}$		
$b =$	$\boldsymbol{46.49}$		$\log b = 21.6674{-}20$

Check: $A + B + C = 180°01'$. The slight discrepancy is due to the interpolation process.

A-3. TANGENTS OF THE HALF-ANGLES

In problems 9, 10, and 11 on page 152 the formula

$$\tan \frac{A}{2} = \frac{1}{s-a} \sqrt{\frac{(s-a)(s-b)(s-c)}{s}}$$

was derived. In a similar manner, expressions for $\tan (B/2)$ and $\tan (C/2)$ could be derived. The formulas for the tangents of the half-angles are:

$$\tan \frac{A}{2} = \frac{r}{(s-a)}, \quad \tan \frac{B}{2} = \frac{r}{(s-b)}, \quad \tan \frac{C}{2} = \frac{r}{(s-c)},$$

where $r = \sqrt{\dfrac{(s-a)(s-b)(s-c)}{s}}$ and $s = \frac{1}{2}(a+b+c)$.

Their use in solving a triangle with three sides known is shown in the following example.

Example: Solve the triangle ABC where $a = 46.19$, $b = 71.43$ and $c = 61.42$.

Solution: Sketch the triangle (Fig. A-3-1). Write the formulas

$$\tan \frac{A}{2} = \frac{r}{(s-a)}, \quad \tan \frac{B}{2} = \frac{r}{(s-b)}, \quad \tan \frac{C}{2} = \frac{r}{(s-c)},$$

$$r = \sqrt{\frac{(s-a)(s-b)(s-c)}{s}}, \quad s = \frac{1}{2}(a+b+c).$$

Set up the log scheme and evaluate. (See page 200.)

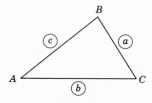

Figure A-3-1

Logarithmic solution for the example on page 199.

$a =$ 46.19
$b =$ 71.43
$c =$ 61.42
$2s =$ 179.04

(r)

$s =$ 89.52 col s = 8.0481–10
$s - a =$ 43.33 log $(s - a)$ = 1.6368
$s - b =$ 18.09 log $(s - b)$ = 1.2575
$s - c =$ 28.10 log $(s - c)$ = 1.4487
$r =$ 15.69 2 log r = 12.3911–10

($\frac{1}{2}A$)

col $(s - a)$ = 8.3632–10
log r = 1.1956
L tan $\frac{1}{2}A$ = 9.5588–10

($\frac{1}{2}B$)

col $(s - b)$ = 8.7425–10
log r = 1.1956
L tan $\frac{1}{2}B$ = 9.9381–10

($\frac{1}{2}C$)

col $(s - c)$ = 8.5513–10
log r = 1.1956
L tan $\frac{1}{2}C$ = 9.7469–10

$\frac{1}{2}A =$ 19°54'
$\frac{1}{2}B =$ 40°56'
$\frac{1}{2}C =$ 29°11'

$A =$	**39°48'**
$B =$	**81°52'**
$C =$	**58°22'**

CHECK: $A + B + C =$ 180°02'.

TABLES

TABLE I

Four-Place Values of Trigonometric Functions
Angle θ in Degrees and Radians

Angle θ									
Degrees	Radians	sin θ	csc θ	tan θ	cot θ	sec θ	cos θ		
0° 00′	.0000	.0000	No value	.0000	No value	1.000	1.0000	1.5708	90° 00′
10	029	029	343.8	029	343.8	000	000	679	50
20	058	058	171.9	058	171.9	000	000	650	40
30	.0087	.0087	114.6	.0087	114.6	1.000	1.0000	1.5621	30
40	116	116	85.95	116	85.94	000	.9999	592	20
50	145	145	68.76	145	68.75	000	999	563	10
1° 00′	.0175	.0175	57.30	.0175	57.29	1.000	.9998	1.5533	89° 00′
10	204	204	49.11	204	49.10	000	998	504	50
20	233	233	42.98	233	42.96	000	997	475	40
30	.0262	.0262	38.20	.0262	38.19	1.000	.9997	1.5446	30
40	291	291	34.38	291	34.37	000	996	417	20
50	320	320	31.26	320	31.24	001	995	388	10
2° 00′	.0349	.0349	28.65	.0349	28.64	1.001	.9994	1.5359	88° 00′
10	378	378	26.45	378	26.43	001	993	330	50
20	407	407	24.56	407	24.54	001	992	301	40
30	.0436	.0436	22.93	.0437	22.90	1.001	.9990	1.5272	30
40	465	465	21.49	466	21.47	001	989	243	20
50	495	494	20.23	495	20.21	001	988	213	10
3° 00′	.0524	.0523	19.11	.0524	19.08	1.001	.9986	1.5184	87° 00′
10	553	552	18.10	553	18.07	002	985	155	50
20	582	581	17.20	582	17.17	002	983	126	40
30	.0611	.0610	16.38	.0612	16.35	1.002	.9981	1.5097	30
40	640	640	15.64	641	15.60	002	980	068	20
50	669	669	14.96	670	14.92	002	978	039	10
4° 00′	.0698	.0698	14.34	.0699	14.30	1.002	.9976	1.5010	86° 00′
10	727	727	13.76	729	13.73	003	974	981	50
20	756	756	13.23	758	13.20	003	971	952	40
30	.0785	.0785	12.75	.0787	12.71	1.003	.9969	1.4923	30
40	814	814	12.29	816	12.25	003	967	893	20
50	844	843	11.87	846	11.83	004	964	864	10
5° 00′	.0873	.0872	11.47	.0875	11.43	1.004	.9962	1.4835	85° 00′
10	902	901	11.10	904	11.06	004	959	806	50
20	931	929	10.76	934	10.71	004	957	777	40
30	.0960	.0958	10.43	.0963	10.39	1.005	.9954	1.4748	30
40	989	987	10.13	992	10.08	005	951	719	20
50	.1018	.1016	9.839	.1022	9.788	005	948	690	10
6° 00′	.1047	.1045	9.567	.1051	9.514	1.006	.9945	1.4661	84° 00′
		cos θ	sec θ	cot θ	tan θ	csc θ	sin θ	Radians	Degrees
								Angle θ	

202

TABLE I—*continued*

Angle θ Degrees	Radians	sin θ	csc θ	tan θ	cot θ	sec θ	cos θ		
6° 00′	.1047	.1045	9.567	.1051	9.514	1.006	.9945	1.4661	84° 00′
10	076	074	9.309	080	9.255	006	942	632	50
20	105	103	9.065	110	9.010	006	939	603	40
30	.1134	.1132	8.834	.1139	8.777	1.006	.9936	1.4573	30
40	164	161	8.614	169	8.556	007	932	544	20
50	193	190	8.405	198	8.345	007	929	515	10
7° 00′	.1222	.1219	8.206	.1228	8.144	1.008	.9925	1.4486	83° 00′
10	251	248	8.016	257	7.953	008	922	457	50
20	280	276	7.834	287	7.770	008	918	428	40
30	.1309	.1305	7.661	.1317	7.596	1.009	.9914	1.4399	30
40	338	334	7.496	346	7.429	009	911	370	20
50	367	363	7.337	376	7.269	009	907	341	10
8° 00′	.1396	.1392	7.185	.1405	7.115	1.010	.9903	1.4312	82° 00′
10	425	421	7.040	435	6.968	010	899	283	50
20	454	449	6.900	465	6.827	011	894	254	40
30	.1484	.1478	6.765	.1495	6.691	1.011	.9890	1.4224	30
40	513	507	6.636	524	6.561	012	886	195	20
50	542	536	6.512	554	6.435	012	881	166	10
9° 00′	.1571	.1564	6.392	.1584	6.314	1.012	.9877	1.4137	81° 00′
10	600	593	277	614	197	013	872	108	50
20	629	622	166	644	084	013	868	079	40
30	.1658	.1650	6.059	.1673	5.976	1.014	.9863	1.4050	30
40	687	679	5.955	703	871	014	858	1.4021	20
50	716	708	855	733	769	015	853	992	10
10° 00′	.1745	.1736	5.759	.1763	5.671	1.015	.9848	1.3963	80° 00′
10	774	765	665	793	576	016	843	934	50
20	804	794	575	823	485	016	838	904	40
30	.1833	.1822	5.487	.1853	5.396	1.017	.9833	1.3875	30
40	862	851	403	883	309	018	827	846	20
50	891	880	320	914	226	018	822	817	10
11° 00′	.1920	.1908	5.241	.1944	5.145	1.019	.9816	1.3788	79° 00′
10	949	937	164	974	066	019	811	759	50
20	978	965	089	.2004	4.989	020	805	730	40
30	.2007	.1994	5.016	.2035	4.915	1.020	.9799	1.3701	30
40	036	.2022	4.945	065	843	021	793	672	20
50	065	051	876	095	773	022	787	643	10
12° 00′	.2094	.2079	4.810	.2126	4.705	1.022	.9781	1.3614	78° 00′
10	123	108	745	156	638	023	775	584	50
20	153	136	682	186	574	024	769	555	40
30	.2182	.2164	4.620	.2217	4.511	1.024	.9763	1.3526	30
40	211	193	560	247	449	025	757	497	20
50	240	221	502	278	390	026	750	468	10
13° 00′	.2269	.2250	4.445	.2309	4.331	1.026	.9744	1.3439	77° 00′
		cos θ	sec θ	cot θ	tan θ	csc θ	sin θ	Radians	Degrees
									Angle θ

TABLE I—*continued*

Angle θ									
Degrees	**Radians**	**sin θ**	**csc θ**	**tan θ**	**cot θ**	**sec θ**	**cos θ**		
13° 00'	.2269	.2250	4.445	.2309	4.331	1.026	.9744	1.3439	**77° 00'**
10	298	278	390	339	275	027	737	410	50
20	327	306	336	370	219	028	730	381	40
30	.2356	.2334	4.284	.2401	4.165	1.028	.9724	1.3352	30
40	385	363	232	432	113	029	717	323	20
50	414	391	182	462	061	030	710	294	10
14° 00'	.2443	.2419	4.134	.2493	4.011	1.031	.9703	1.3265	**76° 00'**
10	473	447	086	524	3.962	031	696	235	50
20	502	476	039	555	914	032	689	206	40
30	.2531	.2504	3.994	.2586	3.867	1.033	.9681	1.3177	30
40	560	532	950	617	821	034	674	148	20
50	589	560	906	648	776	034	667	119	10
15° 00'	.2618	.2588	3.864	.2679	3.732	1.035	.9659	1.3090	**75° 00'**
10	647	616	822	711	689	036	652	061	50
20	676	644	782	742	647	037	644	032	40
30	.2705	.2672	3.742	.2773	3.606	1.038	.9636	1.3003	30
40	734	700	703	805	566	039	628	974	20
50	763	728	665	836	526	039	621	945	10
16° 00'	.2793	.2756	3.628	.2867	3.487	1.040	.9613	1.2915	**74° 00'**
10	822	784	592	899	450	041	605	886	50
20	851	812	556	931	412	042	596	857	40
30	.2880	.2840	3.521	.2962	3.376	1.043	.9588	1.2828	30
40	909	868	487	994	340	044	580	799	20
50	938	896	453	.3026	305	045	572	770	10
17° 00'	.2967	.2924	3.420	.3057	3.271	1.046	.9563	1.2741	**73° 00'**
10	996	952	388	089	237	047	555	712	50
20	.3025	979	357	121	204	048	546	683	40
30	.3054	.3007	3.326	.3153	3.172	1.048	.9537	1.2654	30
40	083	035	295	185	140	049	528	625	20
50	113	062	265	217	108	050	520	595	10
18° 00'	.3142	.3090	3.236	.3249	3.078	1.051	.9511	1.2566	**72° 00'**
10	171	118	207	281	047	052	502	537	50
20	200	145	179	314	018	053	492	2508	40
30	.3229	.3173	3.152	.3346	2.989	1.054	.9483	1.2479	30
40	258	201	124	378	960	056	474	450	20
50	287	228	098	411	932	057	465	421	10
19° 00'	.3316	.3256	3.072	.3443	2.904	1.058	.9455	1.2392	**71° 00'**
10	345	283	046	476	877	059	446	363	50
20	374	311	021	508	850	060	436	334	40
30	.3403	.3338	2.996	.3541	2.824	1.061	.9426	1.2305	30
40	432	365	971	574	798	062	417	275	20
50	462	393	947	607	773	063	407	246	10
20° 00'	.3491	.3420	2.924	.3640	2.747	1.064	.9397	1.2217	**70° 00'**
		cos θ	**sec θ**	**cot θ**	**tan θ**	**csc θ**	**sin θ**	**Radians**	**Degrees**
									Angle θ

TABLE I—*continued*

| Angle θ | | sin θ | csc θ | tan θ | cot θ | sec θ | cos θ | | |
Degrees	Radians	sin θ	csc θ	tan θ	cot θ	sec θ	cos θ		
20° 00′	.3491	.3420	2.924	.3640	2.747	1.064	.9397	1.2217	70° 00′
10	520	448	901	673	723	065	387	188	50
20	549	475	878	706	699	066	377	159	40
30	.3578	.3502	2.855	.3739	2.675	1.068	.9367	1.2130	30
40	607	529	833	772	651	069	356	101	20
50	636	557	812	805	628	070	346	072	10
21° 00′	.3665	.3584	2.790	.3839	2.605	1.071	.9336	1.2043	69° 00′
10	694	611	769	872	583	072	325	1.2014	50
20	723	638	749	906	560	074	315	985	40
30	.3752	.3665	2.729	.3939	2.539	1.075	.9304	1.1956	30
40	782	692	709	973	517	076	293	926	20
50	811	719	689	.4006	496	077	283	897	10
22° 00′	.3840	.3746	2.669	.4040	2.475	1.079	.9272	1.1868	68° 00′
10	869	773	650	074	455	080	261	839	50
20	898	800	632	108	434	081	250	810	40
30	.3927	.3827	2.613	.4142	2.414	1.082	.9239	1.1781	30
40	956	854	595	176	394	084	228	752	20
50	985	881	577	210	375	085	216	723	10
23° 00′	.4014	.3907	2.559	.4245	2.356	1.086	.9205	1.1694	67° 00′
10	043	934	542	279	337	088	194	665	50
20	072	961	525	314	318	089	182	636	40
30	.4102	.3987	2.508	.4348	2.300	1.090	.9171	1.1606	30
40	131	.4014	491	383	282	092	159	577	20
50	160	041	475	417	264	093	147	548	10
24° 00′	.4189	.4067	2.459	.4452	2.246	1.095	.9135	1.1519	66° 00′
10	218	094	443	487	229	096	124	490	50
20	247	120	427	522	211	097	112	461	40
30	.4276	.4147	2.411	.4557	2.194	1.099	.9100	1.1432	30
40	305	173	396	592	177	100	088	403	20
50	334	200	381	628	161	102	075	374	10
25° 00′	.4363	.4226	2.366	.4663	2.145	1.103	.9063	1.1345	65° 00′
10	392	253	352	699	128	105	051	316	50
20	422	279	337	734	112	106	038	286	40
30	.4451	.4305	2.323	.4770	2.097	1.108	.9026	1.1257	30
40	480	331	309	806	081	109	013	228	20
50	509	358	295	841	066	111	001	199	10
26° 00′	.4538	.4384	2.281	.4877	2.050	1.113	.8988	1.1170	64° 00′
10	567	410	268	913	035	114	975	141	50
20	596	436	254	950	020	116	962	112	40
30	.4625	.4462	2.241	.4986	2.006	1.117	.8949	1.1083	30
40	654	488	228	.5022	1.991	119	936	054	20
50	683	514	215	059	977	121	923	1.1025	10
27° 00′	.4712	.4540	2.203	.5095	1.963	1.122	.8910	1.0996	63° 00′
		cos θ	sec θ	cot θ	tan θ	csc θ	sin θ	Radians	Degrees
									Angle θ

TABLE I—*continued*

Degrees	Radians	sin θ	csc θ	tan θ	cot θ	sec θ	cos θ		
Angle θ									
27° 00′	.4712	.4540	2.203	.5095	1.963	1.122	.8910	1.0996	**63° 00′**
10	741	566	190	132	949	124	897	966	50
20	771	592	178	169	935	126	884	937	40
30	.4800	.4617	2.166	.5206	1.921	1.127	.8870	1.0908	30
40	829	643	154	243	907	129	857	879	20
50	858	669	142	280	894	131	843	850	10
28° 00′	.4887	.4695	2.130	.5317	1.881	1.133	.8829	1.0821	**62° 00′**
10	916	720	118	354	868	134	816	792	50
20	945	746	107	392	855	136	802	763	40
30	.4974	.4772	2.096	.5430	1.842	1.138	.8788	1.0734	30
40	.5003	797	085	467	829	140	774	705	20
50	032	823	074	505	816	142	760	676	10
29° 00′	.5061	.4848	2.063	.5543	1.804	1.143	.8746	1.0647	**61° 00′**
10	091	874	052	581	792	145	732	617	50
20	120	899	041	619	780	147	718	588	40
30	.5149	.4924	2.031	.5658	1.767	1.149	.8704	1.0559	30
40	178	950	020	696	756	151	689	530	20
50	207	975	010	735	744	153	675	501	10
30° 00′	.5236	.5000	2.000	.5774	1.732	1.155	.8660	1.0472	**60° 00′**
10	265	025	1.990	812	720	157	646	443	50
20	294	050	980	851	709	159	631	414	40
30	.5323	.5075	1.970	.5890	1.698	1.161	.8616	1.0385	30
40	352	100	961	930	686	163	601	356	20
50	381	125	951	969	675	165	587	327	10
31° 00′	.5411	.5150	1.942	.6009	1.664	1.167	.8572	1.0297	**59° 00′**
10	440	175	932	048	653	169	557	268	50
20	469	200	923	088	643	171	542	239	40
30	.5498	.5225	1.914	.6128	1.632	1.173	.8526	1.0210	30
40	527	250	905	168	621	175	511	181	20
50	556	275	896	208	611	177	496	152	10
32° 00′	.5585	.5299	1.887	.6249	1.600	1.179	.8480	1.0123	**58° 00′**
10	614	324	878	289	590	181	465	094	50
20	643	348	870	330	580	184	450	065	40
30	.5672	.5373	1.861	.6371	1.570	1.186	.8434	1.0036	30
40	701	398	853	412	560	188	418	1.0007	20
50	730	422	844	453	550	190	403	977	10
33° 00′	.5760	.5446	1.836	.6494	1.540	1.192	.8387	.9948	**57° 00′**
10	789	471	828	536	530	195	371	919	50
20	818	495	820	577	520	197	355	890	40
30	.5847	.5519	1.812	.6619	1.511	1.199	.8339	.9861	30
40	876	544	804	661	501	202	323	832	20
50	905	568	796	703	1.492	204	307	803	10
34° 00′	.5934	.5592	1.788	.6745	1.483	1.206	.8290	.9774	**56° 00′**
		cos θ	sec θ	cot θ	tan θ	csc θ	sin θ	**Radians**	**Degrees**
								Angle θ	

206

TABLE I—*continued*

Angle θ									
Degrees	**Radians**	**sin θ**	**csc θ**	**tan θ**	**cot θ**	**sec θ**	**cos θ**		
34° 00′	.5934	.5592	1.788	.6745	1.483	1.206	.8290	.9774	**56° 00′**
10	963	616	781	787	473	209	274	745	50
20	992	640	773	830	464	211	258	716	40
30	.6021	.5664	1.766	.6873	1.455	1.213	.8241	.9687	30
40	050	688	758	916	446	216	225	657	20
50	080	712	751	959	437	218	208	628	10
35° 00′	.6109	.5736	1.743	.7002	1.428	1.221	.8192	.9599	**55° 00′**
10	138	760	736	046	419	223	175	570	50
20	167	783	729	089	411	226	158	541	40
30	.6196	.5807	1.722	.7133	1.402	1.228	.8141	.9512	30
40	225	831	715	177	393	231	124	483	20
50	254	854	708	221	385	233	107	454	10
36° 00′	.6283	.5878	1.701	.7265	1.376	1.236	.8090	.9425	**54° 00′**
10	312	901	695	310	368	239	073	396	50
20	341	925	688	355	360	241	056	367	40
30	.6370	.5948	1.681	.7400	1.351	1.244	.8039	.9338	30
40	400	972	675	445	343	247	021	308	20
50	429	995	668	490	335	249	004	279	10
37° 00′	.6458	.6018	1.662	.7536	1.327	1.252	.7986	.9250	**53° 00′**
10	487	041	655	581	319	255	969	221	50
20	516	065	649	627	311	258	951	192	40
30	.6545	.6088	1.643	.7673	1.303	1.260	.7934	.9163	30
40	574	111	636	720	295	263	916	134	20
50	603	134	630	766	288	266	898	105	10
38° 00′	.6632	.6157	1.624	.7813	1.280	1.269	.7880	.9076	**52° 00′**
10	661	180	618	860	272	272	862	047	50
20	690	202	612	907	265	275	844	.9018	40
30	.6720	.6225	1.606	.7954	1.257	1.278	.7826	.8988	30
40	749	248	601	.8002	250	281	808	959	20
50	778	271	595	050	242	284	790	930	10
39° 00′	.6807	.6293	1.589	.8098	1.235	1.287	.7771	.8901	**51° 00′**
10	836	316	583	146	228	290	753	872	50
20	865	338	578	195	220	293	735	843	40
30	.6894	.6361	1.572	.8243	1.213	1.296	.7716	.8814	30
40	923	383	567	292	206	299	698	785	20
50	952	406	561	342	199	302	679	756	10
40° 00′	.6981	.6428	1.556	.8391	1.192	1.305	.7660	.8727	**50° 00′**
10	.7010	450	550	441	185	309	642	698	50
20	039	472	545	491	178	312	623	668	40
30	.7069	.6494	1.540	.8541	1.171	1.315	.7604	.8639	30
40	098	517	535	591	164	318	585	610	20
50	127	539	529	642	157	322	566	581	10
41° 00′	.7156	.6561	1.524	.8693	1.150	1.325	.7547	.8552	**49° 00′**
		cos θ	**sec θ**	**cot θ**	**tan θ**	**csc θ**	**sin θ**	**Radians**	**Degrees**
								Angle θ	

TABLE I—*continued*

Angle θ									
Degrees	**Radians**	**sin θ**	**csc θ**	**tan θ**	**cot θ**	**sec θ**	**cos θ**		
41° 00′	.7156	.6561	1.524	.8693	1.150	1.325	.7547	.8552	**49° 00′**
10	185	583	519	744	144	328	528	523	50
20	214	604	514	796	137	332	509	494	40
30	.7243	.6626	1.509	.8847	1.130	1.335	.7490	.8465	30
40	272	648	504	899	124	339	470	436	20
50	301	670	499	952	117	342	451	407	10
42° 00′	.7330	.6691	1.494	.9004	1.111	1.346	.7431	.8378	**48° 00′**
10	359	713	490	057	104	349	412	348	50
20	389	734	485	110	098	353	392	319	40
30	.7418	.6756	1.480	.9163	1.091	1.356	.7373	.8290	30
40	447	777	476	217	085	360	353	261	20
50	476	799	471	271	079	364	333	232	10
43° 00′	.7505	.6820	1.466	.9325	1.072	1.367	.7314	.8203	**47° 00′**
10	534	841	462	380	066	371	294	174	50
20	563	862	457	435	060	375	274	145	40
30	.7592	.6884	1.453	.9490	1.054	1.379	.7254	.8116	30
40	621	905	448	545	048	382	234	087	20
50	650	926	444	601	042	386	214	058	10
44° 00′	.7679	.6947	1.440	.9657	1.036	1.390	.7193	.8029	**46° 00′**
10	709	967	435	713	030	394	173	.7999	50
20	738	988	431	770	024	398	153	970	40
30	.7767	.7009	1.427	.9827	1.018	1.402	.7133	.7941	30
40	796	030	423	884	012	406	112	912	20
50	825	050	418	942	006	410	092	883	10
45° 00′	.7854	.7071	1.414	1.000	1.000	1.414	.7071	.7854	**45° 00′**
		cos θ	**sec θ**	**cot θ**	**tan θ**	**csc θ**	**sin θ**	**Radians**	**Degrees**
								Angle θ	

TABLE II
Four-Place Values of Trigonometric Functions
Real Numbers *u*, or Angles θ, in Radians and Degrees

Real Number *u* or θ radians	θ degrees	sin *u* or sin θ	csc *u* or csc θ	tan *u* or tan θ	cot *u* or cot θ	sec *u* or sec θ	cos *u* or cos θ
0.00	0° 00′	0.0000	No value	0.0000	No value	1.000	1.000
.01	0° 34′	.0100	100.0	.0100	100.0	1.000	1.000
.02	1° 09′	.0200	50.00	.0200	49.99	1.000	0.9998
.03	1° 43′	.0300	33.34	.0300	33.32	1.000	0.9996
.04	2° 18′	.0400	25.01	.0400	24.99	1.001	0.9992
0.05	2° 52′	0.0500	20.01	0.0500	19.98	1.001	0.9988
.06	3° 26′	.0600	16.68	.0601	16.65	1.002	.9982
.07	4° 01′	.0699	14.30	.0701	14.26	1.002	.9976
.08	4° 35′	.0799	12.51	.0802	12.47	1.003	.9968
.09	5° 09′	.0899	11.13	.0902	11.08	1.004	.9960
0.10	5° 44′	0.0998	10.02	0.1003	9.967	1.005	0.9950
.11	6° 18′	.1098	9.109	.1104	9.054	1.006	.9940
.12	6° 53′	.1197	8.353	.1206	8.293	1.007	.9928
.13	7° 27′	.1296	7.714	.1307	7.649	1.009	.9916
.14	8° 01′	.1395	7.166	.1409	7.096	1.010	.9902
0.15	8° 36′	0.1494	6.692	0.1511	6.617	1.011	0.9888
.16	9° 10′	.1593	6.277	.1614	6.197	1.013	.9872
.17	9° 44′	.1692	5.911	.1717	5.826	1.015	.9856
.18	10° 19′	.1790	5.586	.1820	5.495	1.016	.9838
.19	10° 53′	.1889	5.295	.1923	5.200	1.018	.9820
0.20	11° 28′	0.1987	5.033	0.2027	4.933	1.020	0.9801
.21	12° 02′	.2085	4.797	.2131	4.692	1.022	.9780
.22	12° 36′	.2182	4.582	.2236	4.472	1.025	.9759
.23	13° 11′	.2280	4.386	.2341	4.271	1.027	.9737
.24	13° 45′	.2377	4.207	.2447	4.086	1.030	.9713
0.25	14° 19′	0.2474	4.042	0.2553	3.916	1.032	0.9689
.26	14° 54′	.2571	3.890	.2660	3.759	1.035	.9664
.27	15° 28′	.2667	3.749	.2768	3.613	1.038	.9638
.28	16° 03′	.2764	3.619	.2876	3.478	1.041	.9611
.29	16° 37′	.2860	3.497	.2984	3.351	1.044	.9582
0.30	17° 11′	0.2955	3.384	0.3093	3.233	1.047	0.9553
.31	17° 46′	.3051	3.278	.3203	3.122	1.050	.9523
.32	18° 20′	.3146	3.179	.3314	3.018	1.053	.9492
.33	18° 54′	.3240	3.086	.3425	2.920	1.057	.9460
.34	19° 29′	.3335	2.999	.3537	2.827	1.061	.9428
0.35	20° 03′	0.3429	2.916	0.3650	2.740	1.065	0.9394
Real Number *u* or θ radians	θ degrees	sin *u* or sin θ	csc *u* or csc θ	tan *u* or tan θ	cot *u* or cot θ	sec *u* or sec θ	cos *u* or cos θ

TABLE II—*continued*

Real Number *u* or θ radians	θ degrees	sin *u* or sin θ	csc *u* or csc θ	tan *u* or tan θ	cot *u* or cot θ	sec *u* or sec θ	cos *u* or cos θ
0.35	20° 03′	0.3429	2.916	0.3650	2.740	1.065	0.9394
.36	20° 38′	.3523	2.839	.3764	2.657	1.068	.9359
.37	21° 12′	.3616	2.765	.3879	2.578	1.073	.9323
.38	21° 46′	.3709	2.696	.3994	2.504	1.077	.9287
.39	22° 21′	.3802	2.630	.4111	2.433	1.081	.9249
0.40	22° 55′	0.3894	2.568	0.4228	2.365	1.086	0.9211
.41	23° 29′	.3986	2.509	.4346	2.301	1.090	.9171
.42	24° 04′	.4078	2.452	.4466	2.239	1.095	.9131
.43	24° 38′	.4169	2.399	.4586	2.180	1.100	.9090
.44	25° 13′	.4259	2.348	.4708	2.124	1.105	.9048
0.45	25° 47′	0.4350	2.299	0.4831	2.070	1.111	0.9004
.46	26° 21′	.4439	2.253	.4954	2.018	1.116	.8961
.47	26° 56′	.4529	2.208	.5080	1.969	1.122	.8916
.48	27° 30′	.4618	2.166	.5206	1.921	1.127	.8870
.49	28° 04′	.4706	2.125	.5334	1.875	1.133	.8823
0.50	28° 39′	0.4794	2.086	0.5463	1.830	1.139	0.8776
.51	29° 13′	.4882	2.048	.5594	1.788	1.146	.8727
.52	29° 48′	.4969	2.013	.5726	1.747	1.152	.8678
.53	30° 22′	.5055	1.978	.5859	1.707	1.159	.8628
.54	30° 56′	.5141	1.945	.5994	1.668	1.166	.8577
0.55	31° 31′	0.5227	1.913	0.6131	1.631	1.173	0.8525
.56	32° 05′	.5312	1.883	.6269	1.595	1.180	.8473
.57	32° 40′	.5396	1.853	.6410	1.560	1.188	.8419
.58	33° 14′	.5480	1.825	.6552	1.526	1.196	.8365
.59	33° 48′	.5564	1.797	.6696	1.494	1.203	.8309
0.60	34° 23′	0.5646	1.771	0.6841	1.462	1.212	0.8253
.61	34° 57′	.5729	1.746	.6989	1.431	1.220	.8196
.62	35° 31′	.5810	1.721	.7139	1.401	1.229	.8139
.63	36° 06′	.5891	1.697	.7291	1.372	1.238	.8080
.64	36° 40′	.5972	1.674	.7445	1.343	1.247	.8021
0.65	37° 15′	0.6052	1.652	0.7602	1.315	1.256	0.7961
.66	37° 49′	.6131	1.631	.7761	1.288	1.266	.7900
.67	38° 23′	.6210	1.610	.7923	1.262	1.276	.7838
.68	38° 58′	.6288	1.590	.8087	1.237	1.286	.7776
.69	39° 32′	.6365	1.571	.8253	1.212	1.297	.7712
0.70	40° 06′	0.6442	1.552	0.8423	1.187	1.307	0.7648
Real Number *u* or θ radians	θ degrees	sin *u* or sin θ	csc *u* or csc θ	tan *u* or tan θ	cot *u* or cot θ	sec *u* or sec θ	cos *u* or cos θ

TABLE II—*continued*

Real Number u or θ radians	θ degrees	sin u or sin θ	csc u or csc θ	tan u or tan θ	cot u or cot θ	sec u or sec θ	cos u or cos θ
0.70	40° 06′	0.6442	1.552	0.8423	1.187	1.307	0.7648
.71	40° 41′	.6518	1.534	.8595	1.163	1.319	.7584
.72	41° 15′	.6594	1.517	.8771	1.140	1.330	.7518
.73	41° 50′	.6669	1.500	.8949	1.117	1.342	.7452
.74	42° 24′	.6743	1.483	.9131	1.095	1.354	.7385
0.75	42° 58′	0.6816	1.467	0.9316	1.073	1.367	0.7317
.76	43° 33′	.6889	1.452	.9505	1.052	1.380	.7248
.77	44° 07′	.6961	1.436	.9697	1.031	1.393	.7179
.78	44° 41′	.7033	1.422	.9893	1.011	1.407	.7109
.79	45° 16′	.7104	1.408	1.009	.9908	1.421	.7038
0.80	45° 50′	0.7174	1.394	1.030	0.9712	1.435	0.6967
.81	46° 25′	.7243	1.381	1.050	.9520	1.450	.6895
.82	46° 59′	.7311	1.368	1.072	.9331	1.466	.6822
.83	47° 33′	.7379	1.355	1.093	.9146	1.482	.6749
.84	48° 08′	.7446	1.343	1.116	.8964	1.498	.6675
0.85	48° 42′	0.7513	1.331	1.138	0.8785	1.515	0.6600
.86	49° 16′	.7578	1.320	1.162	.8609	1.533	.6524
.87	49° 51′	.7643	1.308	1.185	.8437	1.551	.6448
.88	50° 25′	.7707	1.297	1.210	.8267	1.569	.6372
.89	51° 00′	.7771	1.287	1.235	.8100	1.589	.6294
0.90	51° 34′	0.7833	1.277	1.260	0.7936	1.609	0.6216
.91	52° 08′	.7895	1.267	1.286	.7774	1.629	.6137
.92	52° 43′	.7956	1.257	1.313	.7615	1.651	.6058
.93	53° 17′	.8016	1.247	1.341	.7458	1.673	.5978
.94	53° 51′	.8076	1.238	1.369	.7303	1.696	.5898
0.95	54° 26′	0.8134	1.229	1.398	0.7151	1.719	0.5817
.96	55° 00′	.8192	1.221	1.428	.7001	1.744	.5735
.97	55° 35′	.8249	1.212	1.459	.6853	1.769	.5653
.98	56° 09′	.8305	1.204	1.491	.6707	1.795	.5570
.99	56° 43′	.8360	1.196	1.524	.6563	1.823	.5487
1.00	57° 18′	0.8415	1.188	1.557	0.6421	1.851	0.5403
1.01	57° 52′	.8468	1.181	1.592	.6281	1.880	.5319
1.02	58° 27′	.8521	1.174	1.628	.6142	1.911	.5234
1.03	59° 01′	.8573	1.166	1.665	.6005	1.942	.5148
1.04	59° 35′	.8624	1.160	1.704	.5870	1.975	.5062
1.05	60° 10′	0.8674	1.153	1.743	0.5736	2.010	0.4976
Real Number u or θ radians	θ degrees	sin u or sin θ	csc u or csc θ	tan u or tan θ	cot u or cot θ	sec u or sec θ	cos u or cos θ

TABLE II—*continued*

Real Number *u* or θ radians	θ degrees	sin *u* or sin θ	csc *u* or csc θ	tan *u* or tan θ	cot *u* or cot θ	sec *u* or sec θ	cos *u* or cos θ
1.05	60° 10′	0.8674	1.153	1.743	0.5736	2.010	0.4976
1.06	60° 44′	8724	1.146	1.784	.5604	2.046	.4889
1.07	61° 18′	.8772	1.140	1.827	.5473	2.083	.4801
1.08	61° 53′	.8820	1.134	1.871	.5344	2.122	.4713
1.09	62° 27′	.8866	1.128	1.917	.5216	2.162	.4625
1.10	63° 02′	0.8912	1.122	1.965	0.5090	2.205	0.4536
1.11	63° 36′	.8957	1.116	2.014	.4964	2.249	.4447
1.12	64° 10′	.9001	1.111	2.066	.4840	2.295	.4357
1.13	64° 45′	.9044	1.106	2.120	.4718	2.344	.4267
1.14	65° 19′	.9086	1.101	2.176	.4596	2.395	.4176
1.15	65° 53′	0.9128	1.096	2.234	0.4475	2.448	0.4085
1.16	66° 28′	.9168	1.091	2.296	.4356	2.504	.3993
1.17	67° 02′	.9208	1.086	2.360	.4237	2.563	.3902
1.18	67° 37′	.9246	1.082	2.247	.4120	2.625	.3809
1.19	68° 11′	.9284	1.077	2.498	.4003	2.691	.3717
1.20	68° 45′	0.9320	1.073	2.572	0.3888	2.760	0.3624
1.21	69° 20′	.9356	1.069	2.650	.3773	2.833	.3530
1.22	69° 54′	.9391	1.065	2.733	.3659	2.910	.3436
1.23	70° 28′	.9425	1.061	2.820	.3546	2.992	.3342
1.24	71° 03′	.9458	1.057	2.912	.3434	3.079	.3248
1.25	71° 37′	0.9490	1.054	3.010	0.3323	3.171	0.3153
1.26	72° 12′	.9521	1.050	3.113	.3212	3.270	.3058
1.27	72° 46′	.9551	1.047	3.224	.3102	3.375	.2963
1.28	73° 20′	.9580	1.044	3.341	.2993	3.488	.2867
1.29	73° 55′	.9608	1.041	3.467	.2884	3.609	.2771
1.30	74° 29′	0.9636	1.038	3.602	0.2776	3.738	0.2675
1.31	75° 03′	.9662	1.035	3.747	.2669	3.878	.2579
1.32	75° 38′	.9687	1.032	3.903	.2562	4.029	.2482
1.33	76° 12′	.9711	1.030	4.072	.2456	4.193	.2385
1.34	76° 47′	.9735	1.027	4.256	.2350	4.372	.2288
1.35	77° 21′	0.9757	1.025	4.455	0.2245	4.566	0.2190
1.36	77° 55′	.9779	1.023	4.673	.2140	4.779	.2092
1.37	78° 30′	.9799	1.021	4.913	.2035	5.014	.1994
1.38	79° 04′	.9819	1.018	5.177	.1931	5.273	.1896
1.39	79° 38′	.9837	1.017	5.471	.1828	5.561	.1798
1.40	80° 13′	0.9854	1.015	5.798	0.1725	5.883	0.1700
Real Number *u* or θ radians	θ degrees	sin *u* or sin θ	csc *u* or csc θ	tan *u* or tan θ	cot *u* or cot θ	sec *u* or sec θ	cos *u* or cos θ

TABLE II—*continued*

Real Number *u* or θ radians	θ degrees	sin *u* or sin θ	csc *u* or csc θ	tan *u* or tan θ	cot *u* or cot θ	sec *u* or sec θ	cos *u* or cos θ
1.40	80° 13′	0.9854	1.015	5.798	0.1725	5.883	0.1700
1.41	80° 47′	.9871	1.013	6.165	.1622	6.246	.1601
1.42	81° 22′	.9887	1.011	6.581	.1519	6.657	.1502
1.43	81° 56′	.9901	1.010	7.055	.1417	7.126	.1403
1.44	82° 30′	.9915	1.009	7.602	.1315	7.667	.1304
1.45	83° 05′	0.9927	1.007	8.238	0.1214	8.299	0.1205
1.46	83° 39′	.9939	1.006	8.989	.1113	9.044	.1106
1.47	84° 13′	.9949	1.005	9.887	.1011	9.938	.1006
1.48	84° 48′	.9959	1.004	10.98	.0910	11.03	.0907
1.49	85° 22′	.9967	1.003	12.35	.0810	12.39	.0807
1.50	85° 57′	0.9975	1.003	14.10	0.0709	14.14	0.0707
1.51	86° 31′	.9982	1.002	16.43	.0609	16.46	.0608
1.52	87° 05′	.9987	1.001	19.67	.0508	19.69	.0508
1.53	87° 40′	.9992	1.001	24.50	.0408	24.52	.0408
1.54	88° 14′	.9995	1.000	32.46	.0308	32.48	.0308
1.55	88° 49′	0.9998	1.000	48.08	0.0208	48.09	0.0208
1.56	89° 23′	.9999	1.000	92.62	.0108	92.63	.0108
1.57	89° 57′	1.000	1.000	1256	.0008	1256	.0008
Real Number *u* or θ radians	θ degrees	sin *u* or sin θ	csc *u* or csc θ	tan *u* or tan θ	cot *u* or cot θ	sec *u* or sec θ	cos *u* or cos θ

TABLE III

Four-Place Logarithms of Numbers from 1 to 10
To extend the table write the number N as

$$N = n \times 10^c, \; 1 \leqq n < 10, \; c \text{ an integer, and use}$$
$$\log N = \log n + c.$$

n	0	1	2	3	4	5	6	7	8	9
1.0	+0.0000	0043	0086	0128	0170	0212	0253	0294	0334	0374
1.1	.0414	0453	0492	0531	0569	0607	0645	0682	0719	0755
1.2	.0792	0828	0864	0899	0934	0969	1004	1038	1072	1106
1.3	.1139	1173	1206	1239	1271	1303	1335	1367	1399	1430
1.4	.1461	1492	1523	1553	1584	1614	1644	1673	1703	1732
1.5	.1761	1790	1818	1847	1875	1903	1931	1959	1987	2014
1.6	.2041	2068	2095	2122	2148	2175	2201	2227	2253	2279
1.7	.2304	2330	2355	2380	2405	2430	2455	2480	2504	2529
1.8	.2553	2577	2601	2625	2648	2672	2695	2718	2742	2765
1.9	.2788	2810	2833	2856	2878	2900	2923	2945	2967	2989
2.0	.3010	3032	3054	3075	3096	3118	3139	3160	3181	3201
2.1	.3222	3243	3263	3284	3304	3324	3345	3365	3385	3404
2.2	.3424	3444	3464	3483	3502	3522	3541	3560	3579	3598
2.3	.3617	3636	3655	3674	3692	3711	3729	3747	3766	3784
2.4	.3802	3820	3838	3856	3874	3892	3909	3927	3945	3962
2.5	.3979	3997	4014	4031	4048	4065	4082	4099	4116	4133
2.6	.4150	4166	4183	4200	4216	4232	4249	4265	4281	4298
2.7	.4314	4330	4346	4362	4378	4393	4409	4425	4440	4456
2.8	.4472	4487	4502	4518	4533	4548	4564	4579	4594	4609
2.9	.4624	4639	4654	4669	4683	4698	4713	4728	4742	4757
3.0	.4771	4786	4800	4814	4829	4843	4857	4871	4886	4900
3.1	.4914	4928	4942	4955	4969	4983	4997	5011	5024	5038
3.2	.5051	5065	5079	5092	5105	5119	5132	5145	5159	5172
3.3	.5185	5198	5211	5224	5237	5250	5263	5276	5289	5302
3.4	.5315	5328	5340	5353	5366	5378	5391	5403	5416	5428
3.5	.5441	5453	5465	5478	5490	5502	5514	5527	5539	5551
3.6	.5563	5575	5587	5599	5611	5623	5635	5647	5658	5670
3.7	.5682	5694	5705	5717	5729	5740	5752	5763	5775	5786
3.8	.5798	5809	5821	5832	5843	5855	5866	5877	5888	5899
3.9	.5911	5922	5933	5944	5955	5966	5977	5988	5999	6010
4.0	.6021	6031	6042	6053	6064	6075	6085	6096	6107	6117
4.1	.6128	6138	6149	6160	6170	6180	6191	6201	6212	6222
4.2	.6232	6243	6253	6263	6274	6284	6294	6304	6314	6325
4.3	.6335	6345	6355	6365	6375	6385	6395	6405	6415	6425
4.4	.6435	6444	6454	6464	6474	6484	6493	6503	6513	6522
4.5	.6532	6542	6551	6561	6571	6580	6590	6599	6609	6618
4.6	.6628	6637	6646	6656	6665	6675	6684	6693	6702	6712
4.7	.6721	6730	6739	6749	6758	6767	6776	6785	6794	6803
4.8	.6812	6821	6830	6839	6848	6857	6866	6875	6884	6893
4.9	.6902	6911	6920	6928	6937	6946	6955	6964	6972	6981

TABLE III—*continued*

n	0	1	2	3	4	5	6	7	8	9
5.0	+.6990	6998	7007	7016	7024	7033	7042	7050	7059	7067
5.1	.7076	7084	7093	7101	7110	7118	7126	7135	7143	7152
5.2	.7160	7168	7177	7185	7193	7202	7210	7218	7226	7235
5.3	.7243	7251	7259	7267	7275	7284	7292	7300	7308	7316
5.4	.7324	7332	7340	7348	7356	7364	7372	7380	7388	7396
5.5	.7404	7412	7419	7427	7435	7443	7451	7459	7466	7474
5.6	.7482	7490	7497	7505	7513	7520	7528	7536	7543	7551
5.7	.7559	7566	7574	7582	7589	7597	7604	7612	7619	7627
5.8	.7634	7642	7649	7657	7664	7672	7679	7686	7694	7701
5.9	.7709	7716	7723	7731	7738	7745	7752	7760	7767	7774
6.0	.7782	7789	7796	7803	7810	7818	7825	7832	7839	7846
6.1	.7853	7860	7868	7875	7882	7889	7896	7903	7910	7917
6.2	.7924	7931	7938	7945	7952	7959	7966	7973	7980	7987
6.3	.7993	8000	8007	8014	8021	8028	8035	8041	8048	8055
6.4	.8062	8069	8075	8082	8089	8096	8102	8109	8116	8122
6.5	.8129	8136	8142	8149	8156	8162	8169	8176	8182	8189
6.6	.8195	8202	8209	8215	8222	8228	8235	8241	8248	8254
6.7	.8261	8267	8274	8280	8287	8293	8299	8306	8312	8319
6.8	.8325	8331	8338	8344	8351	8357	8363	8370	8376	8382
6.9	.8388	8395	8401	8407	8414	8420	8426	8432	8439	8445
7.0	.8451	8457	8463	8470	8476	8482	8488	8494	8500	8506
7.1	.8513	8519	8525	8531	8537	8543	8549	8555	8561	8567
7.2	.8573	8579	8585	8591	8597	8603	8609	8615	8621	8627
7.3	.8633	8639	8645	8651	8657	8663	8669	8675	8681	8686
7.4	.8692	8698	8704	8710	8716	8722	8727	8733	8739	8745
7.5	.8751	8756	8762	8768	8774	8779	8785	8791	8797	8802
7.6	.8808	8814	8820	8825	8831	8837	8842	8848	8854	8859
7.7	.8865	8871	8876	8882	8887	8893	8899	8904	8910	8915
7.8	.8921	8927	8932	8938	8943	8949	8954	8960	8965	8971
7.9	.8976	8982	8987	8993	8998	9004	9009	9015	9020	9025
8.0	.9031	9036	9042	9047	9053	9058	9063	9069	9074	9079
8.1	.9085	9090	9096	9101	9106	9112	9117	9122	9128	9133
8.2	.9138	9143	9149	9154	9159	9165	9170	9175	9180	9186
8.3	.9191	9196	9201	9206	9212	9217	9222	9227	9232	9238
8.4	.9243	9248	9253	9258	9263	9269	9274	9279	9284	9289
8.5	.9294	9299	9304	9309	9315	9320	9325	9330	9335	9340
8.6	.9345	9350	9355	9360	9365	9370	9375	9380	9385	9390
8.7	.9395	9400	9405	9410	9415	9420	9425	9430	9435	9440
8.8	.9445	9450	9455	9460	9465	9469	9474	9479	9484	9489
8.9	.9494	9499	9504	9509	9513	9518	9523	9528	9533	9538
9.0	.9542	9547	9552	9557	9562	9566	9571	9576	9581	9586
9.1	.9590	9595	9600	9605	9609	9614	9619	9624	9628	9633
9.2	.9638	9643	9647	9652	9657	9661	9666	9671	9675	9680
9.3	.9685	9689	9694	9699	9703	9708	9713	9717	9722	9727
9.4	.9731	9736	9741	9745	9750	9754	9759	9763	9768	9773
9.5	.9777	9782	9786	9791	9795	9800	9805	9809	9814	9818
9.6	.9823	9827	9832	9836	9841	9845	9850	9854	9859	9863
9.7	.9868	9872	9877	9881	9886	9890	9894	9899	9903	9908
9.8	.9912	9917	9921	9926	9930	9934	9939	9943	9948	9952
9.9	.9956	9961	9965	9969	9974	9978	9983	9987	9991	9996

TABLE IV
Four-Place Logarithms of Trigonometric Functions
Angle θ in Degrees

Attach − 10 to Logarithms Obtained from This Table

Angle θ	L sin θ	L csc θ	L tan θ	L cot θ	L sec θ	L cos θ	
0° 00′	No value	No value	No value	No value	10.0000	10.0000	90° 00′
10′	7.4637	12.5363	7.4637	12.5363	.0000	.0000	50′
20′	.7648	.2352	.7648	.2352	.0000	.0000	40′
30′	7.9408	12.0592	7.9409	12.0591	.0000	.0000	30′
40′	8.0658	11.9342	8.0658	11.9342	.0000	.0000	20′
50′	.1627	.8373	.1627	.8373	.0000	10.0000	10′
1° 00′	8.2419	11.7581	8.2419	11.7581	10.0001	9.9999	89° 00′
10′	.3088	.6912	.3089	.6911	.0001	.9999	50′
20′	.3668	.6332	.3669	.6331	.0001	.9999	40′
30′	.4179	.5821	.4181	.5819	.0001	.9999	30′
40′	.4637	.5363	.4638	.5362	.0002	.9998	20′
50′	.5050	.4950	.5053	.4947	.0002	.9998	10′
2° 00′	8.5428	11.4572	8.5431	11.4569.	10.0003	9.9997	88° 00′
10′	.5776	.4224	.5779	.4221	.0003	.9997	50′
20′	.6097	.3903	.6101	.3899	.0004	.9996	40′
30′	.6397	.3603	.6401	.3599	.0004	.9996	30′
40′	.6677	.3323	.6682	.3318	.0005	.9995	20′
50′	.6940	.3060	.6945	.3055	.0005	.9995	10′
3° 00′	8.7188	11.2812	8.7194	11.2806	10.0006	9.9994	87° 00′
10′	.7423	.2577	.7429	.2571	.0007	.9993	50′
20′	.7645	.2355	.7652	.2348	.0007	.9993	40′
30′	.7857	.2143	.7865	.2135	.0008	.9992	30′
40′	.8059	.1941	.8067	.1933	.0009	.9991	20′
50′	.8251	.1749	.8261	.1739	.0010	.9990	10′
4° 00′	8.8436	11.1564	8.8446	11.1554	10.0011	9.9989	86° 00′
10′	.8613	.1387	.8624	.1376	.0011	.9989	50′
20′	.8783	.1217	.8795	.1205	.0012	.9988	40′
30′	.8946	.1054	.8960	.1040	.0013	.9987	30′
40′	.9104	.0896	.9118	.0882	.0014	.9986	20′
50′	.9256	.0744	.9272	.0728	.0015	.9985	10′
5° 00′	8.9403	11.0597	8.9420	11.0580	10.0017	9.9983	85° 00′
10′	.9545	.0455	.9563	.0437	.0018	.9982	50′
20′	.9682	.0318	.9701	.0299	.0019	.9981	40′
30′	.9816	.0184	.9836	.0164	.0020	.9980	30′
40′	8.9945	11.0055	8.9966	11.0034	.0021	.9979	20′
50′	9.0070	10.9930	9.0093	10.9907	.0023	.9977	10′
6° 00′	9.0192	10.9808	9.0216	10.9784	10.0024	9.9976	84° 00′
	L cos θ	L sec θ	L cot θ	L tan θ	L csc θ	L sin θ	Angle θ

TABLE IV—*continued*

Attach — 10 to Logarithms Obtained from This Table

Angle θ	L sin θ	L csc θ	L tan θ	L cot θ	L sec θ	L cos θ	
6° 00′	9.0192	10.9808	9.0216	10.9784	10.0024	9.9976	84° 00′
10′	.0311	.9689	.0336	.9664	.0025	.9975	50′
20′	.0426	.9574	.0453	.9547	.0027	.9973	40′
30′	.0539	.9461	.0567	.9433	.0028	.9972	30′
40′	.0648	.9352	.0678	.9322	.0029	.9971	20′
50′	.0755	.9245	.0786	.9214	.0031	.9969	10′
7° 00′	9.0859	10.9141	9.0891	10.9109	10.0032	9.9968	83° 00′
10′	.0961	.9039	.0995	.9005	.0034	.9966	50′
20′	.1060	.8940	.1096	.8904	.0036	.9964	40′
30′	.1157	.8843	.1194	.8806	.0037	.9963	30′
40′	.1252	.8748	.1291	.8709	.0039	.9961	20′
50′	.1345	.8655	.1385	.8615	.0041	.9959	10′
8° 00′	9.1436	10.8564	9.1478	10.8522	10.0042	9.9958	82° 00′
10′	.1525	.8475	.1569	.8431	.0044	.9956	50′
20′	.1612	.8388	.1658	.8342	.0046	.9954	40′
30′	.1697	.8303	.1745	.8255	.0048	.9952	30′
40′	.1781	.8219	.1831	.8169	.0050	.9950	20′
50′	.1863	.8137	.1915	.8085	.0052	.9948	10′
9° 00′	9.1943	10.8057	9.1997	10.8003	10.0054	9.9946	81° 00′
10′	.2022	.7978	.2078	.7922	.0056	.9944	50′
20′	.2100	.7900	.2158	.7842	.0058	.9942	40′
30′	.2176	.7824	.2236	.7764	.0060	.9940	30′
40′	.2251	.7749	.2313	.7687	.0062	.9938	20′
50′	.2324	.7676	.2389	.7611	.0064	.9936	10′
10° 00′	9.2397	10.7603	9.2463	10.7537	10.0066	9.9934	80° 00′
10′	.2468	.7532	.2536	.7464	.0069	.9931	50′
20′	.2538	.7462	.2609	.7391	.0071	.9929	40′
30′	.2606	.7394	.2680	.7320	.0073	.9927	30′
40′	.2674	.7326	.2750	.7250	.0076	.9924	20′
50′	.2740	.7260	.2819	.7181	.0078	.9922	10′
11° 00′	9.2806	10.7194	9.2887	10.7113	10.0081	9.9919	79° 00′
10′	.2870	.7130	.2953	.7047	.0083	.9917	50′
20′	.2934	.7066	.3020	.6980	.0086	.9914	40′
30′	.2997	.7003	.3085	.6915	.0088	.9912	30′
40′	.3058	.6942	.3149	.6851	.0091	.9909	20′
50′	.3119	.6881	.3212	.6788	.0093	.9907	10′
12° 00′	9.3179	10.6821	9.3275	10.6725	10.0096	9.9904	78° 00′
10′	.3238	.6762	.3336	.6664	.0099	.9901	50′
20′	.3296	.6704	.3397	.6603	.0101	.9899	40′
30′	.3353	.6647	.3458	.6542	.0104	.9896	30′
40′	.3410	.6590	.3517	.6483	.0107	.9893	20′
50′	.3466	.6534	.3576	.6424	.0110	.9890	10′
13° 00′	9.3521	10.6479	9.3634	10.6366	10.0113	9.9887	77° 00′
	L cos θ	L sec θ	L cot θ	L tan θ	L csc θ	L sin θ	Angle θ

TABLE IV—*continued*

Attach − 10 to Logarithms Obtained from This Table

Angle θ	L sin θ	L csc θ	L tan θ	L cot θ	L sec θ	L cos θ	
13° 00′	9.3521	10.6479	9.3634	10.6366	10.0113	9.9887	**77° 00′**
10′	.3575	.6425	.3691	.6309	.0116	.9884	50′
20′	.3629	.6371	.3748	.6252	.0119	.9881	40′
30′	.3682	.6318	.3804	.6196	.0122	.9878	30′
40′	.3734	.6266	.3859	.6141	.0125	.9875	20′
50′	.3786	.6214	.3914	.6086	.0128	.9872	10′
14° 00′	9.3837	10.6163	9.3968	10.6032	10.0131	9.9869	**76° 00′**
10′	.3887	.6113	.4021	.5979	.0134	.9866	50′
20′	.3937	.6063	.4074	.5926	.0137	.9863	40′
30′	.3986	.6014	.4127	.5873	.0141	.9859	30′
40′	.4035	.5965	.4178	.5822	.0144	.9856	20′
50′	.4083	.5917	.4230	.5770	.0147	.9853	10′
15° 00′	9.4130	10.5870	9.4281	10.5719	10.0151	9.9849	**75° 00′**
10′	.4177	.5823	.4331	.5669	.0154	.9846	50′
20′	.4223	.5777	.4381	.5619	.0157	.9843	40′
30′	.4269	.5731	.4430	.5570	.0161	.9839	30′
40′	.4314	.5686	.4479	.5521	.0164	.9836	20′
50′	.4359	.5641	.4527	.5473	.0168	.9832	10′
16° 00′	9.4403	10.5597	9.4575	10.5425	10.0172	9.9828	**74° 00′**
10′	.4447	.5553	.4622	.5378	.0175	.9825	50′
20′	.4491	.5509	.4669	.5331	.0179	.9821	40′
30′	.4533	.5467	.4716	.5284	.0183	.9817	30′
40′	.4576	.5424	.4762	.5238	.0186	.9814	20′
50′	.4618	.5382	.4808	.5192	.0190	.9810	10′
17° 00′	9.4659	10.5341	9.4853	10.5147	10.0194	9.9806	**73° 00′**
10′	.4700	.5300	.4898	.5102	.0198	.9802	50′
20′	.4741	.5259	.4943	.5057	.0202	.9798	40′
30′	.4781	.5219	.4987	.5013	.0206	.9794	30′
40′	.4821	.5179	.5031	.4969	.0210	.9790	20′
50′	.4861	.5139	.5075	.4925	.0214	.9786	10′
18° 00′	9.4900	10.5100	9.5118	10.4882	10.0218	9.9782	**72° 00′**
10′	.4939	.5061	.5161	.4839	.0222	.9778	50′
20′	.4977	.5023	.5203	.4797	.0226	.9774	40′
30′	.5015	.4985	.5245	.4755	.0230	.9770	30′
40′	.5052	.4948	.5287	.4713	.0235	.9765	20′
50′	.5090	.4910	.5329	.4671	.0239	.9761	10′
19° 00′	9.5126	10.4874	9.5370	10.4630	10.0243	9.9757	**71° 00′**
10′	.5163	.4837	.5411	.4589	.0248	.9752	50′
20′	.5199	.4801	.5451	.4549	.0252	.9748	40′
30′	.5235	.4765	.5491	.4509	.0257	.9743	30′
40′	.5270	.4730	.5531	.4469	.0261	.9739	20′
50′	.5306	.4694	.5571	.4429	.0266	.9734	10′
20° 00′	9.5341	10.4659	9.5611	10.4389	10.0270	9.9730	**70° 00′**
	L cos θ	L sec θ	L cot θ	L tan θ	L csc θ	L sin θ	Angle θ

TABLE IV—*continued*

Attach — 10 to Logarithms Obtained from This Table

Angle θ	L sin θ	L csc θ	L tan θ	L cot θ	L sec θ	L cos θ	
20° 00′	9.5341	10.4659	9.5611	10.4389	10.0270	9.9730	**70° 00′**
10′	.5375	.4625	.5650	.4350	.0275	.9725	50′
20′	.5409	.4591	.5689	.4311	.0279	.9721	40′
30′	.5443	.4557	.5727	.4273	.0284	.9716	30′
40′	.5477	.4523	.5766	.4234	.0289	.9711	20′
50′	.5510	.4490	.5804	.4196	.0294	.9706	10′
21° 00′	9.5543	10.4457	9.5842	10.4158	10.0298	9.9702	**69° 00′**
10′	.5576	.4424	.5879	.4121	.0303	.9797	50′
20′	.5609	.4391	.5917	.4083	.0308	.9692	40′
30′	.5641	.4359	.5954	.4046	.0313	.9687	30′
40′	.5673	.4327	.5991	.4009	.0318	.9682	20′
50′	.5704	.4296	.6028	.3972	.0323	.9677	10′
22° 00′	9.5736	10.4264	9.6064	10.3936	10.0328	9.9672	**68° 00′**
10′	.5767	.4233	.6100	.3900	.0333	.9667	50′
20′	.5798	.4202	.6136	.3864	.0339	.9661	40′
30′	.5828	.4172	.6172	.3828	.0344	.9656	30′
40′	.5859	.4141	.6208	.3792	.0349	.9651	20′
50′	.5889	.4111	.6243	.3757	.0354	.9646	10′
23° 00′	9.5919	10.4081	9.6279	10.3721	10.0360	9.9640	**67° 00′**
10′	.5948	.4052	.6314	.3686	.0365	.9635	50′
20′	.5978	.4022	.6348	.3652	.0371	.9629	40′
30′	.6007	.3993	.6383	.3617	.0376	.9624	30′
40′	.6036	.3964	.6417	.3583	.0382	.9618	20′
50′	.6065	.3935	.6452	.3548	.0387	.9613	10′
24° 00′	9.6093	10.3907	9.6486	10.3514	10.0393	9.9607	**66° 00′**
10′	.6121	.3879	.6520	.3480	.0398	.9602	50′
20′	.6149	.3851	.6553	.3447	.0404	.9596	40′
30′	.6177	.3823	.6587	.3413	.0410	.9590	30′
40′	.6205	.3795	.6620	.3380	.0416	.9584	20′
50′	.6232	.3768	.6654	.3346	.0421	.9579	10′
25° 00′	9.6259	10.3741	9.6687	10.3313	10.0427	9.9573	**65° 00′**
10′	.6286	.3714	.6720	.3280	.0433	.9567	50′
20′	.6313	.3687	.6752	.3248	.0439	.9561	40′
30′	.6340	.3660	.6785	.3215	.0445	.9555	30′
40′	.6366	.3634	.6817	.3183	.0451	.9549	20′
50′	.6392	.3608	.6850	.3150	.0457	.9543	10′
26° 00′	9.6418	10.3582	9.6882	10.3118	10.0463	9.9537	**64° 00′**
10′	.6444	.3556	.6914	.3086	.0470	.9530	50′
20′	.6470	.3530	.6946	.3054	.0476	.9524	40′
30′	.6495	.3505	.6977	.3023	.0482	.9518	30′
40′	.6521	.3479	.7009	.2991	.0488	.9512	20′
50′	.6546	.3454	.7040	.2960	.0495	.9505	10′
27° 00′	9.6570	10.3430	9.7072	10.2928	10.0501	9.9499	**63° 00′**
	L cos θ	L sec θ	L cot θ	L tan θ	L csc θ	L sin θ	Angle θ

219

TABLE IV—*continued*

Attach − 10 to Logarithms Obtained from This Table

Angle θ	L sin θ	L csc θ	L tan θ	L cot θ	L sec θ	L cos θ	
27° 00′	9.6570	10.3430	9.7072	10.2928	10.0501	9.9499	63° 00′
10′	.6595	.3405	.7103	.2897	.0508	.9492	50′
20′	.6620	.3380	.7134	.2866	.0514	.9486	40′
30′	.6644	.3356	.7165	.2835	.0521	.9479	30′
40′	.6668	.3332	.7196	.2804	.0527	.9473	20′
50′	.6692	.3308	.7226	.2774	.0534	.9466	10′
28° 00′	9.6716	10.3284	9.7257	10.2743	10.0541	9.9459	62° 00′
10′	.6740	.3260	.7287	.2713	.0547	.9453	50′
20′	.6763	.3237	.7317	.2683	.0554	.9446	40′
30′	.6787	.3213	.7348	.2652	.0561	.9439	30′
40′	.6810	.3190	.7378	.2622	.0568	.9432	20′
50′	.6833	.3167	.7408	.2592	.0575	.9425	10′
29° 00′	9.6856	10.3144	9.7438	10.2562	10.0582	9.9418	61° 00′
10′	.6878	.3122	.7467	.2533	.0589	.9411	50′
20′	.6901	.3099	.7497	.2503	.0596	.9404	40′
30′	.6923	.3077	.7526	.2474	.0603	.9397	30′
40′	.6946	.3054	.7556	.2444	.0610	.9390	20′
50′	.6968	.3032	.7585	.2415	.0617	.9383	10′
30° 00′	9.6990	10.3010	9.7614	10.2386	10.0625	9.9375	60° 00′
10′	.7012	.2988	.7644	.2356	.0632	.9368	50′
20′	.7033	.2967	.7673	.2327	.0639	.9361	40′
30′	.7055	.2945	.7701	.2299	.0647	.9353	30′
40′	.7076	.2924	.7730	.2270	.0654	.9346	20′
50′	.7097	.2903	.7759	.2241	.0662	.9338	10′
31° 00′	9.7118	10.2882	9.7788	10.2212	10.0669	9.9331	59° 00′
10′	.7139	.2861	.7816	.2184	.0677	.9323	50′
20′	.7160	.2840	.7845	.2155	.0685	.9315	40′
30′	.7181	.2819	.7873	.2127	.0692	.9308	30′
40′	.7201	.2799	.7902	.2098	.0700	.9300	20′
50′	.7222	.2778	.7930	.2070	.0708	.9292	10′
32° 00′	9.7242	10.2758	9.7958	10.2042	10.0716	9.9284	58° 00′
10′	.7262	.2738	.7986	.2014	.0724	.9276	50′
20′	.7282	.2718	.8014	.1986	.0732	.9268	40′
30′	.7302	.2698	.8042	.1958	.0740	.9260	30′
40′	.7322	.2678	.8070	.1930	.0748	.9252	20′
50′	.7342	.2658	.8097	.1903	.0756	.9244	10′
33° 00′	9.7361	10.2639	9.8125	10.1875	10.0764	9.9236	57° 00′
10′	.7380	.2620	.8153	.1847	.0772	.9228	50′
20′	.7400	.2600	.8180	.1820	.0781	.9219	40′
30′	.7419	.2581	.8208	.1792	.0789	.9211	30′
40′	.7438	.2562	.8235	.1765	.0797	.9203	20′
50′	.7457	.2543	.8263	.1737	.0806	.9194	10′
34° 00′	9.7476	10.2524	9.8290	10.1710	10.0814	9.9186	56° 00′
	L cos θ	L sec θ	L cot θ	L tan θ	L csc θ	L sin θ	Angle θ

TABLE IV—*continued*

Attach − 10 to Logarithms Obtained from This Table

Angle θ	L sin θ	L csc θ	L tan θ	L cot θ	L sec θ	L cos θ	
34° 00′	9.7476	10.2524	9.8290	10.1710	10.0814	9.9186	56° 00′
10′	.7494	.2506	.8317	.1683	.0823	.9177	50′
20′	.7513	.2487	.8344	.1656	.0831	.9169	40′
30′	.7531	.2469	.8371	.1629	.0840	.9160	30′
40′	.7550	.2450	.8398	.1602	.0849	.9151	20′
50′	.7568	.2432	.8425	.1575	.0858	.9142	10′
35° 00′	9.7586	10.2414	9.8452	10.1548	10.0866	9.9134	55° 00′
10′	.7604	.2396	.8479	.1521	.0875	.9125	50′
20′	.7622	.2378	.8506	.1494	.0884	.9116	40′
30′	.7640	.2360	.8533	.1467	.0893	.9107	30′
40′	.7657	.2343	.8559	.1441	.0902	.9098	20′
50′	.7675	.2325	.8586	.1414	.0911	.9089	10′
36° 00′	9.7692	10.2308	9.8613	10.1387	10.0920	9.9080	54° 00′
10′	.7710	.2290	.8639	.1361	.0930	.9070	50′
20′	.7727	.2273	.8666	.1334	.0939	.9061	40′
30′	.7744	.2256	.8692	.1308	.0948	.9052	30′
40′	.7761	.2239	.8718	.1282	.0958	.9042	20′
50′	.7778	.2222	.8745	.1255	.0967	.9033	10′
37° 00′	9.7795	10.2205	9.8771	10.1229	10.0977	9.9023	53° 00′
10′	.7811	.2189	.8797	.1203	.0986	.9014	50′
20′	.7828	.2172	.8824	.1176	.0996	.9004	40′
30′	.7844	.2156	.8850	.1150	.1005	.8995	30′
40′	.7861	.2139	.8876	.1124	.1015	.8985	20′
50′	.7877	.2123	.8902	.1098	.1025	.8975	10′
38° 00′	9.7893	10.2107	9.8928	10.1072	10.1035	9.8965	52° 00′
10′	.7910	.2090	.8954	.1046	.1045	.8955	50′
20′	.7926	.2074	.8980	.1020	.1055	.8945	40′
30′	.7941	.2059	.9006	.0994	.1065	.8935	30′
40′	.7957	.2043	.9032	.0968	.1075	.8925	20′
50′	.7973	.2027	.9058	.0942	.1085	.8915	10′
39° 00′	9.7989	10.2011	9.9084	10.0916	10.1095	9.8905	51° 00′
10′	.8004	.1996	.9110	.0890	.1105	.8895	50′
20′	.8020	.1980	.9135	.0865	.1116	.8884	40′
30′	.8035	.1965	.9161	.0839	.1126	.8874	30′
40′	.8050	.1950	.9187	.0813	.1136	.8864	20′
50′	.8066	.1934	.9212	.0788	.1147	.8853	10′
40° 00′	9.8081	10.1919	9.9238	10.0762	10.1157	9.8843	50° 00′
10′	.8096	.1904	.9264	.0736	.1168	.8832	50′
20′	.8111	.1889	.9289	.0711	.1179	.8821	40′
30′	.8125	.1875	.9315	.0685	.1190	.8810	30′
40′	.8140	.1860	.9341	.0659	.1200	.8800	20′
50′	.8155	.1845	.9366	.0634	.1211	.8789	10′
41° 00′	9.8169	10.1831	9.9392	10.0608	10.1222	9.8778	49° 00′
	L cos θ	L sec θ	L cot θ	L tan θ	L csc θ	L sin θ	Angle θ

221

TABLE IV—*continued*

Attach − 10 to Logarithms Obtained from This Table

Angle θ	L sin θ	L csc θ	L tan θ	L cot θ	L sec θ	L cos θ	
41° 00′	9.8169	10.1831	9.9392	10.0608	10.1222	9.8778	**49° 00′**
10′	.8184	.1816	.9417	.0583	.1233	.8767	50′
20′	.8198	.1802	.9443	.0557	.1244	.8756	40′
30′	.8213	.1787	.9468	.0532	.1255	.8745	30′
40′	.8227	.1773	.9494	.0506	.1267	.8733	20′
50′	.8241	.1759	.9519	.0481	.1278	.8722	10′
42° 00′	9.8255	10.1745	9.9544	10.0456	10.1289	9.8711	**48° 00′**
10′	.8269	.1731	.9570	.0430	.1301	.8699	50′
20′	.8283	.1717	.9595	.0405	.1312	.8688	40′
30′	.8297	.1703	.9621	.0379	.1324	.8676	30′
40′	.8311	.1689	.9646	.0354	.1335	.8665	20′
50′	.8324	.1676	.9671	.0329	.1347	.8653	10′
43° 00′	9.8338	10.1662	9.9697	10.0303	10.1359	9.8641	**47° 00′**
10′	.8351	.1649	.9722	.0278	.1371	.8629	50′
20′	.8365	.1635	.9747	.0253	.1382	.8618	40′
30′	.8378	.1622	.9772	.0228	.1394	.8606	30′
40′	.8391	.1609	.9798	.0202	.1406	.8594	20′
50′	.8405	.1595	.9823	.0177	.1418	.8582	10′
44° 00′	9.8418	10.1582	9.9848	10.0152	10.1431	9.8569	**46° 00′**
10′	.8431	.1569	.9874	.0126	.1443	.8557	50′
20′	.8444	.1556	.9899	.0101	.1455	.8545	40′
30′	.8457	.1543	.9924	.0076	.1468	.8532	30′
40′	.8469	.1531	.9949	.0051	.1480	.8520	20′
50′	.8482	.1518	9.9975	.0025	.1493	.8507	10′
45° 00′	9.8495	10.1505	10.0000	10.0000	10.1505	9.8495	**45° 00′**
	L cos θ	L sec θ	L cot θ	L tan θ	L csc θ	L sin θ	Angle θ

Answers to Exercises

For problems containing lettered parts, the answers are given for parts (a), (c), (e), (g), etc. Otherwise the answers are given for the odd-numbered problems. For problems not involving logarithms a "10-inch" slide rule was used as an aid in computations. Answers to some problems have been intentionally omitted.

Page 4. Art. 1-2

8. (a) 5, (c) 5. **9.** (a) $-6, 6$; (c) $-4, 4$.

Page 7. Art. 1-3

1. (a) $(+, +)$, (c) $(-, -)$. **3.** (a) $r = 5$, QI, (c) $r = 10$, QII, (e) $r = 5$, QIV, (g) $r = \sqrt{5}$, QIII. **4.** (a) 25, (c) -2, (e) $\pm 3\sqrt{6}$. **5.** (a) $\sqrt{41}$, (c) $\sqrt{29}$, (e) 10.

Page 13. Art. 1-5

1. (a) $\dfrac{\pi}{4}$, (c) $\dfrac{\pi}{3}$, (e) 0.055, (g) 0.0822, (i) 2.12, (k) 5.95. **2.** (a) $360°$, (c) $34°$,

(e) 3.2°, (g) 172°, (i) 36.5°, (k) 72.9°. **3.** 5 ft. **5.** 2880 ft. **7.** 13.4 rev.
9. 71.5 in.^{2} **11.** 0.007. **13.** 0.066 mi^2.

Page 17. Art. 1-7

1. -1, -3, -9. **3.** $-\frac{4}{5}$, $-\frac{4}{5}$. **4.** (a) x, (c) z, (e) θ, (g) t. **5.** $\sqrt{\dfrac{A}{\pi}}$.
6. (a) domain—all real numbers, range—all real numbers; (c) domain—
all real numbers except $x = 1$, range—all real numbers; (e) domain—
$|x| \geqq 5$, range—all real numbers; (g) domain—$-1 \leqq x \leqq 3$, range—
$-1 \leqq f(x) \leqq 7$. **7.** $\pm\sqrt{r^2 - y^2}$.

Page 24. Art. 2-2

Answers to problems requiring all of the trigonometric functions are
listed in the order: sin θ, cos θ, tan θ, cot θ, sec θ, and csc θ.

1. (a) 0.77, 0.64, 1.19, 0.84, 1.56, 1.3; (c) 0.82, -0.57, -1.43, -0.7,
-1.74, 1.22; (e) -0.34, 0.94, -0.36, -2.75, 1.06, -2.92; (g) -0.95,
-0.31, 3.08, 0.32, -3.24, -1.05; (i) -0.64, -0.77, 0.84, 1.19, -1.30,
-1.56; (k) 0.71, -0.71, -1, -1, -1.41, 1.41. **2.** (a) -0.64, 0.77, -0.84,
-1.19, 1.30, -1.56; (c) 0.5, -0.87, -0.58, -1.73, -1.16, 2; (e) 0.94,
0.34, 2.75, 0.36, 2.92, 1.06; (g) 0.34, -0.94, -0.36, -2.75, -1.06, 2.92.
3. (a) QI, QII; (c) QI, QIII; (e) QII, QIII. **5.** (a) $\frac{7}{58}\sqrt{58}$, $\frac{3}{58}\sqrt{58}$, $\frac{7}{3}$, $\frac{3}{7}$,
$\frac{1}{3}\sqrt{58}$, $\frac{1}{7}\sqrt{58}$; (c) $-\frac{13}{313}\sqrt{313}$, $-\frac{12}{313}\sqrt{313}$, $\frac{13}{12}$, $\frac{12}{13}$, $-\frac{1}{12}\sqrt{313}$, $-\frac{1}{13}\sqrt{313}$;
(e) $-\frac{3}{5}$, $-\frac{4}{5}$, $\frac{3}{4}$, $\frac{4}{3}$, $-\frac{5}{4}$, $-\frac{5}{3}$; (g) $-\frac{1}{2}\sqrt{2}$, $\frac{1}{2}\sqrt{2}$, -1, -1, $\sqrt{2}$, $-\sqrt{2}$;
(i) $\frac{5}{29}\sqrt{29}$, $-\frac{2}{29}\sqrt{29}$, $-\frac{5}{2}$, $-\frac{2}{5}$, $-\frac{1}{2}\sqrt{29}$, $\frac{1}{5}\sqrt{29}$.

Page 27. Art. 2-3

1. $\frac{4}{5}$, $\frac{3}{5}$, $\frac{4}{3}$, $\frac{3}{4}$, $\frac{5}{5}$, $\frac{5}{4}$. **3.** $-\frac{3}{5}$, $\frac{4}{5}$, $-\frac{3}{4}$, $-\frac{4}{3}$, $\frac{5}{4}$, $-\frac{5}{3}$. **5.** $\frac{15}{17}$, $-\frac{8}{17}$, $-\frac{15}{8}$, $-\frac{8}{15}$, $-\frac{17}{8}$,
$\frac{17}{15}$. **7.** $-\frac{1}{10}$, $\frac{3}{10}\sqrt{11}$, $-\frac{1}{33}\sqrt{11}$, $-3\sqrt{11}$, $\frac{10}{33}\sqrt{11}$, -10. **9.** $-\frac{3}{29}\sqrt{93}$, $\frac{2}{29}$,
$-\frac{3}{2}\sqrt{93}$, $-\frac{2}{279}\sqrt{93}$, $\frac{29}{2}$, $-\frac{29}{279}\sqrt{93}$. **11.** $-\frac{9}{41}$, $\frac{40}{41}$, $-\frac{9}{40}$, $-\frac{40}{9}$, $\frac{41}{40}$, $-\frac{41}{9}$.
13. $\pm\frac{5}{13}$, $\mp\frac{12}{13}$, $-\frac{5}{12}$, $-\frac{12}{5}$, $\mp\frac{13}{12}$, $\pm\frac{13}{5}$. **15.** $\pm\frac{1}{12}\sqrt{119}$, $-\frac{5}{12}$, $\mp\frac{1}{5}\sqrt{119}$,
$\mp\frac{5}{119}\sqrt{119}$, $-\frac{12}{5}$, $\pm\frac{12}{119}\sqrt{119}$. **17.** $\pm\frac{4}{5}$, $\frac{3}{5}$, $\pm\frac{4}{3}$, $\pm\frac{3}{4}$, $\frac{5}{3}$, $\pm\frac{5}{4}$. **19.** $\pm\frac{1}{2}\sqrt{2}$,
$\pm\frac{1}{2}\sqrt{2}$, 1, 1, $\pm\sqrt{2}$, $\pm\sqrt{2}$. **21.** $\pm\frac{1}{5}\sqrt{21}$, $\frac{2}{5}$, $\pm\frac{1}{2}\sqrt{21}$, $\pm\frac{2}{21}\sqrt{21}$,
$\frac{5}{2}$, $\pm\frac{5}{21}\sqrt{21}$. **23.** $\pm\frac{9}{41}$, $\pm\frac{40}{41}$, $\frac{9}{40}$, $\frac{40}{9}$, $\pm\frac{41}{40}$, $\pm\frac{41}{9}$. **25.** 0.62, 0.785, 0.79,
1.27, 1.27, 1.61. **27.** -0.93, 0.36, -2.6, -0.38, 2.8, -1.08. **29.** 0.99,
0.132, 7.53, 0.133, 7.6, 1.01. **31.** 90°, 180°, 270°.

Page 32. Art. 2-5

1. (a) $\frac{1}{2}$, $-\frac{1}{2}\sqrt{3}$, $-\frac{1}{3}\sqrt{3}$, $-\sqrt{3}$, $-\frac{2}{3}\sqrt{3}$, 2; (c) $-\frac{1}{2}\sqrt{3}$, $-\frac{1}{2}$, $\sqrt{3}$, $\frac{1}{3}\sqrt{3}$, -2,
$-\frac{2}{3}\sqrt{3}$; (e) 0, 1, 0, does not exist, 1, does not exist; (g) -1, 0, does not
exist, 0, does not exist, -1; (i) $-\frac{1}{2}\sqrt{2}$, $\frac{1}{2}\sqrt{2}$, -1, -1, $\sqrt{2}$, $-\sqrt{2}$;
(k) $\frac{1}{2}\sqrt{3}$, $\frac{1}{2}$, $\sqrt{3}$, $\frac{1}{3}\sqrt{3}$, 2, $\frac{2}{3}\sqrt{3}$; (m) same as for (a). **4.** (a) $\frac{1}{3}\sqrt{2}$, (c) 2,
(e) $\sqrt{3} - 1$, (g) 1.

Page 36. Art. 2-6

1. (a) 0.0998, (c) 0.8415, (e) 0.5000, (g) 0.0523. **2.** (a) 0.9950, (c) 0.5403, (e) 0.8660, (g) 0.9986. **3.** 0.1449. **5.** 0.6111. **7.** 0.5812. **9.** 1.829. **11.** 1.423. **13.** 1.668. **15.** 7°10′. **17.** 56°50′. **19.** 21°20′. **21.** 1.2508. **23.** 0.4218. **25.** 0.7098. **27.** 0.6104. **29.** 0.8025. **31.** 0.4431. **33.** 0.5276. **35.** 3.196. **37.** 0.7676. **39.** 0.1280. **41.** 1.851. **43.** 4°23′. **45.** 41°34′. **47.** 18°16′. **49.** 12°57′. **51.** 32°17′. **53.** 27°18′. **55.** 0.1320. **57.** 1.3226. **59.** 0.3852. **61.** 0.1766. **63.** 0.3563. **65.** 0.8658. **67.** $\sin \theta = \theta$.

Page 41. Art. 2-7

1. (a) $\sin 55°$, (c) $-\tan 7°32′$, (e) $-\sec 82°58′$, (g) $\sin 65°$. **2.** (a) 0.8387. (c) -0.0816, (e) -1.218, (g) 0.5854, (i) 0.3249, (k) -0.1768. **3.** (a) 340°, (c) 233°15′, (e) 28°35′, (g) 37°26′, 142°34′; (i) 143°08′, 323°08′; (k) 139°55′, 220°05′.

Page 43. Art. 2-8

1. (a) -0.6691, (c) 1.376, (e) -0.6598, (g) -3.236.

Page 47. Art. 3-2

1. $B = 90° - A$, $a = c \sin A$, $b = c \cos A$. **3.** $A = 90° - B$, $\cos B = a/c$, $b = a \tan B$. **5.** $A = 90° - B$, $\sin B = b/c$, $a = b \tan A$. **7.** $D = 90° - F$, $d = f \cot F$, $e = f \csc F$. **9.** (a) $y = z \cos \theta$. **10.** (a) $z = x \csc \theta$. **11.** (a) $\tan \theta = x/y$, (c) $\cos \theta = y/z$. **12.** (a) $RQ = \sin \theta$. **13.** (a) $AC = \cot \alpha$. **14.** (a) $ED = \tan x$.

Page 56. Art. 3-4

1. (a) $B = 55°$, $b = 5.7$, $c = 7$; (c) $A = 37°$, $B = 53°$, $c = 10$; (e) $A = 55.2°$, $B = 34.8°$, $c = 15.2$; (g) $B = 37°20′$, $a = 0.605$, $c = 0.759$; (i) $B = 76°40′$, $a = 1.45$, $b = 6.12$; (k) $A = 53.0°$, $B = 37.0°$, $b = 111$; (m) $A = 42°34′$, $a = 3.12$, $b = 3.40$; (o) $A = 83°48′$, $a = 3690$, $b = 402$; (q) $A = 36°45′$, $B = 53°15′$, $c = 41.3$; (s) $A = 65°25′$, $B = 24°35′$, $a = 3.15$. **2.** (a) $C = 100°$, $a = 6.5$, $c = 13$; (c) $B = 28°$, $C = 110°$, $a = 14$; (e) $B = 12°$, $C = 148°$, $c = 12$; (g) $B = 100°10′$, $a = 19.2$, $b = 35.2$. **4.** (a) $A = 37°$, $B = 53°$, $C = 90°$.

Page 62. Art. 3-5

1. 28.3°, 29.5 in. **3.** 14.5°, 19.4 ft. **5.** 158 ft. **7.** Lower, 5 ft. **9.** 50 ft. **11.** 350 ft. **12.** (a) 288 ft. **13.** 245°, 32 miles. **15.** 6.5 miles, 3.5 miles. **17.** 27°10′, 4.82 miles. **19.** 622 yds. **21.** (a) 10, 6; (c) 3, -5; (e) -10, 23; (g) 56, -9. **22.** (a) $v = 13$, $\theta = 23°$; (c) $v = 35$, $\theta = 226°$. **23.** 188.7 lbs, 304.5 lbs. **25.** (a) 54 lbs, 9.6 lbs. **27.** 5.77 ft/sec², 2.39 ft/sec².

Page 69. Art. 4-2

5. Yes. Infinite. **6.** (a) $y = \frac{4}{5}$, (c) $y = -\frac{7}{25}$, (e) $y = \frac{40}{41}$, (g) $y = \frac{17}{145}$.

Page 71. Art. 4-3

1. $\tan u = \dfrac{\sin u}{\cos u}$, $\cot u = \dfrac{\cos u}{\sin u}$, $\sec u = \dfrac{1}{\cos u}$, $\csc u = \dfrac{1}{\sin u}$. **3.** (a) $\frac{4}{5}, \frac{3}{5}$, $\frac{4}{3}, \frac{3}{4}, \frac{5}{3}, \frac{5}{4}$; (c) $\frac{3}{5}, -\frac{4}{5}, -\frac{3}{4}, -\frac{4}{3}, -\frac{5}{4}, \frac{5}{3}$; (e) $-\frac{12}{13}, -\frac{5}{13}, \frac{12}{5}, \frac{5}{12}, -\frac{13}{5}, -\frac{13}{12}$; (g) $-\frac{15}{17}, \frac{8}{17}, -\frac{15}{8}, -\frac{8}{15}, \frac{17}{8}, -\frac{17}{15}$. **5.** (a) 0, 1, 0, does not exist, 1, does not exist; (c) 0, -1, 0, does not exist, -1, does not exist; (e) Same as for (a); (g) Same as for (c); (i) 1, 0, does not exist, 0, does not exist, 1; (k) Same as for (c); **9.** No. **11.** No.

Page 75. Art. 4-4

1. (a) 0.0600, (c) 1.557, (e) 1.127, (g) 0.9950, (i) 0.1256, (k) 3.836. **2.** (a) 0.25, (c) 1.56, (e) 0.49, (g) 0.724, (i) 1.154, (k) 1.429. **3.** (a) 0.985, (c) 0.998, (e) 1.00, one. **4.** (a) 0.498. **5.** (a) 2.08. **6.** (a) $s = 0.478$ ft, $v = -0.443$ ft/sec, $a = -4.3$ ft/sec^2; (c) $s = 0.181$ ft, $v = -1.4$ ft/sec, $a = -1.63$ ft/sec^2. **7.** (a) 3×10^{-5} ft, (c) 4.06×10^{-3} ft, (e) 8.37×10^{-2} ft. **8.** (a) 0.991 in., (c) 0.258 in. **9.** (a) 0.317, (c) 1.2. **10.** (a) $x = 0.0002, y = 0.005$; (c) $x = 0.0106, y = 0.0789$; (e) $x = 0.107$, $y = 0.357$. **11.** (a) $x = 1.005, y = 0.0003$; (c) $x = 1.0769, y = 0.0210$; (e) $x = 1.312, y = 0.204$. **12.** (a) 33.9, (c) 110.

Page 78. Art. 4-5

1. (a) $\sin 1.14$, (c) $\tan 0.86$, (e) $\sec 0.13$, (g) $\sin 0.72$. **2.** (a) 0.7446, (c) -0.6524, (e) -2.162, (g) -0.9854, (i) -0.8415, (k) 0.5994. **4.** (a) -4.71, (c) 0. **5.** (a) $x = 0.358, y = 1.0$; (c) $x = 3.30, y = 3.42$; (e) $x = 9.27$, $y = 3.42$; (g) $x = 12.42, y = 0.58$. **6.** (a) 0.782, (c) -0.707.

Page 82. Art. 5-2

4. (a) $\cot u$, (c) $\tan^2 A$, (e) $\tan B$, (g) $\sec \alpha$, (i) $\sec v$, (k) $\sec \theta$. **6.** (c) 12.209. **8.** (a) $8 \cos^3 u$, (c) $\sin u$, (e) $\frac{8}{9} \tan^2 u \sec u$.

Page 90. Art. 5-4

1. $x^2 + y^2 = 1$. **3.** $y^2 - 4x^2 = 16$. **5.** $2x^2 + y = 1$. **7.** $(x - h)^2 + (y - k)^2 = a^2$. **9.** $x^2 - y^2 = 4$. **11.** $x^2 + y^2 = 4y$. **13.** $y(x^2 + 4) = 8$. **15.** $x^{2/3} y^{2/3}(x^{2/3} + y^{2/3}) = 1$. **17.** $mv_0^2 x^2 + a^2 ky^2 = a^2 mv_0^2$.

Page 97. Art. 6-2

1. 1, 2π. **3.** $\frac{1}{3}, 2\pi$. **5.** 2, 4π. **7.** 3, $\dfrac{2\pi}{3}$. **9.** 2, π. **11.** 3, 4. **13.** $\frac{3}{2}, 12\pi$. **15.** 4, $\dfrac{4\pi}{3}$. **17.** 1, 6.

Page 102. Art. 6-4

1. 1, 2π. **3.** $\frac{1}{2}, 2\pi$. **5.** 3, 4π. **7.** 1, $\dfrac{2\pi}{3}$. **9.** 5, 2π, $\dfrac{\pi}{6}$ left. **11.** 2, π, $\dfrac{\pi}{4}$ left. **13.** 1, 2π, $\dfrac{\pi}{2}$ left. **15.** $\frac{1}{2}, 4\pi$, $\dfrac{2\pi}{3}$ left.

Page 107. Art. 6-6

3. π. **5.** π. **7.** 2π. **9.** 2π. **11.** $\dfrac{\pi}{2}$.

Page 112. Art. 7-2

2. (a) $\dfrac{\sqrt{2}}{4}(\sqrt{3}+1)$, **(c)** 0, **(e)** $-\dfrac{\sqrt{2}}{4}(\sqrt{3}+1)$. **(g)** $\dfrac{\sqrt{2}}{4}(\sqrt{3}-1)$.
5. (a) $-\frac{33}{65}, \frac{63}{65}$; **(c)** $\frac{13}{85}, \frac{77}{85}$. **7. (a)** $\cos 4A$, **(c)** $\cos x$. **9. (a)** $\frac{5}{13}$.

Page 116. Art. 7-3

3. (a) $\dfrac{\sqrt{2}}{4}(\sqrt{3}-1)$, $2-\sqrt{3}$; **(c)** 1, does not exist; **(e)** $\dfrac{\sqrt{2}}{4}(1-\sqrt{3})$,
$2-\sqrt{3}$; **(g)** $-\dfrac{\sqrt{2}}{4}(1+\sqrt{3})$, $-2-\sqrt{3}$. **6. (a)** $-\frac{56}{65}$, **(c)** $\frac{56}{33}$. **7. (a)** $-\frac{3}{5}$,
(c) $-\frac{3}{4}$. **8. (a)** $-\frac{21}{221}$, **(c)** $-\frac{21}{220}$. **9.** $\frac{4}{5}$. **11. (a)** $\sin 8A$, **(c)** $\sin x$, **(e)** $\tan 5A$,
(g) $\tan A$. **13.** $\dfrac{\tan A + \tan B + \tan C - \tan A \tan B \tan C}{1 - \tan A \tan B - \tan A \tan C - \tan B \tan C}$.
14. (a) $5\sin(x+\alpha)$, where $\tan\alpha = \frac{3}{4}$; **(c)** $2\sin(2x+\alpha)$, where $\tan\alpha = \frac{1}{3}\sqrt{3}$.

Page 119. Art. 7-4

1. (a) $\frac{336}{625}, \frac{527}{625}, \frac{336}{527}$; **(c)** $\frac{120}{169}, \frac{119}{169}, \frac{120}{119}$. **2. (a)** $\sin 6x$, **(c)** $\tan 6t$, **(e)** $\frac{1}{2}\sin 8A$,
(g) $\frac{1}{2}\tan 8t$, **(i)** $\cos 2A$. **3. (a)** $3\sin A - 4\sin^3 A$, **(c)** $\dfrac{3\tan A - \tan^3 A}{1 - 3\tan^2 A}$.

Page 120. Art. 7-5

1. (a) $\frac{1}{2}\sqrt{2-\sqrt{3}}$, **(c)** $2-\sqrt{3}$, **(e)** $\frac{1}{2}\sqrt{2+\sqrt{2}}$, **(g)** $\frac{1}{2}\sqrt{2+\sqrt{3}}$, **(i)** $2+\sqrt{3}$,
(k) $-\frac{1}{2}\sqrt{2-\sqrt{2}}$. **2. (a)** $\frac{3}{5}, \frac{4}{5}, \frac{3}{4}$; **(c)** $\frac{5}{26}\sqrt{26}, \frac{1}{26}\sqrt{26}, 5$. **3. (a)** $\cos 2\alpha$,
(c) $\tan\frac{3}{2}\alpha$, **(e)** $2\sin 6y$.

Page 133. Art. 8-2

1. (a) 2.3096, **(c)** $8.7905 - 10$, **(e)** 2.5174, **(g)** $9.7134 - 10$, **(i)** 0.0086,
(k) $9.4525 - 10$, **(m)** $9.7647 - 10$, **(o)** 0.7847. **2. (a)** 560.0, **(c)** 9.554×10^9,
(e) 11.14, **(g)** $15°30'$, **(i)** $74°23'$, **(k)** $64°27'$, **(m)** $57°15'$, **(o)** $30°11'$.

Page 135. Art. 8-3

1. (a) 103, **(c)** 0.2336, **(e)** 5.521, **(g)** 3795, **(i)** 0.01863. **2. (a)** 86.518,
(c) 0.95178, **(e)** 361.72.

Page 137. Art. 8-4

1. (a) $B = 39°30'$, $b = 65.37$, $c = 102.8$; (c) $A = 26°53'$, $b = 5.605$, $c = 6.284$; (e) $A = 75°50'$, $B = 14°10'$, $c = 9.56$; (g) $B = 37°51'$, $a = 58.13$, $b = 45.18$; (i) $A = 7°53'$, $B = 82°07'$, $b = 17.75$; (k) $A = 20°00'$, $B = 70°00'$, $b = 140.9$; (m) $B = 46°00'$, $a = 434.2$, $b = 449.6$; (o) $A = 42°15'$, $B = 47°45'$, $c = 1144$. **2.** (a) $A = 51°45.3'$, $B = 38°14.7'$, $c = 670.01$; (c) $B = 1°00.8'$, $a = 126.36$, $c = 126.37$; (e) $B = 37°50.0'$, $a = 236.94$, $b = 184.01$.

Page 141. Art. 9-2

1. (a) $4\sqrt{2}$, (c) 2, (e) 45°, 135°.

Page 148. Art. 9-3

1. (a) $b = 5.38$, $c = 5.16$, $C = 52°10'$; (c) $a = 0.4038$, $c = 0.2915$, $C = 28°28'$; (e) $a = 21.446$, $b = 4.5198$, $C = 98°35.5'$ **2.** (a) none, (c) two, (e) one. **3.** (a) $c_1 = 10.08$, $B_1 = 43°25'$, $C_1 = 113°55'$, $c_2 = 3.906$, $B_2 = 136°35'$, $C_2 = 20°45'$; (c) no solution; (e) $b = 3476.2$, $A = 32°28.3'$, $B = 21°19.5'$. **4.** (a) 3.709×10^6. **5.** 1228 ft. **7.** 1078 ft. **9.** 20.12 miles.

Page 152. Art. 9-4

1. $\sqrt{21}$. **3.** 9.22. **5.** $S = \frac{1}{2}bc \sin A$.

Page 157. Art. 9-5

1. (a) $a = 61.36$, $B = 55°56'$, $C = 52°53'$; (c) $c = 267.6$, $A = 123°23'$, $B = 28°46'$; (e) $c = 120.24$, $A = 110°05.3'$, $B = 39°14.2'$. **2.** (a) $c = 67.53$, $A = 102°09'$, $B = 62°40'$; (c) $b = 18.87$, $A = 67°28'$, $C = 55°12'$; (e) $c = 2479$, $A = 133°52'$, $B = 11°59'$. **3.** (a) $A = 65°34'$, $B = 54°48'$, $C = 59°36'$; (c) $A = 55°29'$, $B = 72°08'$, $C = 52°21'$; (e) $A = 84°21.9'$, $B = 25°38.2'$, $C = 70°00.0'$. **5.** 90°. **7.** $172°08'$, $274°56'$. **9.** $248°56'$, 28.94 miles.

Page 164. Art. 10-2

2. If y denotes the given function; (a) $u = \operatorname{Sin} y$, (c) $x = \operatorname{Sin}\left(\dfrac{y}{3}\right)$, (e) $u + v = \operatorname{Tan} y$, (g) $1 + x^2 = \operatorname{Cos}^2 y$. **3.** (a) $\dfrac{\pi}{6}$, (c) 0, (e) $-\dfrac{\pi}{2}$, (g) $-\dfrac{\pi}{4}$, (i) $-\dfrac{\pi}{6}$, (k) $\dfrac{3\pi}{4}$. **4.** (a) 0.838, (c) 1.93, (e) -0.97. **5.** (a) $\frac{5}{13}$, (c) $\frac{1}{2}$, (e) $\frac{24}{25}$, (g) $-\frac{4}{3}$, (i) $-\frac{7}{24}$, (k) $\frac{15}{8}$.

Page 166. Art. 10-3

1. (a) $2x$, (c) $\dfrac{y}{\sqrt{1 - y^2}}$; (e) $1 - 2u^2$, (g) $\dfrac{2v}{1 + v^2}$; (i) $\frac{16}{65}$, (k) $\frac{56}{65}$, (m) $-\frac{36}{325}$.

Page 171. Art. 11-2

1. $120°, 300°$. **3.** $0, \dfrac{\pi}{6}, \dfrac{5\pi}{6}, \pi$. **5.** $90°, 41°20', 270°, 318°40'$. **7.** $\dfrac{\pi}{4}, \dfrac{\pi}{2}, \dfrac{5\pi}{4}, \dfrac{3\pi}{2}$.
9. $0°, 60°, 180°, 300°$. **11.** $\dfrac{\pi}{2}, \dfrac{7\pi}{6}, \dfrac{11\pi}{6}$. **13.** $71°30', 135°, 251°30', 315°$.
15. $\dfrac{2\pi}{3}, \pi, \dfrac{4\pi}{3}$. **17.** $30°, 150°, 210°, 270°, 330°$. **19.** $1.91, 1.98, 4.30, 4.37$.
21. $67°30', 157°30', 247°30', 337°30'$. **23.** No solution. **25.** $45°, 135°, 225°,$
$315°$. **27.** $0.46, 0.78, 2.36, 2.68, 3.60, 3.92, 5.50, 5.82$. **29.** No solution.

Page 173. Art. 11-3

1. $0°, 45°, 135°, 180°, 225°, 315°$. **3.** $\dfrac{\pi}{2}, \dfrac{2\pi}{3}, \dfrac{4\pi}{3}, \dfrac{3\pi}{2}$. **5.** $90°, 210°, 270°,$
$330°$. **7.** $\dfrac{\pi}{6}, \dfrac{5\pi}{6}, \dfrac{3\pi}{2}$. **9.** $137°, 223°$. **11.** $\dfrac{\pi}{2}, \pi, \dfrac{3\pi}{2}$. **13.** $60°, 300°$. **15.** $\dfrac{\pi}{4},$
$\dfrac{3\pi}{4}, \dfrac{5\pi}{4}, \dfrac{7\pi}{4}$. **17.** $0°$. **19.** $\dfrac{\pi}{2}$. **21.** $30°, 150°, 210°, 330°$. **23.** $\dfrac{2\pi}{3}, \dfrac{4\pi}{3}$. **25.** $45°,$
$225°$. **27.** $\dfrac{2\pi}{3}, \pi$. **29.** $45°$.

Page 175. Art. 11-4

1. $0°, 120°$. **3.** $180°, 300°$. **5.** $9°, 145°$. **7.** $83°, 161°$. **9.** $111°30', 198°30'$.
11. $192°30', 285°30'$. **13.** $74°50', 215°50'$. **15.** $\dfrac{7\pi}{12}, \dfrac{23\pi}{12}$. **17.** $\dfrac{\pi}{2}, \dfrac{11\pi}{6}$.
19. $0, 3.86$.

Page 183. Art. 12-1

1. (a) $\left[\dfrac{5\sqrt{2}}{2}, \dfrac{5\sqrt{2}}{2}\right]$, (c) $\left[-\dfrac{3\sqrt{2}}{2}, \dfrac{3\sqrt{2}}{2}\right]$, (e) $[1.29, -1.53]$. **2.** (a) $[5, 90°]$,
(c) $[25, 106°15']$, (e) $[3.61, 303°40']$, (g) $[88.2, 145°]$. **4.** (a) $[1, 10]$, (c)
$[-5, -6]$, (e) $[7.73, -2]$, (g) $[7.5, -15.6]$. **6.** (a) 2, (c) 0, (e) $\sqrt{3} + 3$,
(g) θ. **7.** (a) -16, (c) -6, (e) $1 - 3\sqrt{3}$, (g) 10. **9.** (a) $82°53'$, (c) $58°40'$.
11. (a) $[87.2$ lb, $306°35']$, (c) $[17.7$ lb, $350°17']$. **14.** (a) 8, (c) 27.5.

Page 186. Art. 12-2

2. (a) $2 + 7i$, (c) $1 + 6i$, (e) $-2 + 3i$, (g) $-7 - i$, (i) $(-6 + \sqrt{14})$
$+ (3\sqrt{7} + 2\sqrt{2})i$, (k) $-\frac{1}{2} - \frac{5}{2}i$, (m) $\frac{5}{4} - \frac{3}{4}i$. **3.** (a) $x = 2, y = -16$,
(c) $x = -2, y = -3$.

Page 189. Art. 12-3

1. (a) $2(\cos 30° + i \sin 30°)$, (c) $\sqrt{2}(\cos 315° + i \sin 315°)$, (e) $2(\cos 90°$
$+ i \sin 90°)$, (g) $4(\cos 0° + i \sin 0°)$, (i) $13(\cos 237°30' + i \sin 237°30')$,

(**k**) 15 (cos 200° + i sin 200°), (**m**) 20 (cos 60° + i sin 60°), (**o**) 3 (cos 110° + i sin 110°).　**2.** (**a**) $\frac{5}{2}\sqrt{3} + \frac{5}{2}i$, (**c**) $-1 - \sqrt{3}i$, (**e**) $2i$, (**g**) -3, (**i**) $7 + 10.95i$.　(**k**) $7 - 10.95i$,　(**m**) $-14.1 - 5.13i$, (**o**) $-33 + 56i$.　**3.** (**a**) $3.6 + 3.2i$.　**5.** (**a**) $1 + 3i$, (**c**) $5i$.

Page 192.　Art. 12-4

1. (**a**) 6 cis 60°, (**c**) 6 cis 45°, (**e**) 4 cis 90°, (**g**) 4 cis 90°, (**i**) 3 cis 120°, (**k**) $\frac{1}{2}$ cis 120°.　**2.** (**a**) 65 cis 120°30′, (**c**) 25 cis 253°45′, (**e**) 13 cis 67°24′, (**g**) 125 cis 290°24′, (**i**) cis 212°40′, (**k**) 1.61 cis $(-29°45')$.　**3.** cos $2\theta \equiv$ $\cos^2 \theta - \sin^2 \theta$, sin $2\theta \equiv 2 \sin \theta \cos \theta$.

Page 194.　Art. 12-5

1. (**a**) 2 cis 40°, 2 cis 160°, 2 cis 280°; (**c**) 4 cis 100°, 4 cis 220°, 4 cis 340°; (**e**) 3 cis 70°, 3 cis 190°, 3 cis 310°.　**2.** (**a**) $2i$, $\pm\sqrt{3} - i$; (**c**) $3 + 2i$, $-3 - 2i$; (**e**) $3.70 + 3.36i$, $-4.76 + 1.53i$, $1.06 - 4.89i$; (**g**) 5 cis 83.1°, 5 cis 203.1°, 5 cis 323.1°; (**i**) 1, $-\dfrac{1}{2} \pm \dfrac{\sqrt{3}}{2}i$.　**3.** (**a**) 1, $0.31 \pm 0.95i$, $-0.81 \pm 0.59i$; (**c**) ± 2, $\pm 2i$.

Page 196.　Art. A-1

2. (**a**) 177.78 mils, (**c**) 2133.36 mils, (**e**) 1528 mils, (**g**) 10.2 mils.　**3.** (**a**) 0.562°, (**c**) 5°37.5′, (**e**) 112°30′.　**4.** (**a**) 0.231 radian, (**c**) 0.785 radian, **5.** 10 yds.　**7.** 21,650 ft.　**9.** 6160 ft.

Index

231